AF820656

Digestive Diseases

Clinical Reviews

Formerly 'Survey of Digestive Diseases'
Founded in 1983 by T.S.N. Chen and R.K. Zetterman
Former Editor: S.R. Achem (1993–2000)

KARGER

Printed in Switzerland on acid-free paper by Reinhardt Druck, Basel

Appears quarterly: 1 volume per year (4 issues)

Digestive Diseases

General Information

Publication data: 'Digestive Diseases' is published 4 times a year. Volume 22 with 4 issues appears in 2004.

Subscription rates: Subscriptions run for a full calendar year. Prices are given per year.

Personal subscription:

Print or Online	Print/Online combined
CHF 119.–	CHF 160.–
EUR 88.–	EUR 118.–
USD 95.00	USD 128.00
postage and handling	(added to print and print/online)
CHF 21.20 Europe,	CHF 31.40 Overseas
EUR 15.20	
USD 21.20	

Institutional subscription:

Print or Online	Print/Online combined
CHF 1158.–	CHF 1251.–
EUR 858.–	EUR 927.–
USD 926.00	USD 1001.00
postage and handling	(added to print and print/online)
CHF 26.40 Europe,	CHF 39.20 Overseas
EUR 19.–	
USD 26.40	

Airmail surcharge: CHF 26.40 / USD 22.00
Discount subscription prices:
Please enquire about reduced rates for residents.

Microforms: Please direct all enquiries and orders to:
University Microfilms Inc.
300 North Zeeb Road, P.O. Box 1346
Ann Arbor, MI 48106-1346 (USA)

Subscription orders: Orders can be placed at agencies, bookstores, directly with the Publisher
S. Karger AG, P.O. Box
CH–4009 Basel (Switzerland)
or with any of the following distributors:
Deutschland: S. Karger GmbH, Postfach
D–79095 Freiburg
France: Librairie Luginbühl
36, bd de Latour-Maubourg
F–75007 Paris
Great Britain, Ireland: S. Karger AG
4 Rickett Street
London SW6 1RU, UK
USA: S. Karger Publishers, Inc.
26 West Avon Road, P.O. Box 529
Farmington, CT 06085, USA
India, Bangladesh, Sri Lanka:
Panther Publishers Private Ltd.
33, First Main
Koramangala First Block
Bangalore 560 034, India
Japan: Karger Japan, Inc.
Yushima S Bld. 3F
4-2-3, Yushima, Bunkyo-ku
Tokyo 113-0034, Japan

Change of address: Both old and new address should be sent to the subscription source.

Single issues and back volumes: Information can be obtained through the Publisher.

Advertising: Correspondence and rate requests should be addressed to the Publisher.

Bibliographic indices: This journal is regularly listed in bibliographic services, including *Current Contents®* and Index Medicus/MEDLINE.

KARGER
Fax +41 61 306 12 34
E-Mail karger@karger.ch
www.karger.com

The Journal Home Page is available at:
www.karger.com/ddi

Digestive
Diseases

New Developments in the Management of Gastric Cancer

Editors
Peter Malfertheiner, Magdeburg
Matthias Ebert, Magdeburg

18 figures, 10 in color and 18 tables, 2004

KARGER

Basel · Freiburg · Paris · London · New York ·
Bangalore · Bangkok · Singapore · Tokyo · Sydney

S. Karger
Medical and Scientific Publishers
Basel • Freiburg • Paris • London
New York • Bangalore • Bangkok
Singapore • Tokyo • Sydney

Drug Dosage
The authors and the publisher have exerted every effort to ensure that drug selection and dosage set forth in this text are in accord with current recommendations and practice at the time of publication. However, in view of ongoing research, changes in government regulations, and the constant flow of information relating to drug therapy and drug reactions, the reader is urged to check the package insert for each drug for any change in indications and dosage and for added warnings and precautions. This is particularly important when the recommended agent is a new and/or infrequently employed drug.

P.O. Box, CH–4009 Basel (Switzerland)
Printed in Switzerland on acid-free paper by
Reinhardt Druck, Basel
ISBN 3–8055–7923–3

KARGER

Fax +41 61 306 12 34
E-Mail karger@karger.ch
www.karger.com

Vol. 22, No. 4, 2004

Digestive Diseases

Contents

KARGER

Fax +41 61 306 12 34
E-Mail karger@karger.ch
www.karger.com

Access to full text and tables of contents, including tentative ones for forthcoming issues:
www.karger.com/ddi_issues

Digestive Diseases

Dig Dis 2004;22:301
DOI: 10.1159/000083589

Editorial

Gastric cancer continues to remain a major challenge for its high mortality because of the diagnosis in advanced stages of disease. Despite new developments and technical advances in endoscopic diagnosis and therapy, the overall prognosis of these patients is poor. The identification of *Helicobacter pylori* as the single most important risk factor for the development of gastric cancer has changed our understanding of the pathogenesis of this malignancy. In this issue of *Digestive Diseases* we have invited the world's leading experts in the field of basic research and clinical management of gastric cancer to share their expertise with the clinical community. Important insight is given in this issue on the pathogenesis and the most important risk factors for the development of gastric cancer, as well as the potential benefits of chemoprevention and *H. pylori* eradication. A further focus of this edition is the presentation of advances in diagnosis and treatment of gastric cancer. New diagnostic modalities and surgical therapy, including the potential benefits of neoadjuvant and adjuvant therapy, are also covered in state-of-the-art reviews. Most patients require palliative therapy because of locally advanced or metastasized cancers, and, therefore, a large amount of space is dedicated to advances in the chemotherapy of advanced gastric cancers and peritoneal metastasis. Finally, future approaches towards a molecular diagnosis and therapy are also described. We believe that despite the still limited prognosis for patients with gastric cancer today, these advancements will help to improve the management of gastric cancer patients. We hope that with this issue we will not only help clinicians in the clinical routine management of gastric cancer patients, but that these reviews will also stimulate the interest for clinical and basic research in the field of gastric cancer.

Matthias Ebert
Peter Malfertheiner

KARGER

Fax +41 61 306 12 34
E-Mail karger@karger.ch
www.karger.com

0257–2753/04/0224–0301$21.00/0

Accessible online at:
www.karger.com/ddi

Review Article

Digestive Diseases

Dig Dis 2004;22:302–305
DOI: 10.1159/000083590

Gastric Cancer: Who Is at Risk?

Rocco Maurizio Zagari Franco Bazzoli

Department of Internal Medicine and Gastroentererology, University of Bologna, Bologna, Italy

Key Words
Gastric cancer · Gastric cancer, dietary factors · Gastric cancer, host genetic factors · *Helicobacter pylori*

Abstract
Gastric cancer is a multifactorial disease. *Helicobacter pylori* infection, host genetic factors and dietetic factors play an important role in the development of gastric cancer. Individuals with a positive family history of gastric cancer and/or pro-inflammatory polymorphisms of the interleukin-1 and tumor necrosis factor A genes infected by *H. pylori* virulent strains (cagA-, vacA s1-, vacA m1- and babA2-positive) have the highest risk of gastric cancer development. Diets rich in salted and smoked food and poor in fresh fruit and vegetables favor gastric carcinogenesis. Genetic combined with bacterial and host genotyping may allow for the identification of patients at high risk of gastric cancer who can benefit from preventive eradication therapy.

Introduction

Despite a decrease in the annual incidence and mortality rates over the past 50 years, gastric cancer remains the second cause of cancer-related death. As with other cancers, the etiology of gastric cancer is unknown. However, putative etiologic factors of gastric cancer have been identified, as detailed below, which play an important role in the pathogenesis and development of gastric cancer. Recent interest has focused on substantiating the causal role of these risk factors in order to develop rational strategies for the active prevention of gastric cancer.

Differences in exposure to environmental factors, such as, different *Helicobacter pylori* strains and diets, and in the genetic predisposition of the host can probably be responsible for the variation of the incidence of gastric cancer between populations. There is a marked geographic variation in the incidence of gastric cancer. The highest incidence rates occur in Costa Rica and Japan while the lowest rates occur in the USA [1].

The most important risk factors for gastric cancer are *H. pylori* infection, host genetic factors, such as a positive family history of gastric cancer and polymorphisms in the interleukin-1 (IL-1) and tumor necrosis factors (TNF)-A genes, and dietetic factors.

Helicobacter pylori

In 1994 *H. pylori* was classified by the International Agency for Research on Cancer as type I (definite) carcinogen [2]. The magnitude of the risk of gastric cancer associated with *H. pylori* has been evaluated by many epidemiological studies and several meta-analyses [3–5]. Probably the best evidence is provided by Forman et al.

KARGER
Fax +41 61 306 12 34
E-Mail karger@karger.ch
www.karger.com

0257–2753/04/0224–0302$21.00/0

Accessible online at:
www.karger.com/ddi

Prof. Franco Bazzoli
Dipartimento di Medicina Interna e Gastroenterologia
Università di Bologna, Policlinico S.Orsola, Via Massarenti 9
IT–40138 Bologna (Italy)
Tel. +39 051 6364106, Fax +39 051 343926, E-Mail bazzoli@alma.unibo.it

[3] that combines data from all case-control studies nested within prospective cohorts. Forman et al. reported that *H. pylori* infection increases two- or threefold the risk of non-cardia gastric cancer. The association was stronger, with risk increased sixfold, when blood samples for *H. pylori* serology were obtained 10 years or more before cancer diagnosis [3]. Furthermore, Uemura et al. [6] reported in a recent prospective study of 1,526 subjects that gastric cancer developed in 2.9% of subjects with *H. pylori* infection over about 8 years but in none of those uninfected. Also studies in animal models, such as Mongolian gerbils, show that *H. pylori* can develop gastric cancer [7]. *H. pylori* cause chronic gastritis in all infected subjects. In a very small proportion of subjects *H. pylori* gastritis progress over time from an initially superficial non-atrophic form to more severe forms, such as atrophic gastritis and intestinal metaplasia which are important precursors of gastric cancer [8]. Subjects with *H. pylori*-related pangastritis or corpus-predominant gastritis are more likely to develop hypochlorhydria, gastric atrophy and intestinal metaplasia and have a higher risk of non-cardia gastric cancer [1, 6, 9–11]. Hypochlorhydria itself increases the risk of developing gastric cancer possibly impairing the mechanisms that protect the gastric mucosa against the action of carcinogens. Hypochlorhydria favors the intragastric overgrowth of anaerobic bacteria which can convert the dietary nitrate and nitrite into carcinogenic nitroso compound [12], and is associated with a marked reduction of intragastric acid ascorbic secretion [13]. *H. pylori* strains are highly diverse and there are *H. pylori* strains of differing virulence. Among the virulence factors, the cytotoxin-associated gene A (cagA), vacuolating toxin A (vacA) and babA2 have been linked to enhanced pathogenicity of *H. pylori*. The cagA gene, which is found in 60–70% of *H. pylori* in the industrialized world, encodes the protein cagA that influences the severity of inflammation and cellular function including proliferation, apoptosis and cytokine release [14, 15]. Numerous studies have reported that the infection with cagA-positive strains further increased the risk of gastric cancer by about two- to threefold [16, 17]. Held et al. [17] show that the odd ratios (ORs) for gastric cancer was 7.4 and 4.2 in patients infected by cagA-positive and cagA-negative *H. pylori* strains, respectively. vacA gene is present in all *H. pylori* strains, but in only half of *H. pylori*-produced cytotoxin vacA, a toxin which induces epithelial cell vacuolation and cell death. vacA expression is determined by variations in the signal sequences (s1a, s1b, s1c, s2) and mid-region (m1, m2) of the vacA gene. *H. pylori* strains with an s1-type signaling sequence all produce functional vacA toxin, whereas those with an s2-type signaling sequence have little cytotoxic activity [19]. Moreover, *H. pylori* vacA s1m1 strains are more toxic than s1m2 strains and associated with more severe atrophic gastritis and intestinal metaplasia [20]. The infection with vacA s1 and vacA m1 *H. pylori* strains was associated with an increased risk for gastric cancer, with ORs of 17 and 6.7, respectively [21]. In addition to vacA and cagA, microbial factors involved in adherence of *H. pylori* to gastric epithelial cells are important in the bacterium's pathogenicity. babA2 geno-positive *H. pylori* encode the adhesin babA that interacts with the blood group antigen Lewis on gastric epithelial cell to enhance *H. pylori* colonization to gastric mucosa. babA2 gene usually coexists with other *H. pylori* virulence factor genes, such as cagA and vacA s1m1. Tripositive strains which have cagA, vacA s1m1 and babA2 genotype further increase the risk of developing gastric atrophy, intestinal metaplasia and finally gastric cancer [22, 23].

Host Genetic Factors

Considerable evidence supports the role of the host genetic factors in the pathogenesis of gastric cancer. Case-control studies indicate that first-degree relatives of patients with gastric cancer have a two- to threefold increase in the risk of this disease [24, 25]. Therefore, El-Omar et al. [26] reported that the first-degree relatives of patients with gastric cancer have an increased prevalence of precancerous gastric abnormalities, such as hypochlorhydria and atrophic gastritis, but this increase was confined to those with *H. pylori* infection. Recently, functional polymorphisms in the IL-1 and TNF-A genes have been associated with an increased risk of non-cardia gastric cancer [27–29]. Subject carriers of pro-inflammatory IL-1B-511T allele and IL-1RN 2/2 genotype are associated with higher production of IL-1β, a potent pro-inflammatory cytokine and powerful inhibitor of gastric acid secretion in the gastric mucosa in response to *H. pylori* infection [30]. Increased IL-1β levels would result in enhanced suppression of gastric acid secretion and severe and sustained inflammation and, consequently, more rapid development of gastric atrophy and hypochlorhydria with a higher risk of gastric cancer development. Individual *H. pylori*-infected carriers of the IL-1B-511T allele and IL-1RN 2/2 genotype have an increased risk of gastric atrophy and non-cardia gastric cancer, with ORs of about 3 [27]. Carriers of the pro-inflammatory TNF-A-308A allele, which is thought to increase the production of TNF-α, a pro-inflammatory and acid inhibitor cytokine, were also associated with higher risk of gastric cancer [27, 28]. Moreover, the risk of gastric cancer seems to increase with the number of high-risk genotypes. Carriage of multiple pro-inflammatory polymorphisms of IL-1B, IL-1RN and TNF-A genes conferred greater risk, with ORs of 2.8 for one, 5.4 for two and 27 for three genotypes [28].

There is an important interaction between host genetic factors and *H. pylori* virulence factors which contribute to the mucosal damage and physiological abnormalities that increase the risk of gastric cancer and its precursors. The risk of atrophic gastritis, intestinal metaplasia and gastric cancer seems to be greater in the presence of pro-inflammatory genotype of IL-1 and of *H. pylori* virulent strains [21, 31]. Rad et al. [31] reported the highest prevalence of atrophic gastritis and intestinal metaplasia in patient carriers of IL-1B-511T and IL-1RN 2 alleles and infected with cagA- and vacA s1-positive strains, with ORs of 6 for atrophic gastritis and 2.4 for intestinal metaplasia. Figureido et al. [21] show that individual IL-1B-511T carriers infected with vacA s1-, vacA m1-, and cagA-positive strains have the highest risk of gastric cancer, with ORs of 87, 7.4, and 25, respectively. Moreover, IL-1RN 2 homozygotes infected with vacA s1-, vacA m1-, and cagA-positive strains also had an increased risk of gastric cancer, with ORs of 32, 8.8, and 23, respectively [21].

Dietary Factors

There is much evidence to suggest that diet plays an important role in the etiology of gastric cancer. Diets rich in fresh fruit and vegetable are associated with a reduced risk of gastric cancer [32]. Dietary antioxidants, such as β-carotene and vitamins A, C and E, may be the components of fruit and vegetables that are of etiological importance [33]. However, supplementation studies [34] and prospective studies on single antioxidants [35] have given contrasting results. Recently, a meta-analysis of Bjelakovic et al. [34] shows that antioxidant supplements cannot prevent gastric cancer. Diets rich in salted, smoked and preserved foods are associated with an increased risk of gastric cancer [36]. Excessive dietary salt has been associated with gastric atrophy in animals [37].

Epidemiological data on dietary nitrates and nitrites have been inconsistent and their role in gastric carcinogenesis remains unclear [38]. Case-control studies have reported a statistically non-significant increased risk of gastric cancer for high vs. low nitrite intake [39].

Other Factors: Age, Sex, Smoking

Other risk factors for gastric cancer are age and sex [40]. The incidence of gastric cancer rises progressively with age, with most patients being between 50 and 70 years. Gastric cancer rarely occurs in subjects younger the 30–40 years. Non-cardia gastric cancer is more common in males than females by a ratio of 2:1.

The relationship between smoking and gastric cancer has been extensively examined yet remains unclear. Smoking has been associated with a mildly increased risk of gastric cancer [41]. The most important limitation of the studies has been a lack of control for correlating particularly *H. pylori* infection and fruit and vegetable intake. No association between alcohol consumption and gastric cancer was reported [40].

Conclusions

Gastric cancer is a multifactorial disease. *H. pylori* infection is an important risk factor for gastric cancer. Nevertheless, gastric cancer develops in only a small proportion of individuals infected, suggesting that genetic and environmental cofactors are required. The combination of genetic factors, such as a positive family history for gastric cancer and/or the presence of pro-inflammatory polymorphisms, and *H. pylori* virulent strains is associated with the highest risk of gastric cancer development. The current data underline that bacterial and host immune factors act in a synergistic manner during gastric carcinogenesis, providing a better understanding of this multifactorial disease. Furthermore, the findings may be of clinical relevance because genetic combined bacterial and host genotyping may allow for the identification of patients at high risk of gastric cancer which can benefit from preventive eradication therapy.

References

1 Hohenberger P, Gretschel S: Gastric cancer. Lancet 2003;362:305–315.

2 International Agency for Research on Cancer: Schistosomes, liver flukes and *Helicobacter pylori*. IARC Monographs on the Evaluation of Carcinogenic Risks to Humans. Lyon, IARC, 1994, vol 61.

3 Forman D, Helicobacter and Cancer Collaborative Group: Gastric cancer and *Helicobacter pylori*: A combined analysis of 12 case-control studies nested within a prospective cohort. Gut 2001;49:347–353.

4 Danesh J: *Helicobacter pylori* infection and gastric cancer: Systematic review of the epidemiological studies. Aliment Pharmacol Ther 1999;13:851–856.

5 Eslick GD, Lim LL, Byles JE, Xia HH, Talley NJ: Association of *Helicobacter pylori* infection with gastric carcinoma: A meta-analysis. Am J Gastroenterol 1999;84:2373–2379.

6 Uemura N, Okamoto S, Yamamoto S, Matsumura N, Yamaguchi S, Yamakido M, Taniyama K, Sasaki N, Schlemper RJ: *Helicobacter pylori* infection and the development of gastric cancer. N Engl J Med 2001;345:784–789.

7 Watanabe T, Tada M, Nagai H, Sasaki S, Nakao M: *Helicobacter pylori* infection induces gastric cancer in Mongolian gerbil. Gastroenterology 1998;115:642–648.

8 Correa P: A human model of gastric carcinogenesis. Cancer Res 1988;48:3554–3560.

9 Axon A: Review article: Gastric cancer and *Helicobacter pylori*. Aliment Pharmacol Ther 2002;16(suppl 4):83–88.

10 Suerbaum S, Michetti P: *Helicobacter pylori* infection. N Engl J Med 2002;347:1175–1186.

11 Matsuhisa T, Matsukura N, Yamada N: Topography of chronic active gastritis in *Helicobacter pylori*-positive Asian populations: Age-, gender- and endoscopic diagnosis-matched study. J Gastroenterol 2004;39:324–328.

12 Correa P: Human gastric carcinogenesis: A multistep and multifactorial process. First American Cancer Society Award Lecture on Cancer Epidemiology and Prevention. Cancer Res 1992;52:6735–6740.

13 Sobala GM, Schorah CJ, Sanderson M: Ascorbic acid in the human stomach. Gastroenterology 1989;97:357–363.

14 Hocker M, Hohenberger P: *Helicobacter pylori* virulence factors – One part of a big picture. Lancet 2003;362:1231–1233.

15 Blaser MJ, Berg DE: *Helicobacter pylori* genetic diversity and risk of human disease. J Clin Invest 2001;107:767–773.

16 Huang JQ, Zheng GF, Sumanac K, Irvine EJ, Hunt RH: Meta-analysis of the relationship between cagA seropositivity and gastric cancer. Gastroenterology 2003;125:1636–1644.

17 Held M, Engstrand L, Hansson LE, Bergstrom R, Wadstrom T, Nyren O: Is the association between *Helicobacter pylori* and gastric cancer confined to cagA-positive strains? Helicobacter 2004;9:271–277.

18 Lopez-Carrillo L, Torres-Lopez J, Galvan-Portillo M, Munoz L, Lopez-Cervantes M: *Helicobacter pylori*-cagA seropositivity and nitrite and ascorbic acid food intake as predictor for gastric cancer. Eur J Cancer 2004;40:1752–1759.

19 Megraud F: Impact of *Helicobacter pylori* virulence on the outcome of gastroduodenal diseases: Lessons from the microbiologist. Dig Dis 2001:19:99–103.

20 Atherton JC, Peek RM, Tham KT, Cover TL, Blaser MJ: Clinical and pathological importance of heterogeneity in vacA, the vacuolating cytotoxin gene of *Helicobacter pylori*. Gastroenterology 1997;112:92–99.

21 Figueiredo C, Machado JC, Pharoah P, Seruca R, Sousa S, Carvalho R, Capelinha AF, Quint W, Caldas C, van Doorn LJ, Carneiro F, Sobrinho-Simoes M: *Helicobacter pylori* and interleukin-1 genotyping: An opportunity to identify high-risk individuals for gastric carcinoma. J Natl Cancer Inst 2002;94:1680–1687.

22 Prinz C, Schoniger M, Rad R, Becker I, Keiditsch E, Wagenpfeil S, Klassen M, Rosch T, Schepp W, Gerhard M: Key importance of the *Helicobacter pylori* adherence factor blood group antigen binding adhesion during chronic gastric inflammation. Cancer Res 2001;61: 1903–1909.

23 Zambon CF, Navaglia F, Basso D, Rugge M, Plebani M: *Helicobacter pylori* babA2, cagA, and s1vacA genes work synergistically in causing intestinal metaplasia. J Clin Pathol 2003; 56:287–291.

24 La Vecchia C, Negri E, Franceschi S, Gentile A: Family history and the risk of stomach and colorectal cancer. Cancer 1992;70:50–55.

25 Dhillon PK, Farrow DC, Vaughan TL, Chow WH, Risch HA, Gammon MD, Mayne ST, Stanford JL, Schoenberg JB, Ahsan H, Dubrow R, Brian West A, Rotterdam H, Blot WJ, Fraumeni JF: Family history of cancer and risk of esophageal and gastric cancers in the United States. Int J Cancer 2001;93:148–152.

26 El-Omar EM, Oien K, Murray LS, El-Nujumi A, Wirz A, Gillen D, Williams C, Fullarton G, McColl KEL: Increased prevalence of precancerous changes in relatives of gastric cancer patients: Critical role of *Helicobacter pylori*. Gastroenterology 2000;118:22–30.

27 Machado JC, Figueiredo C, Canedo P, Pharoah P, Carvalho R, Nabais S, Castro Alves C, Campos ML, Van Doorn LJ, Caldas C, Seruca R, Carneiro F, Sobrinho-Simoes M: A proinflammatory genetic profile increases the risk for chronic atrophic gastritis and gastric carcinoma. Gastroenterology 2003;125:364–371.

28 El-Omar EM, Rabkin CS, Gammon MD, Vaughan TL, Risch HA, Schoenberg JB, Stanford JL, Mayne ST, Goedert J, Blot WJ, Fraumeni JF, Chow WH: Increased risk of noncardia gastric cancer associated with proinflammatory cytokine gene polymorphisms. Gastroenterology 2003;124:1193–1201.

29 Chen A, Li CN, Hsu PI, Lai KH, Tseng HH, Hsu PN, Lo GH, Lo CC, Lin CK, Hwang IR, Yamaoka Y, Chen HC: Risks of interleukin-1 genetic polymorphisms and *Helicobacter pylori* infection in the development of gastric cancer. Aliment Pharmacol Ther 2004;20:203–311.

30 Hwang IR, Kodama T, Kikuchi S, Sakai K, Peterson LE, Graham DY, Yamaoka Y: Effect of interleukin-1 polymorphisms on gastric mucosal interleukin-1β production in *Helicobacter pylori* infection. Gastroenterology 2002; 123:1793–1803.

31 Rad R, Prinz C, Neu B, Neuhofer M, Zeitner M, Voland P, Becker I, Schepp W, Gerhard M: Synergistic effect of *Helicobacter pylori* virulence factors and interleukin-1 polymorphisms for the development of severe histological changes in the gastric mucosa. J Infect Dis 2003;188:272–281.

32 Steinmeitz KA, Potter JD: Vegetable, fruit and cancer prevention: A review. J Am Diet Assoc 1996;96:1027–1039.

33 Serafini M, Bellocco R, Wolk A, Ekstrom AM: Total antioxidant potential of fruit and vegetable and risk of gastric cancer. Gastroenterology 2002;123:985–991.

34 Bjelakovic G, Nikolova D, Simonetti RG, Gluud C: Antioxidant supplements for prevention of gastrointestinal cancer: A systematic review and meta-analysis. Lancet 2004;364: 1193–1194.

35 Botterweck AA, van der Barndt PA, Goldbohm RA: Vitamins, carotenoids, dietary fiber, and the risk of gastric carcinoma: Results from a prospective study after 6.3 years of follow-up. Cancer 2000;88:737–748.

36 Hill MJ: Salt and gastric cancer. Eur J Cancer Prev 1998;7:173–175.

37 Kodama M, Kodama T, Suzuki H, Kondo K: Effect of rice and salty rice diets on the structure of mouse stomach. Nutr Cancer 1984;6: 135–147.

38 Forman D: Gastric cancer, diet and nitrate exposure. BMJ 1987;294:528–529.

39 Kono S, Hiroata T: Nutrition and stomach cancer. Cancer Causes Control 1996;7:41–55.

40 Kelley JR, Duggan JM: Gastric cancer epidemiology and risk factors. J Clin Epidemiol 2003;56:1–9.

41 Tredaniel J, Boffetta P, Buiatti E, Saracci R, Hirsch A: Tobacco smoking and gastric cancer: review and meta-analysis. Int J Cancer 1997; 72:565–573.

Review Article

Digestive Diseases

Dig Dis 2004;22:306–312
DOI: 10.1159/000083591

Pathogenesis of Pre-Neoplastic Lesions of the Stomach: Targets for Prevention

Wai K. Leung Joseph J.Y. Sung

Department of Medicine and Therapeutics, The Chinese University of Hong Kong, Prince of Wales Hospital, Shatin, Hong Kong

Key Words
Atrophy · Gastric cancer · *Helicobacter pylori* · Intestinal metaplasia

Abstract
Gastric atrophy and intestinal metaplasia are generally considered to be precancerous lesions of the stomach. Chronic *Helicobacter pylori* infection is one the most important factors in the development of these pre-malignant gastric lesions. In addition to bacterial factors, polymorphisms in the cytokine genes of the host that modulate inflammatory responses are found to have a synergistic effect in the development of gastric cancer as well as pre-neoplastic lesions. Recently, inappropriate activation of the intestine-specific transcription factor like the homeobox gene complex *CDX1* and *CDX2* are found to be an important contributing factor in the induction of intestinal metaplasia in the stomach. Aberrant expression of cyclooxygenase-2 and epigenetic changes are also frequently detected in pre-neoplastic gastric lesions. One of the most important questions relating to these pre-neoplastic gastric lesions is that whether *H. pylori* eradication could reverse these changes. However, most controlled studies showed no or just modest improvement in intestinal metaplasia after *H. pylori* eradication. Further studies should evaluate the role of other chemopreventive agents, particularly cyclooxygenase-2 inhibitor, on regression of pre-neoplastic lesions.

Introduction

Despite the overall decline in incidence, gastric cancer is still the second leading cause of cancer-related death worldwide which kills more than 700,000 people each year [1]. Gastric cancer, particularly the intestinal type, is generally believed to be a multistep progression triggered by chronic *Helicobacter pylori* infection. Chronic gastritis, glandular atrophy, intestinal metaplasia and dysplasia represent the different stages of the gastric carcinogenesis cascade [2]. Apart from easily recognized phenotypic changes, molecular changes are readily detectable in these pre-neoplastic lesions. This article reviews the role of *H. pylori* and various molecular changes associated with pre-neoplastic gastric lesions and the potential of reversing these pre-neoplastic gastric lesions.

KARGER

Fax +41 61 306 12 34
E-Mail karger@karger.ch
www.karger.com

0257–2753/04/0224–0306$21.00/0

Accessible online at:
www.karger.com/ddi

Prof. Joseph Sung
Department of Medicine and Therapeutics
Prince of Wales Hospital
Shatin (Hong Kong)
Tel. +852 2632 3132, Fax +852 2637 3852, E-Mail joesung@cuhk.edu.hk

H. pylori and Pre-Neoplastic Gastric Lesions

Based on several large-scale epidemiological studies published in the last decade, the World Health Organization classified *H. pylori* infection as a type I carcinogen in 1994 [3]. The risk of stomach cancer based on case-control studies was subsequently summarized in a meta-analysis by Huang et al. [4] which showed that *H. pylori*-infected individuals have at least a 2-fold increase in risk of gastric cancer when compared to uninfected individuals. The most convincing data came from a prospective follow-up study in Japan [5] in which 2.9% of *H. pylori*-infected individuals develop gastric cancer over a mean follow-up of 7.8 years. In particular, those with severe atrophy and intestinal metaplasia have a significant increase in risk of gastric cancer. The corresponding relative risk for cancer was 4.9 and 6.4 in those with severe atrophy and intestinal metaplasia, respectively. Gastric atrophy and intestinal metaplasia are therefore generally regarded as the intermediate steps of gastric cancer development. Notably, *H. pylori* increase the risk of developing both intestinal and diffuse type cancer.

The emergence of intestinal metaplasia in the gastric mucosa is believed to be the result of an adaptive response to an adverse environment as well as selection pressures [6]. The exact mechanisms leading to these phenotypic changes remain contentious but *H. pylori* infection, smoking and high-salt intake are consistently found to be the most important etiological factors.

Interestingly, not all *H. pylori*-infected individuals will develop gastric cancer. It is well recognized that patients with duodenal ulcer are at lower risk of developing gastric cancer while those with gastric ulcer are at higher risk [5, 7]. In keeping with this, a cross-sectional study showed that those with duodenal ulcer disease are less likely to have intestinal metaplasia and glandular atrophy [8]. Thus, *H. pylori* infection appears to produce two distinct phenotypes, namely duodenal ulcer or gastric ulcer/cancer [9]. The duodenal ulcer phenotype is characterized by the antral-predominant non-atrophic type of gastritis, whereas gastric cancer patients tend to have multifocal or extensive corpus atrophic gastritis. This hypothesis is confirmed by the recent Japanese study which showed that those with pangastritis and corpus-predominant gastritis have a 16- and 35-fold increase in risk of gastric cancer when compared to those with antral-predominant gastritis [5].

The reason underlying the development of different patterns of gastritis in different individuals has been recently linked to the genetic make up of the host and more precisely, the interaction between the host and the bacteria. El-Omar et al. [10] first demonstrated that the polymorphisms in interleukin-1β (IL-1B), a pro-inflammatory cytokine as well as a potent inhibitor of gastric acid secretion, may underlie the predisposition to atrophic gastritis development and hence the risk of gastric cancer in susceptible individuals. Subsequent studies from different ethnic groups confirmed this important observation [11–13]. Interestingly, the effect of IL-1B polymorphism is less obvious in areas with high prevalence for gastric cancer since control subjects from the high prevalence region also have a high background frequency of the pro-inflammatory genotype IL-1B-511T/T [13]. Whether this could explain the high geographic variations in gastric cancer incidences in China needs to be verified. In addition to development of gastric cancer, it was also found that carriers of the pro-inflammatory alleles, IL-1B-511T/-31C and IL-1RN*2, had an increased risk for the development of atrophy, intestinal metaplasia and severe inflammation [14].

On the other hand, the presence of certain bacterial virulence factors may increase the risk of having pre-malignant gastric lesions. The presence of *H. pylori* vacA s1, vacA m1, cagA+ genotypes were significantly associated with a higher *H. pylori* density, higher degrees of lymphocytic and neutrophilic infiltrates, atrophy, the type of intestinal metaplasia, and presence of epithelial damage [15]. In populations where cagA+ strains are prevalent, the infection by babA2+ *H. pylori* strains alone or in combination with cagA+ and vacA s1 further increase the risk of pre-neoplastic gastric lesions [16]. Notably, the combination of IL-1B polymorphism and *H. pylori* infection substantially increased the risk of gastric cancer development [12, 13]. The highest prevalence of severe gastric abnormalities is expected to be found in patients with pro-inflammatory cytokine alleles (IL-1B-511T/IL-1RN*2) and virulent bacterial genotypes cagA+/vacAs1+ [14].

Diet and Precancerous Lesions

The association between environmental factors, particularly diet, and gastric cancer has been extensively studied. It has been shown in an animal study that high-salt diet is associated with a higher risk of atrophic gastritis [17]. Salt is shown to facilitate colonization of *H. pylori* in mice and may therefore perpetuate chronic active gastritis and glandular atrophy.

Apart from that, low vitamin C intake has also been associated with a risk of gastric cancer development. Vitamin C, being an important antioxidant in diet, is a logical anti-cancer agent in the stomach. Patients with a normal stomach were found to have lower gastric pH and higher levels of ascorbic acid in gastric juice than patients with atrophic gastritis, intestinal metaplasia, or dysplasia [18]. The reduction in gastric vitamin C concentrations is also found to be related to the presence of *H. pylori* and the cagA antibody status of the individual [19]. In an epidemiological study from Columbia, subjects diagnosed with gastric dysplasia have an approximately 15% reduction in intake of vitamin C when compared to subjects with atrophic gastritis [20].

Cellular Kinetics Changes in Intestinal Metaplasia

Disruption of cell kinetics plays an instrumental role in cancer development. Inhibition of apoptosis and/or increased in proliferation leads to an increased risk of neoplastic development. *H. pylori* infection induces cellular apoptosis and proliferation in normal gastric epithelium [21–23]. We have previously demonstrated that the apoptotic index is significantly attenuated in *H. pylori*-associated intestinal metaplasia [24]. While proliferation was increased in both intestinal metaplasia and non-metaplastic regions, the level of apoptosis was significantly lower in the former. Thus, the apoptosis:proliferation ratio was markedly reduced in intestinal metaplasia which may favor cellular accumulation and neoplasm formation.

Genetic and Epigenetic Alterations in Intestinal Metaplasia

Unlike the colorectal adenoma-carcinoma sequence, the genetic mutations found in gastric pre-neoplastic lesions are less well characterized. Whilst mutation in *p53* is one of the most common genetic alterations found in human cancer, Shiao et al. [25] reported *p53* mutations in 50% of the intestinal metaplasia adjacent to gastric cancer. Accumulation of p53 proteins was also demonstrated in intestinal metaplasia, particularly in type III subtype [26]. On the other hand, *APC* mutation was detected in a subset of gastric cancers only [27].

Cyclooxygenase (COX) is a key enzyme responsible for the conversion of arachidonic acid into prostaglandins. Overexpression of COX-2 is noticed in many neoplastic conditions including colon, breast, and stomach [28–31]. By using immunohistochemistry and in-situ hybridization, we showed that COX-2 is strongly expressed in *H. pylori*-associated gastritis [32] and gastric intestinal metaplasia [30]. It is therefore tempting to speculate that the disrupted cell kinetics found in pre-neoplastic gastric lesions are due to the COX-2 overexpression, which is associated with resistance to apoptosis [33].

Gastric cancer cells express a broad spectrum of growth factors and cytokines. Among them, TGF-α and EGF-RI have been reported in pre-neoplastic gastric lesions. An increased expression of these two growth factors has been found in the intestinal metaplasia of patients with gastric cancer by immunohistochemistry and Western blotting [34]. Cyclins, cyclin-dependent kinases (CDK) and their inhibitors regulate cell growth, differentiation, survival, and cell death. Overexpression of cyclin D2 and diminished p27 expression was detected in *H. pylori*-associated intestinal metaplasia [35]. Notably, these aberrant expressions could be reversed by *H. pylori* eradication.

Inappropriate activation of intestine-specific transcription factors during regeneration of gastric epithelial cells may lead to deviation from normal gastric differentiation process. The intestine-specific caudal-related homeobox transcription factors, CDX1 and CDX2, seem to play a key role in intestinal development and differentiation. CDX2 activates transcription of intestine-specific proteins such as MUC2 [36]. Aberrant CDX2 expression is often seen in intestinal metaplasia of the stomach and in some gastric carcinomas [37]. By using *CDX2* transgenic mice, it was found that ectopic expression of CDX2 in mouse stomach induced the expression of alcian blue-positive intestinal-type goblet cells, a hallmark of intestinal metaplasia [38]. These findings strongly suggest the involvement of CDX2 in the initiation of the process leading to intestinal metaplasia of the gastric mucosa. Moreover, it was recently found that CDX2 and LI-cadherin expression are tightly correlated in intestinal metaplasia [39]. CDX2 regulates LI-cadherin gene expression in normal, metaplastic and neoplastic tissues of the gastrointestinal tract. In addition to *CDX2*, it was recently found that the *CDX1* transgenic mice developed intestinal metaplasia in the stomach which consists of all four intestinal epithelial cell types: absorptive enterocytes, goblet, enteroendocrine, and Paneth cells [40]. The stomach of the *CDX1* transgenic mice was different from *CDX2* transgenic mice by the absence of pseudopyloric gland metaplasia, thicker proliferation zone and with thicker metaplastic mucosa. It thus appears that both

CDX1 and CDX2 are important in the induction of intestinal metaplasia in normal stomach, but whether the aberrant expression of CDX1 and CDX2 could be reversed by *H. pylori* eradication deserves further evaluation.

Microsatellite instability is a form of genetic aberration typically found in patients with hereditary non-polyposis colorectal cancer syndrome. Most of these patients suffered from mutation or epigenetic inactivation of the DNA mismatch repair genes including *hMLH1* and *hMSH2*. Microsatellite instability has also been detected in gastric cancer [41] as well as in intestinal metaplasia [42]. Instead of genetic mutation, these abnormalities are usually accounted by the transcriptional silencing of the DNA mismatch repair gene *hMLH1* by promoter hypermethylation [43].

In this regard, epigenetic alterations have emerged as an important alternative pathway leading to inactivation of tumor suppressor genes in the absence of alteration of genetic sequences. Epigenetic silencing of tumor-associated genes is frequently found in human gastric cancer [44] as well as in gastric intestinal metaplasia [45]. The presence of promoter hypermethylation of multiple tumor-associated genes including *DAP-kinase, E-cadherin, GSTP1, p14, p15, p16, RASSF1A* and *hMLH1* has been demonstrated in gastric intestinal metaplasia [45]. Notably, E-cadherin methylation was frequently found in the non-neoplastic gastric mucosa of *H. pylori*-infected individuals [46]. These findings suggest that hypermethylation occurs early in the multistep gastric carcinogenesis pathway and may play an instrumental role in gastric cancer development.

Is Intestinal Metaplasia Reversible by *H. pylori* Eradication?

Despite the strong links between *H. pylori* infection and gastric cancer, the role of *H. pylori* treatment in the prevention of gastric cancer remains controversial. These interventional studies are extremely difficult to perform due to the long lead-time in gastric cancer development. Instead, most studies attempted to look into changes in pre-neoplastic lesions as a surrogate endpoint. Early studies that reported positive responses to anti-*Helicobacter* therapy were largely uncontrolled and had a small sample size [47, 48]. Thus far, there are conflicting results in the literature due to various reasons including inconsistency in interpretation of histological grading, sampling errors, lack of proper control, and different study populations.

The results of a few large-scale randomized control studies have been published recently. Correa et al. [49] reported 6-year follow-up results of 976 Colombian subjects. In their study, subjects were randomized to receive eight different treatments that included vitamin supplements and anti-*Helicobacter* therapy alone or in combination versus placebo. Of the 79 subjects that received anti-*Helicobacter* therapy, there was a borderline regression of intestinal metaplasia when compared with placebo (15 vs. 6%; relative risk 3.1 (95% confidence interval 1.0–9.3)). Interestingly, the supplementation of β-carotene or ascorbic acid resulted in a similar degree of improvement in intestinal metaplasia (20 and 19%). However, the combinations of antibiotics and vitamins did not confer any additional benefits. More importantly, the progression rate of intestinal metaplasia was comparable irrespective of the treatments received. The progression rate is 23% in placebo whereas 17% of eradicated patients showed progression of intestinal metaplasia. In our interventional study performed in Shandong Province of northern China, 587 *H. pylori*-infected subjects were randomized to receive anti-*Helicobacter* therapy or placebo [50]. At 1 year, though there was no significant improvement in intestinal metaplasia of those treated with antibiotics, patients with persistent infection (placebo group) had a significant deterioration of corpus atrophy. In the 5-year follow up, subjects who had successful eradication of *H. pylori* had significantly reduced progression of intestinal metaplasia than those with persistent infection [51]. Gastric atrophy also appeared to regress after eradication of *H. pylori*. Although our results strongly support the eradication of *H. pylori* in the prevention of metaplasia progression, it is imperative to note that substantial proportions (>50%) of individuals in both treatment groups had deterioration of metaplasia over the 5-year follow-up period. Further analysis showed that persistent *H. pylori* infection, age >45 years, alcohol use, and drinking water from a well were all independent risk factors associated with intestinal metaplasia progression [52]. Conversely, the presence of duodenal ulcer was an independent protective factor against progression.

Many of these results were summarized by Hojo et al. [53] who included all indexed literature from 1992 to 2001. Of the 25 articles that focused on changes in atrophy, 11 reported improvement whereas 13 reported no significant change after *H. pylori* eradication. For changes in intestinal metaplasia, only 5 of the 28 studies reported a significant improvement after treatment of *H. pylori*. Due to heterogeneity in study design, follow-up duration, histological interpretation and statistical methods, it remains undetermined whether *H. pylori* eradication results in any significant improvement in pre-neoplastic lesions other than resolution of inflammation.

Recently, a study using gastric cancer incidence as primary endpoint also failed to show any significant difference between *H. pylori* eradication and placebo groups after the 7.5-year follow-up [54]. It was only in subgroup analysis that individuals with no precancerous gastric lesions at baseline were found to have a marginal lower risk of gastric cancer development. Whether gastric intestinal metaplasia represents a point of no return deserves further evaluation.

Other Chemopreventive Agents

Apart from the study by Correa et al. [49] which showed a borderline improvement of gastric histology after ascorbic acid treatment, a small randomized trial from Italy also found that patients given 6 months of ascorbic acid following *H. pylori* eradication had significant improvement of intestinal metaplasia [55].

With the strong epidemiological link between usage of non-steroidal anti-inflammatory agent (NSAID) or aspirin and risk reduction for gastric cancer [56, 57], NSAID is another attractive chemopreventive agent. A recent meta-analysis showed that the continuous use of NSAID was associated with a reduction in risk of gastric cancer (summary odds ratio of 0.78) [57]. Users of aspirin and non-aspirin NSAIDs experienced similar magnitudes of risk reduction. Due to the gastric toxicity associated with conventional NSAID and even aspirin, this approach may not be clinically feasible. With the recent availability of the COX-2 inhibitors, it is tempting to test whether this agent can be used in the chemoprevention of gastric cancer [58]. In a rat model of gastric cancer, we have recently shown that the use of high-dose celecoxib resulted in a significantly lower number of gastric tumor formations [59]. Interestingly, the use of indomethacin, a non-selective COX inhibitor, failed to suppress tumor development in this model. We further showed that the chemopreventive effect of celecoxib was independent of COX-2 and prostaglandin suppression but more dependent on the induction of apoptosis and inhibition of proliferation [60]. Results of human gastric cancer chemoprevention study by COX-2 inhibitor are eagerly awaited.

Conclusion

If intestinal metaplasia represents an altered gastric phenotype resulting from somatic mutation or epigenetic changes in progency cells, it may not be surprising to find that these pre-neoplastic changes are not reversible with simple *H. pylori* eradication. Future studies should perhaps be directed to the identification of more potent chemopreventive agents or the early detection of gastric cancer in high-risk individuals.

References

1 Ferlay J, Bray F, Pisani P, Parkin DM: GLOBOCAN 2002: Cancer incidence, mortality and prevalence worldwide. IARC Cancer Base No 5, vers 2.0. Lyon, IARC Press, 2004.

2 Correa P: Human gastric carcinogenesis: A multistep and multifactorial process. First American Cancer Society Award Lecture on Cancer Epidemiology and Prevention. Cancer Res 1992;52:6735–6740.

3 IARC Working Group on the Evaluation of Carcinogenic Risks to Humans: Schistosomes, liver flukes and *Helicobacter pylori*, Lyon, June 7–14, 1994. IARC Monogr Eval Carcinog Risks Hum 1994;61:1–241.

4 Huang JQ, Sridhar S, Chen Y, Hunt RH: Meta-analysis of the relationship between *Helicobacter pylori* seropositivity and gastric cancer. Gastroenterology 1998;114:1169–1179.

5 Uemura N, Okamoto S, Yamamoto S, Matsumura N, Yamaguchi S, Yamakido M, Taniyama K, Sasaki N, Schlemper RJ: *Helicobacter pylori* infection and the development of gastric cancer. N Engl J Med 2001;345:784–789.

6 Dixon MF: Prospects for intervention in gastric carcinogenesis: Reversibility of gastric atrophy and intestinal metaplasia. Gut 2001;49:2–4.

7 Hansson LE, Nyren O, Hsing AW, Bergstrom R, Josefsson S, Chow WH, Fraumeni JF Jr, Adami HO: The risk of stomach cancer in patients with gastric or duodenal ulcer disease. N Engl J Med 1996;335:242–249.

8 Tsukui T, Kashiwagi R, Sakane M, Tabata F, Akamatsu T, Wada K, Futagami S, Miyake K, Sueoka N, Hirakawa T, Kobayashi M, Fujimori T, Sakamoto C: Aging increase, and duodenal ulcer reduces the risk of intestinal metaplasia of the gastric corpus in Japanese patients with dyspepsia. J Gastroenterol Hepatol 2001;16:15–21.

9 Chan FKL, Leung WK: Peptic-ulcer disease. Lancet 2002;360:933–941.

10 El-Omar EM, Carrington M, Chow WH, McColl KE, Bream JH, Young HA, Herrera J, Lissowska J, Yuan CC, Rothman N, Lanyon G, Martin M, Fraumeni JF Jr, Rabkin CS: Interleukin-1 polymorphisms associated with increased risk of gastric cancer. Nature 2000;404:398–402.

11 Machado JC, Figueiredo C, Canedo P, Pharoah P, Carvalho R, Nabais S, Castro Alves C, Campos ML, Van Doorn LJ, Caldas C, Seruca R, Carneiro F, Sobrinho-Simoes M: A proinflammatory genetic profile increases the risk for chronic atrophic gastritis and gastric carcinoma. Gastroenterology 2003;125:364–371.

12 Figueiredo C, Machado JC, Pharoah P, Seruca R, Sousa S, Carvalho R, Capelinha AF, Quint W, Caldas C, van Doorn LJ, Carneiro F, Sobrinho-Simoes M: *Helicobacter pylori* and interleukin-1 genotyping: An opportunity to identify high-risk individuals for gastric carcinoma. J Natl Cancer Inst 2002;94:1680–1687.

13 Zeng ZR, Hu PJ, Hu S, Pang RP, Chen MH, Ng M, Sung JJ: Association of interleukin-1B gene polymorphism and gastric cancers in high and low prevalence regions in China. Gut 2003;52:1684–1689.
14 Rad R, Prinz C, Neu B, Neuhofer M, Zeitner M, Voland P, Becker I, Schepp W, Gerhard M: Synergistic effect of *Helicobacter pylori* virulence factors and interleukin-1 polymorphisms for the development of severe histological changes in the gastric mucosa. J Infect Dis 2003;188:272–281.
15 Nogueira C, Figueiredo C, Carneiro F, Gomes AT, Barreira R, Figueira P, Salgado C, Belo L, Peixoto A, Bravo JC, Bravo LE, Realpe JL, Plaisier AP, Quint WG, Ruiz B, Correa P, van Doorn LJ: *Helicobacter pylori* genotypes may determine gastric histopathology. Am J Pathol 2001;158:647–654.
16 Yu J, Leung WK, Go MY, Chan MC, To KF, Ng EK, Chan FK, Ling TK, Chung SC, Sung JJ: Relationship between *Helicobacter pylori* babA2 status with gastric epithelial cell turnover and pre-malignant gastric lesions. Gut 2002;51:480–484.
17 Fox JG, Dangler CA, Taylor NS, King A, Koh TJ, Wang TC: High-salt diet induces gastric epithelial hyperplasia and parietal cell loss and enhances *Helicobacter pylori* colonization in C57BL/6 mice. Cancer Res 1999;59:4823–4828.
18 Rood JC, Ruiz B, Fontham ET, Malcom GT, Hunter FM, Sobhan M, Johnson WD, Correa P: *Helicobacter pylori*-associated gastritis and the ascorbic acid concentration in gastric juice. Nutr Cancer 1994;22:65–72.
19 Zhang ZW, Patchett SE, Perrett D, Katelaris PH, Domizio P, Farthing MJ: The relation between gastric vitamin C concentrations, mucosal histology, and cagA seropositivity in the human stomach. Gut 1998;43:322–326.
20 Su L, Fontham E, Ruiz B, Schmidt S, Correa P, Bravo L: Association of dietary antioxidants on the severity of gastritis in a high risk population. Ann Epidemiol 2000;10:468.
21 Moss SF, Calam J, Agarwal B, Wang S, Holt PR: Induction of gastric epithelial apoptosis by *Helicobacter pylori.* Gut 1996;38:498–501.
22 Peek RM Jr, Moss SF, Tham KT, Perez-Perez GI, Wang S, Miller GG, Atherton JC, Holt PR, Blaser MJ: Helicobacter pylori cagA+ strains and dissociation of gastric epithelial cell proliferation from apoptosis. J Natl Cancer Inst 1997;89:863–868.
23 Leung WK, To KF, Chan FKL, Lee TL, Chung SCS, Sung JJY: Interaction of *H. pylori* and NSAID on gastric epithelial cell apoptosis and proliferation: Implications on ulcerogenesis. Aliment Pharmacol Ther 2000;14:879–885.
24 Leung WK, Yu J, To KF, Go MY, Ma PK, Chan FK, Sung JJ: Apoptosis and proliferation in *Helicobacter pylori*-associated gastric intestinal metaplasia. Aliment Pharmacol Ther 2001;15:1467–1472.
25 Shiao YH, Rugge M, Correa P, Lehmann HP, Scheer WD: p53 alteration in gastric precancerous lesions. Am J Pathol 1994;144:511–517.
26 Wu MS, Shun CT, Lee WC, Chen CJ, Wang HP, Lee WJ, Sheu JC, Lin JT: Overexpression of p53 in different subtypes of intestinal metaplasia and gastric cancer. Br J Cancer 1998;78:971–973.
27 Horii A, Nakatsuru S, Miyoshi Y, Ichii S, Nagase H, Kato Y, Yanagisawa A, Nakamura Y: The APC gene, responsible for familial adenomatous polyposis, is mutated in human gastric cancer. Cancer Res 1992;52:3231–3233.
28 Gupta RA, Dubois RN: Colorectal cancer prevention and treatment by inhibition of cyclooxygenase-2. Nat Rev Cancer 2001;1:11–21.
29 Wang D, Dubois RN: Cyclooxygenase-2: A potential target in breast cancer. Semin Oncol 2004;31(suppl 3):64–73.
30 Sung JJY, Leung WK, Go MYY, To KF, Cheng AS, Ng EK, Chan FK: Cyclooxygenase-2 expression in *Helicobacter pylori*-associated pre-malignant and malignant gastric lesions. Am J Pathol 2000;157:729–735.
31 Leung WK, To KF, Ng YP, Lee TL, Lau JY, Chan FK, Ng EK, Chung SC, Sung JJ: Association between cyclo-oxygenase-2 overexpression and missense p53 mutations in gastric cancer. Br J Cancer 2001;84:335–339.
32 Chan FK, To KF, Ng YP, Lee TL, Cheng AS, Leung WK, Sung JJ: Expression and cellular localization of COX-1 and -2 in *Helicobacter pylori* gastritis. Aliment Pharmacol Ther 2001;15:187–193.
33 Tsujii M, DuBois RN: Alterations in cellular adhesion and apoptosis in epithelial cells overexpressing prostaglandin endoperoxide synthase-2. Cell 1995;83:493–501.
34 Filipe MI, Osborn M, Linehan J, Sanidas E, Brito MJ, Jankowski J: Expression of transforming growth factor-α, epidermal growth factor receptor and epidermal growth factor in precursor lesions to gastric carcinoma. Br J Cancer 1995;71:30–36.
35 Yu J, Leung WK, Ng EK, To KF, Ebert MP, Go MY, Chan WY, Chan FK, Chung SC, Malfertheiner P, Sung JJ: Effect of *H. pylori* eradication on expression of cyclin D2 and p27 in gastric intestinal metaplasia. Aliment Pharmacol Ther 2001;15:1505–1512.
36 Yamamoto H, Bai YQ, Yuasa Y: Homeodomain protein CDX2 regulates goblet-specific MUC2 gene expression. Biochem Biophys Res Commun 2003;300:813–818.
37 Bai YQ, Yamamoto H, Akiyama Y, Tanaka H, Takizawa T, Koike M, Kenji Yagi O, Saitoh K, Takeshita K, Iwai T, Yuasa Y: Ectopic expression of homeodomain protein CDX2 in intestinal metaplasia and carcinomas of the stomach. Cancer Lett 2002;176:47–55.
38 Silberg DG, Sullivan J, Kang E, Swain GP, Moffett J, Sund NJ, Sackett SD, Kaestner KH: CDX2 ectopic expression induces gastric intestinal metaplasia in transgenic mice. Gastroenterology 2002;122:689–696.
39 Hinoi T, Lucas PC, Kuick R, Hanash S, Cho KR, Fearon ER: CDX2 regulates liver intestine-cadherin expression in normal and malignant colon epithelium and intestinal metaplasia. Gastroenterology 2002;123:1565–1577.
40 Mutoh H, Sakurai S, Satoh K, Osawa H, Hakamata Y, Takeuchi T, Sugano K: CDX1 induced intestinal metaplasia in the transgenic mouse stomach: Comparative study with CDX2 transgenic mice. Gut 2004;53:1416–1423.
41 Yamamoto H, Perez-Piteira J, Yoshida T, Terada M, Itoh F, Imai K, Perucho M: Gastric cancers of the microsatellite mutator phenotype display characteristic genetic and clinical features. Gastroenterology 1999;116:1348–1357.
42 Leung WK, Kim JJ, Kim JG, Graham DY, Sepulveda AR: Microsatellite instability in gastric intestinal metaplasia in patients with and without gastric cancer. Am J Pathol 2000;156:537–543.
43 Leung SY, Yuen ST, Chung LP, Chu KM, Chan AS, Ho JC: hMLH1 promoter methylation and lack of hMLH1 expression in sporadic gastric carcinomas with high-frequency microsatellite instability. Cancer Res 1999;59:159–164.
44 Leung WK, Yu J, Ng EK, To KF, Ma PK, Lee TL, Go MY, Chung SC, Sung JJ: Concurrent hypermethylation of multiple tumor-related genes in gastric carcinoma and adjacent normal tissues. Cancer 2001;91:2294–2301.
45 To KF, Leung WK, Lee TL, Yu J, Tong JH, Chan MW, Ng EK, Chung SC, Sung JJ: Promoter hypermethylation of tumor-related genes in gastric intestinal metaplasia of patients with and without gastric cancer. Int J Cancer 2002;102:623–628.
46 Chan AO, Lam SK, Wong BC, Wong WM, Yuen MF, Yeung YH, Hui WM, Rashid A, Kwong YL: Promoter methylation of E-cadherin gene in gastric mucosa associated with *Helicobacter pylori* infection and in gastric cancer. Gut 2003;52:502–506.
47 Uemura N, Mukai T, Okamoto S, Yamaguchi S, Mashiba H, Taniyama K, Sasaki N, Haruma K, Sumii K, Kajiyama G: Effect of *Helicobacter pylori* eradication on subsequent development of cancer after endoscopic resection of early gastric cancer. Cancer Epidemiol Biomarkers Prev 1997;6:639–642.
48 Ohkusa T, Fujiki K, Takashimizu I, Kumagai J, Tanizawa T, Eishi Y, Yokoyama T, Watanabe M: Improvement in atrophic gastritis and intestinal metaplasia in patients in whom *Helicobacter pylori* was eradicated. Ann Intern Med 2001;134:380–386.
49 Correa P, Fontham ET, Bravo JC, Bravo LE, Ruiz B, Zarama G, Realpe JL, Malcom GT, Li D, Johnson WD, Mera R: Chemoprevention of gastric dysplasia: randomized trial of antioxidant supplements and anti-*Helicobacter* therapy. J Natl Cancer Inst 2000;92:1881–1888.

50 Sung JJY, Lin SR, Ching JYL, Zhou LY, To KF, Wang RT, Leung WK, Ng EK, Lau JY, Lee YT, Yeung CK, Chao W, Chung SC: Atrophy and intestinal metaplasia one year after cure of *H. pylori* infection: A prospective, randomized study. Gastroenterology 2000;119:7–14.

51 Zhou L, Sung JJ, Lin S, Jin Z, Ding S, Huang X, Xia Z, Guo H, Liu J, Chao W: A five-year follow-up study on the pathological changes of gastric mucosa after *H. pylori* eradication. Chin Med J 2003;116:11–14.

52 Leung WK, Lin SR, Ching JY, To KF, Ng EK, Chan FK, Lau JY, Sung JJ: Factors predicting progression of gastric intestinal metaplasia: Results of a randomised trial on *Helicobacter pylori* eradication. Gut 2004;53:1244–1249.

53 Hojo M, Miwa H, Ohkusa T, Ohkura R, Kurosawa A, Sato N: Alteration of histological gastritis after cure of *Helicobacter pylori* infection. Aliment Pharmacol Ther 2002;16:1923–1932.

54 Wong BC, Lam SK, Wong WM, Chen JS, Zheng TT, Feng RE, Lai KC, Hu WH, Yuen ST, Leung SY, Fong DY, Ho J, Ching CK, Chen JS; China Gastric Cancer Study Group: *Helicobacter pylori* eradication to prevent gastric cancer in a high-risk region of China. A randomized controlled trial. JAMA 2004;291:187–194.

55 Zullo A, Rinaldi V, Hassan C, Diana F, Winn S, Castagna G, Attili AF: Ascorbic acid and intestinal metaplasia in the stomach: A prospective randomized study. Aliment Pharmacol Ther 2000;14:1303–1309.

56 Langman MJ, Cheng KK, Gilman EA, Lancashire RJ: Effect of anti-inflammatory drugs on overall risk of common cancer: Case-control study in general practice research database. BMJ 2000;320:1642–1646.

57 Wang WH, Huang JQ, Zheng GF, Lam SK, Karlberg J, Wong BC: Non-steroidal anti-inflammatory drug use and the risk of gastric cancer: A systematic review and meta-analysis. J Natl Cancer Inst 2003;95:1784–1791.

58 Dannenberg AJ, Subbaramaiah K: Targeting cyclooxygenase-2 in human neoplasia: Rationale and promise. Cancer Cell 2003;4:431–436.

59 Hu PJ, Yu J, Zeng ZR, Leung WK, Lin HL, Tang BD, Bai AH, Sung JJ: Chemoprevention of gastric cancer by celecoxib in rats. Gut 2004;53:195–200.

60 Yu J, Tang BD, Leung WK, Zeng ZR, Yo KF, Bai AHC, Ma PK, Go MYY, Hu PJ, Sung JJY: Different cell kinetic changes in rat stomach cancer after treatment with celecoxib or indomethacin: Implications on chemoprevention. World J Gastroenterol 2005;11:41–45.

Review Article

Digestive Diseases

Dig Dis 2004;22:313–319
DOI: 10.1159/000083592

Prevention of Gastric Cancer by *Helicobacter pylori* Eradication

A. Leodolter[a] M. Naumann[b] P. Malfertheiner[a]

[a]Department of Gastroenterology and Hepatology, [b]Institute of Experimental Internal Medicine, Otto von Guericke University Magdeburg, Magdeburg, Germany

Key Words

Gastric cancer · *Helicobacter pylori* · Prevention of gastric cancer

Abstract

The evidence supporting the important role of *Helicobacter pylori* causing gastric cancer is getting stronger. The mechanisms by which *H. pylori* can influence the progression to severe changes in the gastric mucosa are under investigation. An increased gastric epithelial cell proliferation has been observed in individuals infected with *H. pylori*. This lifelong increased cell turnover is deemed to be a major risk factor for increased mutational changes and may lead to the development of gastric cancer. Successful eradication of *H. pylori* infection induces the healing of the gastritis and a significant decrease in gastric epithelial cell proliferation. Nevertheless, it is right now unknown at which time the point of no return, meaning at which time an eradication therapy leads to a benefit for the individual to prevent gastric cancer, has been reached. Therefore the major question that arises is to whom an eradication therapy should be offered to prevent gastric cancer. A general elimination of the infection might be worthwhile, but seems to be unrealistic now because of the high prevalence of the infection and the missing of a vaccine. This review reflects possible mechanisms of gastric cancer development induced by chronic *H. pylori* infection and recent investigational trials for prevention of gastric cancer by *H. pylori* eradication therapy will be discussed.

Introduction

Gastric cancer is still the leading cause of cancer-related deaths in many parts of the world [1]. Gastric carcinogenesis is a complex, multifactorial process. The evidence supporting an important role of *Helicobacter pylori* causing gastric cancer is getting stronger. *H. pylori* has been classified by the WHO as a class 1 carcinogen, even though the ultimate mechanism by which this bacterium causes gastric cancer is not known [2]. A combination of virulent *H. pylori* strain, a supporting environment and a genetically susceptible host might be the essential in the pathogenesis of gastric cancer.

Epidemiological studies suggest a strong association between *H. pylori* infection and the development of gastric adenocarcinoma. All over at least 70% of all non-car-

KARGER

Fax +41 61 306 12 34
E-Mail karger@karger.ch
www.karger.com

0257–2753/04/0224–0313$21.00/0

Accessible online at:
www.karger.com/ddi

Andreas Leodolter, MD
Department of Gastroenterology, Hepatology and Infectious Diseases
Otto von Guericke University, Leipziger Strasse 44, DE–39120 Magdeburg (Germany)
Tel. +49 391 6713100, Fax +49 391 6713105
E-Mail Andreas.Leodolter@medizin.uni-magdeburg.de

diac gastric adenocarcinomas are attributable to an *H. pylori* infection [3]. The risk for *H. pylori*-infected individuals to develop gastric cancer is about 6 times higher compared to non-infected individuals [4]. Earlier investigations have found a lower risk, but suffer from the disadvantage that the IgG response to the infection disappears in advanced cases of atrophy, where also the infection can disappear. The above cited study avoids this disadvantage, because blood samples were collected at least 10 years before cancer diagnosis. However, if the selection of patients and methodology is optimized, the risk increases to more than 25 times [5]. In another recent study with more than 4,000 healthy subjects and a follow-up of more than 7 years, the relative risk was 62 times higher for those with a low pepsinogen level and a loss of active *H. pylori* infection, indicating also the importance of immunological markers to identify subjects at a high risk [6].

Gastric adenocarcinoma is divided into two main types according to his histological pattern (Lauren's classification). For the intestinal type a sequence based on a histopathological pattern beginning with gastritis and progressing to atrophy and intestinal metaplasia, dysplasia and finally cancer has been proposed by Correa [7]. Atrophy and intestinal metaplasia are nowadays frequently used as sequential precursor lesions and have been included in several risk scores to estimate the risk for an individual person. The diffuse type appears without any identifiable histological precursor lesion [8]. Both types, the intestinal and the diffuse, show an equally strong association with *H. pylori* infection [9, 10].

Several other gastrointestinal diseases are caused by *H. pylori* like duodenal and gastric ulcer, and gastric MALT lymphoma. The proof of causality is even easier in those diseases, because it is possible to heal these diseases and/or prevent the recurrence of the disease by *H. pylori* eradication. The infection is acquired normally in the childhood; gastric cancer occurs several decades later. Studies of cancer prevention as the primary target need a long-term follow-up because of a very prolonged latency period. Even the point in life is not yet defined until an intervention (i.e., *H. pylori* eradication therapy) makes any sense to prevent development of gastric cancer (point of no return).

This review is structured in two parts, the first deals with the recent knowledge how *H. pylori* triggers cell signalling which might be of importance in gastric carcinogenesis, and secondly the results of several recent trials to prevent gastric cancer are discussed in detail.

Molecular Processes Contributing to the Risk to Develop Gastric Intraepithelial Neoplasia and Adenocarcinoma

Chronic *H. pylori* infection has been associated with the development of gastric neoplasia and adenocarcinoma. The increased risk of developing gastric cancer is the hyperproliferation of gastric epithelial cells induced by *H. pylori*. In vitro infected epithelial cells, and in vivo studies in humans and animal models, have been used to examine bacterial factors involved in the hyperproliferative response in the gastric epithelium. The *cag* pathogenicity island (PAI) [11–13] and host genetic polymorphisms in the interleukin-1β and IL-1 receptor antagonist genes associated with overexpression of IL-1 and hypochlorhydria [14, 15] have each been linked to an increased risk of developing intraepithelial neoplasia and intestinal type gastric cancer. Epithelial proliferation indices have been positively correlated with the degree of histological inflammation in the gastric mucosa in *H. pylori*-infected patients [16–18] and patients with *H. pylori*-negative gastritis do not have increased gastric epithelial cell proliferation compared to uninfected controls [19–21]. A significant decrease in gastric epithelial cell proliferation has been observed following successful eradication of *H. pylori* [19, 22–24].

H. pylori and Inflammation

Inflammation is a critical component of tumor progression and cancer could arise from sites of infection and chronic irritation. *H. pylori* is a genomically diverse pathogen [25] and several bacterial virulence factors are now considered to have a key role on the epithelial response to infection. Only *H. pylori* strains containing the 40 kb *cag* PAI [26, 27] trigger signalling cascades in gastric epithelial cells resulting in the release of proinflammatory cytokines/chemokines and involving the immediate early response transcription factors AP-1 and NF-κB [28]. These transcription factors contribute to the activation of proinflammatory C-X-C chemokines, which in vivo attract neutrophils towards the colonized epithelium and other innate defenses. Of particular interest has been the observation that chemokines such as IL-8 are upregulated in gastric epithelial cells by *cag* PAI-positive *H. pylori* strains [29, 30]. *H. pylori* stimulates the transcription factor NF-κB which involves the activity of the kinases IKKα and IKKβ [31]. AP-1 activation involves C-terminal Jun-kinase (JNK) activity [32]. The bacterial effector injected by the *cag* PAI type IV secretion system is peptidoglycan that is recognized by the intracellular nucleotide-binding oligomerization domain protein (Nod1) receptor molecule [33], which directly activates NF-κB. Nod1 belongs to a family that includes multiple members with NOD and leucine-rich repeats and recognizes peptidoglycan derived primarily from Gram-negative bacteria [33]. Thus, certain signalling cascades that lead to the activation of the IKK complex, JNK kinase and p38 kinase, are only activated by *H. pylori* strains carrying the active *cag* PAI [34]. The *cag* PAI encoded CagA protein, which is translocated into the gastric epithelial cell via the type IV secretion system [35–39], is dispensable for *H. pylori*-induced NF-κB activation.

Activation of Proliferation-Associated Signalling in *H. pylori* Infection

Whilst clinical and animal model studies have investigated several aspects of the bacterial induced hyperproliferative responses, recent in vitro studies with gastric epithelial cells have begun to delineate the importance of specific signalling pathways. Furthermore, the contribution of these pathways to overexpression of key genes potentially involved in gastric neoplasia has been examined.

The epidermal growth factor receptor (EGFR) and related EGFR ligands are thought to have an important role in gastric mucosal repair [40]. Recent studies have demonstrated that *H. pylori* activates the EGFR in gastric epithelial cells [41, 42]. The upregulation of HB-EGF gene transcription by *H. pylori* requires metalloprotease, EGFR and MEK1 activities [42]. EGFR transactivation and increased expression of HB-EGF in gastric epithelial cells is induced by both *cag* PAI-positive and *cag* PAI-negative *H. pylori* strains [42]. *H. pylori* infection in humans is associated with increased gastric mucosal levels of epidermal growth factor (EGF) protein and EGFR transcripts [43]. Recent in vitro studies indicate that *H. pylori* induces the receptor tyrosine kinase HER2/Neu (ErbB-2), another member of the EGF receptor family, in gastric epithelial cells [44]. Gastric expression of EGFR ligands amphiregulin [45, 46] and HB-EGF [47, 48] are also increased in patients with *H. pylori* infection and/or gastric cancer. Additionally, expression of several ADAM metalloprotease disintegrin family genes is strongly increased in gastric cancer mucosa [49].

Recent data show that *H. pylori* induces the activation of c-Met and cell scattering (motogenic response) in AGS gastric epithelial cells [44]. The direct involvement of c-Met in the stimulation of host epithelial cell motogenic response by *H. pylori* was confirmed by using small interfering RNA (siRNA) to silence the expression of the c-Met receptor by RNA interference (RNAi) in epithelial cells. Compared to the PAI-positive wild-type strain, an isogenic *cagA* mutant strain induced only a weak motogenic response in AGS cells and a virB11 mutant strain, that lacks a functional type IV secretion system, to promote the motogenic response [44]. Physical interaction of CagA and PLCγ and activation of PLCγ by *H. pylori* contribute in the motogenic response. Further, MAP kinase signalling events are critical for the induction of the motogenic response in *H. pylori*-infected epithelial cells [44]. The observed interaction of the tyrosine phosphatase SHP-2 and phosphorylated CagA [50, 51] is of high interest in the context of *H. pylori*-induced c-Met regulation. Numerous experimental and clinical data indicate a particular role of HGF and the proto-oncogene c-Met in tumor invasive growth. Thus, *H. pylori*-induced c-Met receptor signal transduction pathways could be responsible for cancer onset and tumor progression.

Based on previous studies, wild-type *H. pylori* strains and the *cagA* mutant strain could activate Rho GTPases Rac1 and Cdc42 in AGS gastric epithelial cells. Furthermore, Rac1 and Cdc42 are recruited to the site of bacterial attachment [52]. Rho GTPases control polarity, protrusion, and adhesion during cell movement [53]. Thus, during *H. pylori* infection the activation of Rho GTPases contribute to the motogenic response in host cells.

As in many human tumor cells, gastric cancer cells overexpress COX-2 [54] and induce nitric oxide synthase [55]. COX-2 and prostaglandin E_2 (PGE_2) are implicated in maintaining the function and structure of the gastric mucosa by modulating diverse cellular functions, such as secretion of fluid and electrolytes, and cell proliferation [56]. COX-2 mRNA expression and PGE_2 synthesis in gastric epithelial cells and experimentally infected mice [57] and in human gastric mucosa [54, 58, 59] has been demonstrated in *H. pylori* infection, indicating that COX-2 is involved in *H. pylori*-related gastric pathology. *H. pylori*-triggered induction of the COX-2 gene appears independent of the *cag* type IV secretion system, and involves activation of the mitogen-activated extracellular signal-regulated kinases MEK and ERK [57]. A rate-limiting step in the control of PGE_2 is the release of arachidonic acid (AA) from membrane phospholipids, which is known to occur via a number of different pathways. *H. pylori* induces the release of PGE_2 and AA in gastric epithelial cells by activation of the cytosolic phospholipase A_2 via pertussis toxin-sensitive heterotrimeric $G\alpha_i$/$G\alpha_o$ proteins and the p38 kinase. PGE_2 production via AA release is predominately synthesized from phosphatidylinositol. In contrast to the *H. pylori* wild-type strain, an isogenic strain with a polar mutation in the *cag* PAI only weakly activates AA synthesis [60].

H. pylori-Induced Cell Cycle Control and Apoptosis

Exposure of epithelial cells to *H. pylori* alters cell proliferation rates and apoptosis in vitro and in vivo. In vitro studies have demonstrated that cyclin D1 [61] expression induced in *H. pylori*-infected epithelial cells is partly dependent on the *cag* PAI. Cyclin D1 regulates passage through the G1 phase, and cyclin D1 overexpression shortens the G1 phase and increases the rate of cellular proliferation. Cyclin D3 is frequently detected in the antral mucosa of *H. pylori*-infected patients [62], and cyclin D2 overexpression, together with reduced $p27^{kip1}$ expression, are closely associated with *H. pylori* infection and intestinal metaplasia [63, 64]. In AGS cells, *H. pylori* is capable of inhibiting cell cycle progression and induces apoptosis, which is associated with a reduced expression of the cell cycle inhibitor $p27^{kip1}$ [63]. Other reports by Peek et al. [16, 65] show that *H. pylori* induces cell cycle progression and apoptosis, which does not affect the expression of p53 or the cell cycle inhibitor p21. Further, expression of the intestine-specific homeobox gene CDX2 has also been observed in patients with chronic gastritis and is also closely associated with intestinal metaplasia [66]. CDX2 plays an important role in differentiation and maintenance of intestinal epithelial cells. Presumably in the progression to neoplasia in the human gastric mucosa, apoptosis in epithelial cells decreases but proliferation increases.

H. pylori triggers apoptosis via a Fas-dependent pathway, which depends on the expression of the *cag* PAI [67], whereas activation of the nuclear hormone transcription factor peroxisome proliferator-activated receptor γ (PPARγ) suppresses *H. pylori*-induced apoptosis, which depends presumably on the ability of PPARγ to inhibit *H. pylori*-induced activation of NF-κB [68].

From clinical studies it is currently unclear whether gastric epithelial cell proliferation and apoptosis vary according to the *cag* PAI status of the infecting strain. Two studies have reported that gastric epithelial cell proliferation is greater in patients infected with *cagA*-positive strains than *cagA*-negative strains [16, 69], although another study in patients with non-ulcer dyspepsia failed to confirm these observations [18]. Further, apoptosis was greater in patients infected with *cagA*-negative strains than *cagA*+ strains [16, 69], whilst one reported the converse [18]. A recent study in a Chinese population where 98% of patients were infected with *cagA*+ *H. pylori* strains, identified increased epithelial cell proliferation in those infected with strains expressing the blood group antigen-binding adhesin babA2 [70].

Regression of Precancerous Lesions and Prevention of Gastric Cancer by *H. pylori* Eradication – Evidence from Clinical Trials

Atrophy and intestinal metaplasia are well-known histological precursor lesions with an elevated risk for development of gastric adenocarcinoma [71]. Beside these well-known lesions, the phenotype of gastritis has also been shown to correlate strongly with the risk of gastric adenocarcinoma. *H. pylori*-positive individuals with a pangastritis and even stronger corpus-predominant gastritis are at a markedly higher risk of developing gastric adenocarcinoma. In the study by Uemura et al. [71] the presence of a corpus-predominant gastritis was associated with the highest risk for gastric cancer (RR = 34.5) and significantly higher compared to all other histological risk factors (atrophy, intestinal metaplasia, pangastritis). The finding of a corpus-predominant gastritis in combination with the appearance of intestinal metaplasia is a very common finding in early gastric cancer cases [72]. The latter study also provides that the combination of different histological features might be a simple method of identifying patients infected with *H. pylori* and carrying a higher risk for gastric carcinoma.

The effect of a *H. pylori* eradication therapy on gastritis is well known, the neutrophilic infiltration disappears and infiltration with lymphocytes and plasma cell will be reduced significantly [73]. The effect of eradication of *H. pylori* on atrophy and intestinal metaplasia is not that clear. Based on a systematic review from the literature in 2002, no definite trend of regression was observable, but at this time it was difficult to analyze this topic due to methodological problems of the studies including statistical power. Very recent publications indicate a clear benefit of *H. pylori* eradication. These studies are much more reliable because of outstanding design with a sufficient power.

One such randomized trial was conducted in Colombia and a beneficial effect of *H. pylori* eradication on atrophy and intestinal metaplasia was observed after the 6-year follow-up period [74]. In another trial, even with a very short follow-up of only 1 year, a significant benefit regarding atrophy and intestinal metaplasia was proven. The authors used a combination of several histopathological features. This new index score was based on weights for degree of severity and extension of preneoplastic lesions in gastric biopsies. Because of the short follow-up period the authors were not able to find any effect on the progression of atrophy and intestinal metaplasia in those with remaining *H. pylori* infection [75]. That *H. pylori* eradication has a substantial effect on precancerous lesions was impressively shown in a trial carried out in China. Patients with persistent infection had a 2.1 risk of progression of intestinal metaplasia, whereas *H. pylori* eradication therapy reduces the risk of progression of intestinal metaplasia significantly [76]. In this trial the authors also looked at the incidence of gastric cancer and found no significant difference between the treated and the placebo group. This reminds how difficult it is to conduct a study where gastric cancer is the endpoint. It would require a follow-up of cohorts of tens of thousands of individuals for several decades to achieve a sufficiently large enough number of cases [77]. Therefore there is strong need for trials which focus on precancerous lesions to obtain data of the effect of *H. pylori* eradication. Nevertheless, it is clear that not all patients, especially those with advanced changes in the gastric mucosa, benefit from *H. pylori* eradication therapy to prevent all cases of cancer. The incomplete regression of gastric precancerous lesions suggests but does not prove that eradication of *H. pylori* decreases the risk of gastric adenocarcinoma. But there is evidence that *H. pylori* eradication is able to prevent gastric cancer. In the non-randomized study by Uemura et al. [71] from Japan, no gastric cancer was observed in patients with successful *H. pylori* eradication therapy, whereas in the control group with persistent infection 3.7% of the patients developed gastric cancer in a mean follow-up period of 7.8 years. Especially those with corpus-predominant gastritis, pangastritis, atrophy or intestinal metaplasia had the highest risk. On the other hand, a large randomized trial from China indicates that the point of no return might be already achieved when atrophy or intestinal metaplasia are observable. In this trial, performed in more than 1,600 healthy volunteers from Fujian Province, no significant reduction of gastric cancer incidence by *H. pylori* eradication compared to placebo was observed in the entire group of subjects in an 8-year follow-up period [78]. Only in the subgroup of patients without precancerous lesions at the beginning of the study, none developed gastric cancer. The consequence from this study should be that patients with precancerous lesions have to be included in an endoscopic surveillance program, but it is unknown which intervals are necessary and how cost-effective such a strategy might be. Even if advanced histopathological changes have occurred, *H. pylori* eradication therapy should be recommended because the progression of precancerous lesions can be avoided. The final proof of efficiency of the latter recommendation is still missing. Nevertheless, the recent data of effects of *H. pylori* eradication on precancerous lesions as well as the reduced risk for gastric cancer development strongly support early *H. pylori* therapy.

Conclusion

There is increasing scientific evidence that *H. pylori* infection is involved in the development of gastric adenocarcinoma. In recent years, several pathophysiological mechanisms have been identified and improved our understanding of the crucial role of *H. pylori*. Investigational trials have proven that *H. pylori* eradication therapy is able to prevent progression of cancerous precursor lesions in the gastric mucosa or, even better, to regress these lesions in parts. Furthermore, for the first time, prevention of gastric adenocarcinoma by *H. pylori* eradication therapy has been proven, not in all individuals but in a significant subset. Prevention is therefore possible; the challenge now is to identify those *H. pylori*-infected individuals who are at a higher risk of developing gastric adenocarcinoma and to consequentially eradicate the infection in these individuals.

Acknowledgement

The work was supported in part by the Deutsche Forschungsgemeinschaft (Na 292/7-1) by a grant to M.N.

References

1 Murray CJ, Lopez AD: Alternative projections of mortality and disability by cause 1990–2020: Global Burden of Disease Study. Lancet 1997;349:1498–1504.

2 IARC Working Group on the Evaluation of Carcinogenic Risks to Humans: Schistosomes, liver flukes and *Helicobacter pylori*, Lyon, June 7–14, 1994. IARC Monogr Eval Carcinog Risks Hum 1994;61:1–241:1–241.

3 Ekstrom AM, Held M, Hansson LE, Engstrand L, Nyren O: *Helicobacter pylori* in gastric cancer established by CagA immunoblot as a marker of past infection. Gastroenterology 2001;121:784–791.

4 Helicobacter and Cancer Collaborative Group: Gastric cancer and *Helicobacter pylori*: A combined analysis of 12 case-control studies nested within prospective cohorts. Gut 2001;49:347–353.

5 Brenner H, Arndt V, Stegmaier C, Ziegler H, Rothenbacher D: Is *Helicobacter pylori* infection a necessary condition for noncardia gastric cancer? Am J Epidemiol 2004;159:252–258.

6 Ohata H, Kitauchi S, Yoshimura N, et al: Progression of chronic atrophic gastritis associated with *Helicobacter pylori* infection increases risk of gastric cancer. Int J Cancer 2004;109:138–143.

7 Correa P: Human gastric carcinogenesis: A multistep and multifactorial process. First American Cancer Society Award Lecture on Cancer Epidemiology and Prevention. Cancer Res 1992;52:6735–6740.

8 Sipponen P, Marshall BJ: Gastritis and gastric cancer. Western countries. Gastroenterol Clin North Am 2000;29:579–592.

9 Meining A, Bayerdorffer E, Muller P, et al: Gastric carcinoma risk index in patients infected with *Helicobacter pylori*. Virchows Arch 1998;432:311–314.

10 Huang JQ, Sridhar S, Chen Y, Hunt RH: Meta-analysis of the relationship between *Helicobacter pylori* seropositivity and gastric cancer. Gastroenterology 1998;114:1169–1179.

11 Blaser MJ, Perez-Perez GI, Kleanthous H, et al: Infection with *Helicobacter pylori* strains possessing cagA is associated with an increased risk of developing adenocarcinoma of the stomach. Cancer Res 1995;55:2111–2115.

12 Kuipers EJ, Perez-Perez GI, Meuwissen SG, Blaser MJ: *Helicobacter pylori* and atrophic gastritis: Importance of the cagA status. J Natl Cancer Inst 1995;87:1777–1780.

13 Webb PM, Crabtree JE, Forman D: Gastric cancer, cytotoxin-associated gene A-positive *Helicobacter pylori*, and serum pepsinogens: An international study. The Eurogst Study Group. Gastroenterology 1999;116:269–276.

14 El-Omar EM, Carrington M, Chow WH, et al: Interleukin-1 polymorphisms associated with increased risk of gastric cancer. Nature 2000;404:398–402.

15 Machado JC, Pharoah P, Sousa S, et al: Interleukin-1B and interleukin-1RN polymorphisms are associated with increased risk of gastric carcinoma. Gastroenterology 2001;121:823–829.

16 Peek RM Jr, Moss SF, Tham KT, et al: *Helicobacter pylori* cagA+ strains and dissociation of gastric epithelial cell proliferation from apoptosis. J Natl Cancer Inst 1997;89:863–868.

17 Lynch DA, Mapstone NP, Clarke AM, et al: Correlation between epithelial cell proliferation and histological grading in gastric mucosa. J Clin Pathol 1999;52:367–371.

18 Moss SF, Sordillo EM, Abdalla AM, et al: Increased gastric epithelial cell apoptosis associated with colonization with cagA + *Helicobacter pylori* strains. Cancer Res 2001;61:1406–1411.

19 Lynch DA, Mapstone NP, Clarke AM, et al: Cell proliferation in *Helicobacter pylori* associated gastritis and the effect of eradication therapy. Gut 1995;36:346–350.

20 Cahill RJ, Kilgallen C, Beattie S, Hamilton H, O'Morain C: Gastric epithelial cell kinetics in the progression from normal mucosa to gastric carcinoma. Gut 1996;38:177–181.

21 Panella C, Ierardi E, Polimeno L, et al: Proliferative activity of gastric epithelium in progressive stages of *Helicobacter pylori* infection. Dig Dis Sci 1996;41:1132–1138.

22 Fraser AG, Sim R, Sankey EA, Dhillon AP, Pounder RE: Effect of eradication of *Helicobacter pylori* on gastric epithelial cell proliferation. Aliment Pharmacol Ther 1994;8:167–173.

23 Cahill RJ, Xia H, Kilgallen C, Beattie S, Hamilton H, O'Morain C: Effect of eradication of *Helicobacter pylori* infection on gastric epithelial cell proliferation. Dig Dis Sci 1995;40:1627–1631.

24 Leung WK, To KF, Chan FK, Lee TL, Chung SC, Sung JJ: Interaction of *Helicobacter pylori* eradication and non-steroidal anti-inflammatory drugs on gastric epithelial apoptosis and proliferation: Implications on ulcerogenesis. Aliment Pharmacol Ther 2000;14:879–885.

25 Suerbaum S, Smith JM, Bapumia K, et al: Free recombination within *Helicobacter pylori*. Proc Natl Acad Sci USA 1998;95:12619–12624.

26 Censini S, Lange C, Xiang Z, et al: cag, a pathogenicity island of *Helicobacter pylori*, encodes type I-specific and disease-associated virulence factors. Proc Natl Acad Sci USA 1996;93:14648–14653.

27 Akopyants NS, Clifton SW, Kersulyte D, et al: Analyses of the cag pathogenicity island of *Helicobacter pylori*. Mol Microbiol 1998;28:37–53.

28 Naumann M: Host cell signaling in *Helicobacter pylori* infection. Int J Med Microbiol 2001;291:299–305.

29 Crabtree JE, Farmery SM, Lindley IJ, Figura N, Peichl P, Tompkins DS: CagA/cytotoxic strains of *Helicobacter pylori* and interleukin-8 in gastric epithelial cell lines. J Clin Pathol 1994;47:945–950.

30 Sharma SA, Tummuru MK, Miller GG, Blaser MJ: Interleukin-8 response of gastric epithelial cell lines to *Helicobacter pylori* stimulation in vitro. Infect Immun 1995;63:1681–1687.

31 Foryst-Ludwig A, Naumann M: p21-activated kinase 1 activates the NF-κB-inducing kinase-IκB kinases NF-κB pathway and proinflammatory cytokines in *Helicobacter pylori* infection. J Biol Chem 2000;275:39779–39785.

32 Naumann M, Wessler S, Bartsch C, et al: Activation of activator protein 1 and stress response kinases in epithelial cells colonized by *Helicobacter pylori* encoding the cag pathogenicity island. J Biol Chem 1999;274:31655–31662.

33 Viala J, Chaput C, Boneca IG, et al: Nod1 responds to peptidoglycan delivered by the *Helicobacter pylori* cag pathogenicity island. Nat Immunol 2004;5:1166–1174.

34 Naumann M, Crabtree JE: *Helicobacter pylori*-induced epithelial cell signalling in gastric carcinogenesis. Trends Microbiol 2004;12:29–36.

35 Segal ED, Cha J, Lo J, Falkow S, Tompkins LS: Altered states: Involvement of phosphorylated CagA in the induction of host cellular growth changes by *Helicobacter pylori*. Proc Natl Acad Sci USA 1999;96:14559–14564.

36 Asahi M, Azuma T, Ito S, et al: *Helicobacter pylori* CagA protein can be tyrosine phosphorylated in gastric epithelial cells. J Exp Med 2000;191:593–602.

37 Backert S, Ziska E, Brinkmann V, et al: Translocation of the *Helicobacter pylori* CagA protein in gastric epithelial cells by a type IV secretion apparatus. Cell Microbiol 2000;2:155–164.

38 Odenbreit S, Puls J, Sedlmaier B, Gerland E, Fischer W, Haas R: Translocation of *Helicobacter pylori* CagA into gastric epithelial cells by type IV secretion. Science 2000;287:1497–1500.

39 Stein M, Rappuoli R, Covacci A: Tyrosine phosphorylation of the *Helicobacter pylori* CagA antigen after cag-driven host cell translocation. Proc Natl Acad Sci USA 2000;97:1263–1268.

40 Barnard JA, Beauchamp RD, Russell WE, Dubois RN, Coffey RJ: Epidermal growth factor-related peptides and their relevance to gastrointestinal pathophysiology. Gastroenterology 1995;108:564–580.

41 Keates S, Sougioultzis S, Keates AC, et al: cag+ *Helicobacter pylori* induce transactivation of the epidermal growth factor receptor in AGS gastric epithelial cells. J Biol Chem 2001;276:48127–48134.

42 Wallasch C, Crabtree JE, Bevec D, Robinson PA, Wagner H, Ullrich A: *Helicobacter pylori*-stimulated EGF receptor transactivation requires metalloprotease cleavage of HB-EGF. Biochem Biophys Res Commun 2002;295:695–701.

43 Wong BC, Wang WP, So WH, et al: Epidermal growth factor and its receptor in chronic active gastritis and gastroduodenal ulcer before and after *Helicobacter pylori* eradication. Aliment Pharmacol Ther 2001;15:1459–1465.
44 Churin Y, Al Ghoul L, Kepp O, Meyer TF, Birchmeier W, Naumann M: *Helicobacter pylori* CagA protein targets the c-Met receptor and enhances the motogenic response. J Cell Biol 2003;161:249–255.
45 Cook PW, Pittelkow MR, Keeble WW, Graves-Deal R, Coffey RJ Jr, Shipley GD: Amphiregulin messenger RNA is elevated in psoriatic epidermis and gastrointestinal carcinomas. Cancer Res 1992;52:3224–3227.
46 Cox JM, Clayton CL, Tomita T, Wallace DM, Robinson PA, Crabtree JE: cDNA array analysis of cag pathogenicity island-associated *Helicobacter pylori* epithelial cell response genes. Infect Immun 2001;69:6970–6980.
47 Naef M, Yokoyama M, Friess H, Büchler MW, Korc M: Co-expression of heparin-binding EGF-like growth factor and related peptides in human gastric carcinoma. Int J Cancer 1996; 66:315–321.
48 Murayama Y, Miyagawa J, Shinomura Y, et al: Significance of the association between heparin-binding epidermal growth factor-like growth factor and CD9 in human gastric cancer. Int J Cancer 2002;98:505–513.
49 Yoshimura T, Tomita T, Dixon MF, Axon AT, Robinson PA, Crabtree JE: ADAMs (a disintegrin and metalloproteinase) messenger RNA expression in *Helicobacter pylori*-infected, normal, and neoplastic gastric mucosa. J Infect Dis 2002;185:332–340.
50 Higashi H, Tsutsumi R, Muto S, et al: SHP-2 tyrosine phosphatase as an intracellular target of *Helicobacter pylori* CagA protein. Science 2002;295:683–686.
51 Higashi H, Tsutsumi R, Fujita A, et al: Biological activity of the *Helicobacter pylori* virulence factor CagA is determined by variation in the tyrosine phosphorylation sites. Proc Natl Acad Sci USA 2002;99:14428–14433.
52 Churin Y, Kardalinou E, Meyer TF, Naumann M: Pathogenicity island-dependent activation of Rho GTPases Rac1 and Cdc42 in *Helicobacter pylori* infection. Mol Microbiol 2001; 40:815–823.
53 Nobes CD, Hall A: Rho GTPases control polarity, protrusion, and adhesion during cell movement. J Cell Biol 1999;144:1235–1244.
54 Sung JJ, Leung WK, Go MY, et al: Cyclooxygenase-2 expression in *Helicobacter pylori*-associated premalignant and malignant gastric lesions. Am J Pathol 2000;157:729–735.
55 Fu S, Ramanujam KS, Wong A, et al: Increased expression and cellular localization of inducible nitric oxide synthase and cyclooxygenase 2 in *Helicobacter pylori* gastritis. Gastroenterology 1999;116:1319–1329.
56 Eberhart CE, Dubois RN: Eicosanoids and the gastrointestinal tract. Gastroenterology 1995; 109:285–301.
57 Juttner S, Cramer T, Wessler S, et al: *Helicobacter pylori* stimulates host cyclooxygenase-2 gene transcription: Critical importance of MEK/ERK-dependent activation of USF1/-2 and CREB transcription factors. Cell Microbiol 2003;5:821–834.
58 Sawaoka H, Kawano S, Tsuji S, et al: *Helicobacter pylori* infection induces cyclooxygenase-2 expression in human gastric mucosa. Prostaglandins Leukot Essent Fatty Acids 1998;59: 313–316.
59 McCarthy CJ, Crofford LJ, Greenson J, Scheiman JM: Cyclooxygenase-2 expression in gastric antral mucosa before and after eradication of *Helicobacter pylori* infection. Am J Gastroenterol 1999;94:1218–1223.
60 Pomorski T, Meyer TF, Naumann M: *Helicobacter pylori*-induced prostaglandin E_2 synthesis involves activation of cytosolic phospholipase A_2 in epithelial cells. J Biol Chem 2001; 276:804–810.
61 Hirata Y, Maeda S, Mitsuno Y, et al: *Helicobacter pylori* activates the cyclin D1 gene through mitogen-activated protein kinase pathway in gastric cancer cells. Infect Immun 2001;69:3965–3971.
62 Miehlke S, Yu J, Ebert M, et al: Expression of G1 phase cyclins in human gastric cancer and gastric mucosa of first-degree relatives. Dig Dis Sci 2002;47:1248–1256.
63 Shirin H, Sordillo EM, Kolevska TK, et al: Chronic *Helicobacter pylori* infection induces an apoptosis-resistant phenotype associated with decreased expression of $p27^{kip1}$. Infect Immun 2000;68:5321–5328.
64 Yu J, Leung WK, Ng EK, et al: Effect of *Helicobacter pylori* eradication on expression of cyclin D2 and p27 in gastric intestinal metaplasia. Aliment Pharmacol Ther 2001;15: 1505–1511.
65 Peek RM Jr, Blaser MJ, Mays DJ, et al: *Helicobacter pylori* strain-specific genotypes and modulation of the gastric epithelial cell cycle. Cancer Res 1999;59:6124–6131.
66 Satoh K, Mutoh H, Eda A, et al: Aberrant expression of CDX2 in the gastric mucosa with and without intestinal metaplasia: Effect of eradication of *Helicobacter pylori*. Helicobacter 2002;7:192–198.
67 Le'Negrate G, Ricci V, Hofman V, Mograbi B, Hofman P, Rossi B: Epithelial intestinal cell apoptosis induced by *Helicobacter pylori* depends on expression of the cag pathogenicity island phenotype. Infect Immun 2001;69: 5001–5009.
68 Gupta RA, Polk DB, Krishna U, et al: Activation of peroxisome proliferator-activated receptor-γ suppresses nuclear factor κB-mediated apoptosis induced by *Helicobacter pylori* in gastric epithelial cells. J Biol Chem 2001;276: 31059–31066.
69 Rokkas T, Ladas S, Liatsos C, et al: Relationship of *Helicobacter pylori* CagA status to gastric cell proliferation and apoptosis. Dig Dis Sci 1999;44:487–493.
70 Yu J, Leung WK, Go MY, et al: Relationship between *Helicobacter pylori* babA2 status with gastric epithelial cell turnover and premalignant gastric lesions. Gut 2002;51:480–484.
71 Uemura N, Okamoto S, Yamamoto S, et al: *Helicobacter pylori* infection and the development of gastric cancer. N Engl J Med 2001;345: 784–789.
72 Meining A, Bayerdorffer E, Muller P, et al: Gastric carcinoma risk index in patients infected with *Helicobacter pylori*. Virchows Arch 1998;432:311–314.
73 Hojo M, Miwa H, Ohkusa T, Ohkura R, Kurosawa A, Sato N: Alteration of histological gastritis after cure of *Helicobacter pylori* infection. Aliment Pharmacol Ther 2002;16:1923–1932.
74 Correa P, Fontham ET, Bravo JC, et al: Chemoprevention of gastric dysplasia: Randomized trial of antioxidant supplements and anti-*Helicobacter pylori* therapy. J Natl Cancer Inst 2000;92:1881–1888.
75 Ley C, Mohar A, Guarner J, et al: *Helicobacter pylori* eradication and gastric preneoplastic conditions: A randomized, double-blind, placebo-controlled trial. Cancer Epidemiol Biomarkers Prev 2004;13:4–10.
76 Leung WK, Lin SR, Ching JY, et al: Factors predicting progression of gastric intestinal metaplasia: Results of a randomised trial on *Helicobacter pylori* eradication. Gut 2004;53: 1244–1249.
77 Correa P: Is gastric cancer preventable? Gut 2004;53:1217–1219.
78 Wong BC, Lam SK, Wong WM, et al: *Helicobacter pylori* eradication to prevent gastric cancer in a high-risk region of China: A randomized controlled trial. JAMA 2004;291: 187–194.

Review Article

Digestive Diseases

Dig Dis 2004;22:320–326
DOI: 10.1159/000083593

Chemoprevention of Gastric Cancer: Role of COX-2 Inhibitors and Other Agents

Gerardo Nardone Alba Rocco

Department of Clinical and Experimental Medicine, Gastroenterology Unit, University 'Federico II', Naples, Italy

Key Words
Gastric cancer · Chemoprevention · *Helicobacter pylori* · COX-2 inhibitors

Abstract
Despite the decrease in incidence, gastric cancer remains the second leading cause of cancer-related death worldwide. Prevention is likely to be the most effective means of not only reducing the incidence but also mortality from this disease. The term 'chemoprevention' has been referred to the prevention of cancer using specific agents to suppress or reverse the carcinogenic process. In recent years, attention has been focused on the anticancer properties of non-steroidal anti-inflammatory drugs (NSAIDs), *Helicobacter pylori* eradication therapy and diet life-style. In vitro and in vivo studies show that widespread and long-term use of NSAIDs may be adopted in the healthy population for gastric chemoprevention. Albeit, enthusiasm has been thwarted by the potential toxic effects, i.e., risk of peptic ulcer disease. The new NSAIDs, selective cyclooxygenase-2 inhibitors, causing less injury to the mucosa of the upper gastrointestinal tract may be a valid alternative. However, fundamental questions such as safety, efficacy, mechanisms of actions, and optimal treatment regimens need to be defined. *H. pylori* triggers gastric carcinogenesis, however, cost-effect analyses suggest that only a subgroup of *H. pylori*-infected subjects present beneficial changes following eradication therapy. Diet plays an important role in the pathogenesis of gastric cancer either increasing the risks of or protecting against, cancer development. Thus, a reasonable suggestion for the general population is a natural chemoprevention based on life-style *'eat to live, not live to eat'*.

Despite the decrease in incidence, gastric cancer (GC) remains the second leading cause of cancer-related death worldwide [1]. The American Cancer Society still reports 876,000 new cases and more than 649,000 deaths from GC every year, estimating a 5-year relative survival rate of <20% [2]. Diagnosis in advanced stages and the intrinsic resistance to radio- and chemotherapy of GC may account for these dismal statistics [3]. Thus, prevention is likely to be the most effective means of reducing the incidence and mortality from this disease even though, as yet, there are no effective measures to prevent GC.

The term 'chemoprevention', first introduced by Sporn [4] in 1976, has been referred to the prevention of cancer using specific agents to suppress or reverse the carcinogenic process.

KARGER

Fax +41 61 306 12 34
E-Mail karger@karger.ch
www.karger.com

0257–2753/04/0224–0320$21.00/0

Accessible online at:
www.karger.com/ddi

Gerardo Nardone, MD
Dipartimento di Medicina Clinica e Sperimentale, Gastroenterologia
Università 'Federico II', Via S. Pansini 5
IT–80131 Naples (Italy)
Tel./Fax +39 081 7464293, E-Mail nardone@unina.it

Table 1. In vitro experimental studies of COX inhibitors in gastric cancer lines

Author	Year	Cultured cell lines	Intervention	Molecular mechanism	Results	Ref.
Tsuji	1996	Kato III; MKN28; MKN45	NS-398; indomethacin	↓ COX-2 mRNA	↓ proliferation	16
Sawaoka	1998	Kato III; MKN28; MKN45	NS-398; indomethacin	↓ COX-2 mRNA	↓ proliferation	17
Uefuji	2000	MKN28; MKN45	JTE-522	↑ c-myc; ↓ bcl-2	↓ proliferation ↑ apoptosis	18
Husain	2001	MKN28	NS-398; indomethacin	↓ MAPK (ERK2)	↓ proliferation ↑ apoptosis	19
Zhou	2001	AGS; MKN28	Aspirin; indomethacin	↑ bax; ↑ bak; ↑ caspase 3	↓ proliferation ↑ apoptosis	20
Li	2002	SGC7901	Nimesulide	↑ $P27^{kip1}$	↓ proliferation ↑ apoptosis	21
Jiang	2002	AGS	SC236	↓ PKC-β	↑ apoptosis	22
Wong	2003	AGS; MKN28	SC236	↓ NF-κB	↑ apoptosis	23
Wu	2003	AGS; MKN45; MKN28	SC236	↑ 15-LOX-1	↑ apoptosis	24
Liu	2003	SGC7901	Melecoxicam; celecoxib; rofecoxib	↓ COX-2 mRNA	↓ proliferation ↑ apoptosis	25
Wang	2003	SGC7901	Aspirin	↓ COX-2 mRNA; ↓ fos	↓ proliferation	26
Leung	2003	Kato III	NS398	↓ COX-2	↓ VEGF proliferation	27
Hu	2004	SGC7901	Nimesulide	↓ TERT; ↓ PKB	↓ proliferation	28

In 1998, the Physician's Health Study showed that use of aspirin may reduce the risk of colorectal cancer [5]. Recently, attention has been focused on the anticancer properties of non-steroidal anti-inflammatory drugs (NSAIDs) in GC. The main target of NSAIDs is the cyclooxygenase (COX) enzyme which catalyses the conversion of arachidonic acid to prostaglandins (PG) [6]. Since 1991, two distinctive isoforms of COX have been recognized: COX-1 and COX-2 sharing >60% identity at amino acid level and a similar enzymatic activity [7]. COX-1 is constitutively expressed in many tissues where it regulates housekeeping cellular functions, while COX-2, usually low or undetectable, is up-regulated by hormones, proinflammatory cytokines and tumor promoters [8]. The induction of COX-2 is associated with inhibition of apoptosis, promotion of neoangiogenesis and increase in metastatic potential [9].

COX-2 expression is up-regulated in GC as well as in precancerous lesions and in *Helicobacter pylori*-induced inflammation [10–15]. Thus, the relatively early role of COX-2 in gastric carcinogenesis makes it an attractive target for cancer chemoprevention.

The purpose of this review is to provide a comprehensive examination of the COX-2 inhibitors and other agents potentially useful in the prevention of GC. Research using Medline has been carried out focusing on in vitro and in vivo studies as well as epidemiological observations.

COX-2 Inhibitors in the Prevention of Gastric Cancer

In vitro Experimental Studies

Several studies have analyzed the effect of the selective and non-selective COX-2 inhibitors on gastric cell lines focusing on cell proliferation and apoptosis. Cellular hyperproliferation and inhibition of apoptosis are considered to be important mechanisms in human carcinogenesis [29]. COX-2 plays a role in controlling apoptosis through two possible mechanisms: removal of the substrate arachidonic acid via COX-catalytic activity or generation of PG products. In addition, COX-2 and the COX-2 product PGE_2 are involved in the apoptosis pathway by up-regulating p53, p21, c-myc, bcl-2 and bcl-xl, and down-regulating bax or bak [30].

Regardless of the cancer cell lines used and gene markers analyzed, all in vitro studies [16–28] showed inhibition of cell proliferation and induction of apoptosis (table 1). The MKN45 and CACO-2 cell lines, which abundantly express COX-2, showed a reduction of both COX-2 mRNA and protein expression as well as cell proliferation rate when exposed to selective and non-selective COX-2 inhibitors NS-398 and indomethacin [16, 17, 19]. In addition, both selective and non-selective COX-2 inhibitors exerted minimal effects on proliferation of Kato III and MKN28 which express significantly lower levels of COX-2 [16, 17, 19]. The COX-2-specific inhibitor JTE-522 induced apoptosis and suppressed cell pro-

Table 2. In vivo experimental studies of COX inhibitors in gastric cancer

Author	Year	Animal model	Trigger factor	Drug tested	Result	Ref.
Lehnert	1987	Rat	MNNG	Flurbiprofen	↑ Tumor incidence	31
Bespalov	1989	Rat	NSEE	Indomethacin + dexamethasone	↓ Tumor incidence	32
Lehnert	1990	Rat	MNNG	Flurbiprofen	↑ Tumor incidence	33
Jalbert	1992	Mouse	NNK	Sulindac; ibuprofen; piroxicam; naproxen	↓ Tumor number	34
Sawaoka	1998	Nude mouse	MKN45	NS-398; indomethacin	↓ Xenograft tumor volume	35
Liu	2003	Nude mouse	SGC7901	Rofecoxib	↓ Xenograft tumor implant	25
Fu	2004	Nude mouse	SGC7901	Sulindac; celecoxib	↓ Xenograft tumor volume	36
Hu	2004	Rat	SGC7901	Indomethacin; rofecoxib	↓ Tumor incidence and growth	37

MNNG = N-methyl-N'-nitro-N-nitrosoguanidine; NSEE = N-nitrososarcosine ethyl ester; NNK = 4-(methylnitrosamino)-1-(3-pyridyl)-1-butanone.

liferation in MKN28 and MKN45 cell lines by up-regulation of c-myc and down-regulation of bcl-2 protein expression [18]. In the SGC7901 cell line, nimesulide, a selective COX-2 inhibitor, suppressed proliferation and cell viability in a time- and dose-dependent fashion by reducing PGE_2 release and telomerase activity [21]. Furthermore, Leung et al. [27] demonstrated that treatment with NS398 reduced VEGF expression in Kato III cell lines transfected with COX-2 expressing vector.

Animal Models or in vivo Experimental Studies

In vivo experimental studies would be helpful in better understanding the mechanism of tumor suppression by COX-2 inhibitors before use in human protocols. Animal models involve the application of cancer-inducing agents such as MNNG (N-methyl-N′-nitro-N-nitrosoguanidine), NSEE (N-nitrososarcosine ethyl ester) and NNK (4-methylnitrosamino-1-3-pyridyl-1-butanone). Using these models, several NSAIDs have been studied in experimentally induced GC in rodent animals (table 2), however the results have been conflicting [31–37]. Lehnert et al. [31, 33], in two different studies, found an increase in gastric tumor incidence in the rodent model of MNNG-induced GC treated with a powerful COX-inhibitor flurbiprofen. In another two studies [32, 34], treatment with indomethacin, sulindac and ibuprofen of rats exposed to NSEE and NNK led to a decrease in tumor size and number, whereas the administration of piroxicam did not produce the same result. Finally, four recent studies have demonstrated that treatment with COX-2-selective inhibitors NS-398, rofecoxib or celecoxib, suppressed the growth or implant rate of a GC xenograft in nude mice by stimulation of apoptosis and inhibition of proliferation and neoangiogenesis [34–37].

Human Studies

A growing body of evidence suggests that COX-2 inhibitors may have some beneficial effect, for GC chemoprevention, even if data retrieved from the literature (table 3) are still limited to case-control or cohort studies [38–44]. Initial reports came from record linkage studies performed in Finland and Sweden on patients with rheumatoid arthritis. In a large cohort study, supported by the American Cancer Society, on 653,031 participants observed at follow-up for approximately 10 years, Thun et al. [38] demonstrated that regular exposure to aspirin exerted a protective effect against GC. In that study, those patients who reported aspirin use for more than 16 times per month showed a reduction of approximately 50% of the GC risk when compared with non-users. Analyzing data from the population-based North Jutland prescription database and the Danish Cancer Registry, comprising 172,057 individuals, a reduced risk was found for GC among non-aspirin NSAIDs users over a 9-year study period [44]. Coogan et al. [41] found that regular NSAIDs use (at least 4 days a week for >3 months) reduced the risk of GC in a hospital-based case-control study of 254 patients. The protective effect was more pronounced in those patients using NSAIDs continually for >5 years (OR 0.2; 95% CI 0.1–0.7) than in those using NSAIDs for less than 5 years (OR 0.4; 95% CI 0.1–0.9). In a case-control study from the UK, Langman et al. [42] found a lower risk of GC in subjects who had used NSAIDs for 13–16 months before cancer diagnosis. Two different case-control studies found that users of aspirin, compared to non-users, were at decreased risk of non-cardia gastric adenocarcinoma but not of gastric cardia adenocarcinoma [39, 43]. Moreover, Zaridze et al. [40] reported that only *H. pylori*-infected patients using NSAIDs were at decreased risk of GC.

Table 3. Epidemiological studies on COX inhibitors in prevention of gastric cancer

Author	Year	Protocol study	Population	Drug	Duration	OR	95% CI	Ref.
Thun	1993	Cohort	635,031	Aspirin	≥ 10 years	0.53	0.34–0.81	38
Farrow[1]	1998	Case-control	629	Aspirin or NSAIDs	–	0.46	0.31–0.68	39
Zaridze[1,2]	1999	Case-control	448	Aspirin or NSAIDs	2 days/week for 6 months	0.60	0.41–0.90	40
Coogan	2000	Case-control	254	NSAIDs	4 days/week for 3 months	0.30	0.10–0.60	41
Langman	2000	Case-control	613	NSAIDs	7 times/last 13–36 months	0.51	0.33–0.79	42
Akre[1]	2001	Case-control	567	Aspirin	>30 tablets/month	0.70	0.60–1.00	43
Sorensen	2003	Cohort	172,057	NSAIDs	>10 prescriptions	0.70[3]	0.40–1.10	44

[1] Data refer to non-cardia gastric cancer.
[2] Reduction of risk limited to *H. pylori*-positive patient.
[3] SIR = Standardized incidence ratio.

Other Factors: H. pylori *and Diet*

GC is a multifactorial disease in which environment plays a key pathogenetic role. The most important environmental factor is *H. pylori* infection. In 1994, just 10 years after the incidental discovery by Warren and Marshal, the International Agency for Research on Cancer [45] declared *H. pylori* to be a group I human carcinogen for gastric adenocarcinoma. The relationship between *H. pylori* and GC has been postulated to exist mainly on the basis of epidemiological investigations and animal models studies. The most powerful evidence comes from a prospective study including 1,526 Japanese patients followed for approximately 7.8 years [46]. GC developed in 36 *H. pylori*-positive patients (2.9%) in contrast to none of the 280 non-infected subjects. The close relationship between *H. pylori* infection and GC leads to the critical question of whether antimicrobial therapy can be considered for GC chemoprevention. Until now, there is only one prospective, randomized, placebo-controlled, population study carried out in a high-risk area of China involving 1,630 subjects observed from 1994 until 2002. A comparable incidence of GC was found in the subjects receiving *H. pylori* eradication treatment and those receiving placebo, while eradication of *H. pylori* significantly decreased the development of GC in a subgroup of *H. pylori* carriers not presenting precancerous lesions [47].

Interventional studies in which cancer diagnosis is the primary end-point are not easily feasible since they require follow-up of a large number of individuals for several decades. An effective alternative could be smaller and shorter-term trials focusing on intermediate steps or precancerous lesions, i.e., atrophy, intestinal metaplasia and dysplasia. Many studies have focused on this issue but the results are still controversial even if more data were obtained showing regression of precancerous lesions following eradication [48–54]. A synergistic interaction between *H. pylori* infection and diet in GC has been suggested [55]. In an Italian study, co-administration of ascorbic acid with *H. pylori* eradication led to a significant improvement in intestinal metaplasia of the gastric mucosa [56]. Likewise, in Columbia, anti-*H. pylori* treatment and dietary supplementation with antioxidant micronutrients induced regression of cancer precursor lesions [57]. Tea is one of the most widely used beverages in the world. The prevalence of GC, caused by a combination of *H. pylori* and salted foods, has been shown to be lower in a tea-drinking population compared to a non-tea-drinking control [58]. Thus, diet and life-style play an important role in the pathogenesis of GC. Indeed, several observational case-control studies in many countries have demonstrated that a diet rich in complex carbohydrates, salted, pickled or smoked foods, dried fish, and cooking oil were linked with an increased GC risk while diets rich in fresh fruit and vegetables were associated with a low GC risk [59–63]. A consistent inverse association between GC and garlic consumption has been reported by a large meta-analysis carried out between January 1996 and August 1999 (RR 0.53; 95% CI 0.31–0.92) [64]. A prospective cohort study on 30,304 Japanese people followed for 7 years, showed that intake of soy isoflavones may reduce the risk of death from GC [65]. In a recent large population-based prospective study with a 10-year follow-up, vegetable and fruit intake, even in low amounts, was associated with a lower risk of GC [66]. The protecting role of diet seemed to be mainly due to the antioxidant potential of the micronutrients. Indeed, using the total radical-trapping antioxidant potential (TRAP) of different plant foods to convert food frequency intake into antioxidant potential, the intake of antioxidant equivalents was inversely related with the risk of GC (OR 0.65; 95% CI 0.48–0.89) [67].

Ideally all the observational results should be confirmed by randomized interventional trials including a large number of individuals and lasting for many years. However, at present there are only very few and conflicting studies. The Linxian chemoprevention trial carried out on 29,584 subjects in a high-risk region of China showed a reduction in GC incidence and mortality after a 5-year follow-up in those subjects who received daily supplements containing β-carotene, vitamin E, and selenium [68]. In contrast, another study, in a low-risk US population including 22,071 male physicians, showed no statistically significant benefit due to β-carotene after a mean follow-up of 12 years [69]. Finally, Xiao et al. [70] reported that a high dose of folic acid significantly reduced the development of N-ethyl-N-nitrosoguanidine-induced GC in beagles, suggesting a role of folic acid in the prevention of GC.

Conclusions

GC remains a major health concern and prevention is the only valid alternative for control of the disease. Widespread and long-term use of NSAIDs has been advocated, in the healthy population, for GC chemoprevention. Albeit, enthusiasm has been thwarted by the potential toxic effects, i.e., risk of peptic ulcer disease.

Selective COX-2 inhibitors causing less injury to the mucosa of the upper gastrointestinal tract may be a valid alternative. However, the mechanisms of the antitumoral action of the COX-2 inhibitors still remain to be defined and may vary from agent to agent and tumor to tumor. In vitro studies have shown a mixture of COX-related mechanisms in controlling proliferation and apoptosis balance. Animal models are often performed with much higher pharmacological doses than those clinically achievable. Human observational studies are prevalently of the case-control type and often suffer from inadequate sample size to avoid a type II statistical error. Furthermore, due to the high cost of these new agents, cost-effectiveness analyses must be carried out to optimize the allocation of resources. The cumulative probability of developing a lesion from birth to 80 years of age is less than 4% thus, in the general population, more than 95% of people treated prophylactically with COX-2 inhibitors will not benefit [71]. Therefore, chemoprevention with selective COX-2 inhibitors may be a worthwhile goal only in those subjects known to be at an increased risk of GC. However, also in these subjects, fundamental questions such as safety, efficacy, mechanisms of actions, and optimal treatment regimens need to be defined. Very recently, rofecoxib, a new selective COX-2 inhibitor, has been withdrawn from the market due to the high risk of coronary heart attack.

Although epidemiological studies have clearly established that *H. pylori* infection is associated with GC, there are, so far, no definitive prospective studies showing that eradication treatment significantly reduces the development of neoplasia. Prospective studies are hampered by the long period of time elapsing between infection and cancer development. Cost-effect analyses suggest that only a subgroup of *H. pylori*-infected subjects may present beneficial changes following eradication therapy, i.e., people living in high-risk areas, relatives of GC patients, subjects with gastric atrophy and intestinal metaplasia. Diet plays an important role in the pathogenesis of GC, either increasing the risk or protecting against cancer development. Thus, a reasonable suggestion for the general population is a natural chemoprevention based on lifestyle *'eat to live, not live to eat'*.

References

1 Murray CJ, Lopez AD: Alternative projections of mortality and disability by cause 1990–2020: Global Burden of Disease Study. Lancet 1997;349:1498–504.
2 American Cancer Society: Estimated New Cancer Cases and Deaths by Sex for all Sites. American Cancer Society, United States, 2000 (table). http://www.cancer.org/statistics/cff2000 /data/newCaseSex.html
3 Landis SH, Murray T, Bolden S, Wingo PA: Cancer statistics, 1999. CA Cancer J Clin 1999; 49:8–31.
4 Sporn MB: Approaches to prevention of epithelial cancer during the preneoplastic period. Cancer Res 1976;36:2689–2702.
5 Sturmer T, Glynn RJ, Lee IM, Manson JE, Buring JE, Hennekens CH: Aspirin use and colorectal cancer: Post-trial follow-up data from the Physician's Health Study. Ann Intern Med 1998;128:713–20.
6 Vane JR, Bakhle YS, Botting RM: Cyclo-oxygenase 1 and 2. Annu Rev Pharmacol Toxicol 1998;38:97–120.
7 Funk CD, Funk LB, Kennedy ME, Pong AS, Fitzgerald GA: Human platelet/erythroleukemia cell prostaglandin G/H synthase: cDNA cloning, expression, and gene chromosomal assignment. FASEB J 1991;5:2304–2312.
8 Smith WL, Garavito RM, DeWitt DL: Prostaglandin endoperoxide H synthases (cyclooxygenases)-1 and -2. J Biol Chem 1996;271: 33157–33160.
9 Dubois RN, Abramson SB, Crofford L, Gupta RA, Simon LS, Van de Putte LB, Lipsky PE: Cyclooxygenase in biology and disease. FASEB J 1998;12:1063–1073.
10 Tatsuguchi A, Sakamoto C, Wada K, Akamatsu T, Tsukui T, Miyake K, Futagami S, Kishida T, Fukuda Y, Yamanaka N, Kobayashi M: Localisation of cyclooxygenase 1 and cyclooxygenase 2 in *Helicobacter pylori*-related gastritis and gastric ulcer tissues in humans. Gut 2000; 46:782–789.
11 Nardone G, Rocco A, Vaira D, Staibano S, Budillon A, Tatangelo F, Scialli MG, Perna F, Salvatore G, Di Benedetto M, De Rosa G, Patrignani P: Expression of COX-2, mPGE-synthase 1, MDR-1 (P-GP) and BCL-X_L: A molecular pathway of *H. pylori*-related gastric carcinogenesis. J Pathol 2004:202:305–312.
12 Sung JJ, Leung WK, Go MY, To KF, Cheng AS, Ng EK, Chan FK: Cyclooxygenase-2 expression in *Helicobacter pylori*-associated premalignant and malignant gastric lesions. Am J Pathol 2000;157:729–735.
13 Ristimaki A, Honkanen N, Jankala H, Sipponen P, Harkonen M: Expression of cyclooxygenase-2 in human gastric carcinoma. Cancer Res 1997;57:1276–1280.
14 Saukkonen K, Nieminen O, van Rees B, Vilkki S, Harkonen M, Juhola M, Mecklin JP, Sipponen P, Ristimaki A: Expression of cyclooxygenase-2 in dysplasia of the stomach and in intestinal-type gastric adenocarcinoma. Clin Cancer Res 2001;7:1923–1931.
15 Yamagata R, Shimoyama T, Fukuda S, Yoshimura T, Tanaka M, Munakata A: Cyclooxygenase-2 expression is increased in early intestinal-type gastric cancer and gastric mucosa with intestinal metaplasia. Eur J Gastroenterol Hepatol 2002;14:359–363.
16 Tsuji S, Kawano S, Sawaoka H, Takei Y, Kobayashi I, Nagano K, Fusamoto H, Kamada T: Evidences for involvement of cyclooxygenase-2 in proliferation of two gastrointestinal cancer cell lines. Prostaglandins Leukot Essent Fatty Acids 1996;55:179–183.
17 Sawaoka H, Kawano S, Tsuji S, Tsujii M, Murata H, Hori M: Effects of NSAIDs on proliferation of gastric cancer cells in vitro: Possible implication of cyclooxygenase-2 in cancer development. J Clin Gastroenterol 1998;27 (suppl 1):47–52.
18 Uefuji K, Ichikura T, Shinomiya N, Mochizuki H: Induction of apoptosis by JTE-522, a specific cyclooxygenase-2 inhibitor, in human gastric cancer cell lines. Anticancer Res 2000;20: 4279–4284.
19 Husain SS, Szabo IL, Pai R, Soreghan B, Jones MK, Tarnawski AS: MAPK (ERK2) kinase – A key target for NSAIDs-induced inhibition of gastric cancer cell proliferation and growth. Life Sci 2001;69:3045–3054.
20 Zhou XM, Wong BC, Fan XM, Zhang HB, Lin MC, Kung HF, Fan DM, Lam SK: Non-steroidal anti-inflammatory drugs induce apoptosis in gastric cancer cells through up-regulation of bax and bak. Carcinogenesis 2001;22:1393–1397.
21 Li JY, Wang XZ, Chen FL, Yu JP, Luo HS: Nimesulide inhibits proliferation via induction of apoptosis and cell cycle arrest in human gastric adenocarcinoma cell line. World J Gastroenterol 2003;9:915–920.
22 Jiang XH, Lam SK, Lin MC, Jiang SH, Kung HF, Slosberg ED, Soh JW, Weinstein IB, Wong BC: Novel target for induction of apoptosis by cyclooxygenase-2 inhibitor SC-236 through a protein kinase C-β_1-dependent pathway. Oncogene 2002;21:6113–6122.
23 Wong BC, Jiang X, Fan XM, Lin MC, Jiang SH, Lam SK, Kung HF: Suppression of RelA/p65 nuclear translocation independent of IκB-α degradation by cyclooxygenase-2 inhibitor in gastric cancer. Oncogene 2003;22:1189–1197.
24 Wu J, Xia HH, Tu SP, Fan DM, Lin MC, Kung HF, Lam SK, Wong BC: 15-Lipoxygenase-1 mediates cyclooxygenase-2 inhibitor-induced apoptosis in gastric cancer. Carcinogenesis 2003;24:243–247.
25 Liu C, Tang C, Wan X, Wang C, Zhou X: The effects of selective cyclooxygenase-2 inhibitors on the growth of gastric adenocarcinoma. Sichuan Da Xue Xue Bao Yi Xue Ban 2003;34: 480–483.
26 Wang C, Tang C: Inhibition effect of aspirin on the growth of gastric cancer and the mechanism therein involved. Sichuan Da Xue Xue Bao Yi Xue Ban 2003;34:468–71.
27 Leung WK, To KF, Go MY, Chan KK, Chan FK, Ng EK, Chung SC, Sung JJ: Cyclooxygenase-2 upregulates vascular endothelial growth factor expression and angiogenesis in human gastric carcinoma. Int J Oncol 2003;23:1317–1322.
28 Hu GY, Yu BP, Yu JP, Ran ZX, Luo HS: Nimesulide, a selective cyclooxygenase-2 inhibitor inhibits telomerase activity by blocking activation of PKB in gastric cancer cell line. Zhonghua Zhong Liu Za Zhi 2004;26:209–212.
29 Moss SF: Cellular markers in the gastric precancerous process. Aliment Pharmacol Ther 1998;12(suppl 1):91–109.
30 Dannenberg AJ, Altorki NK, Boyle JO, Dang C, Howe LR, Weksler BB, Subbaramaiah K: Cyclooxygenase 2: A pharmacological target for the prevention of cancer. Lancet Oncol 2001;ii:544–551.
31 Lehnert T, Deschner EE, Karmali RA, DeCosse JJ: Effect of flurbiprofen and 16,16-dimethyl-prostaglandin E_2 on gastrointestinal tumorigenesis induced by N-methyl-N -nitro-N-nitrosoguanidine in rats. I. Squamous epithelium and mesenchymal tissue. J Natl Cancer Inst 1987;78:923–929.
32 Bespalov VG, Troian DN, Petrov AS, Morozov VG, Khavinson VK: Inhibiting effect of thymogen on the development of tumors of the esophagus and forestomach induced by N-nitrososarcosine ethyl ester in rats. Eksp Onkol 1989;11:23–26.
33 Lehnert T, Deschner EE, Karmali RA, DeCosse JJ: Effect of flurbiprofen and 16,16-dimethyl-prostaglandin E_2 on gastrointestinal tumorigenesis induced by N-methyl-N -nitro-N-nitrosoguanidine in rats: Glandular epithelium of stomach and duodenum. Cancer Res 1990;50:381–384.
34 Jalbert G, Castonguay A: Effects of NSAIDs on NNK-induced pulmonary and gastric tumorigenesis in A/J mice. Cancer Lett 1992;66:21–28.
35 Sawaoka H, Kawano S, Tsuji S, Tsujii M, Gunawan ES, Takei Y, Nagano K, Hori M: Cyclooxygenase-2 inhibitors suppress the growth of gastric cancer xenografts via induction of apoptosis in nude mice. Am J Physiol 1998; 274:G1061–G1067.
36 Fu SL, Wu YL, Zhang YP, Qiao MM, Chen Y: Anti-cancer effects of COX-2 inhibitors and their correlation with angiogenesis and invasion in gastric cancer. World J Gastroenterol 2004;10:1971–1974.
37 Hu PJ, Yu J, Zeng ZR, Leung WK, Lin HL, Tang BD, Bai AH, Sung JJ: Chemoprevention of gastric cancer by celecoxib in rats. Gut 2004; 53:195–200.
38 Thun MJ, Namboodiri MM, Calle EE, Flanders D, Heath CW: Aspirin use and risk of fatal cancer. Cancer Res 1993:1322–1327.

39 Farrow DC, Vaughan TL, Hansten PD, Stanford JL, Risch HA, Gammon MD, Chow WH, Dubrow R, Ahsan H, Mayne ST, Schoenberg JB, West AB, Rotterdam H, Fraumeni JF Jr, Blot WJ: Use of aspirin and other non-steroidal anti-inflammatory drugs and risk of esophageal and gastric cancer. Cancer Epidemiol Biomarkers Prev 1998;7:97–102.
40 Zaridze D, Borisova E, Maximovitch D, Chkhikvadze V: Aspirin protects against gastric cancer: Results of a case-control study from Moscow, Russia. Int J Cancer 1999;82:473–476.
41 Coogan PF, Rosenberg L, Palmer JR, Strom BL, Zauber AG, Stolley PD, Shapiro S: Nonsteroidal anti-inflammatory drugs and risk of digestive cancers at sites other than the large bowel. Cancer Epidemiol Biomarkers Prev 2000;9:119–123.
42 Langman MJ, Cheng KK, Gilman EA, Lancashire RJ: Effect of anti-inflammatory drugs on overall risk of common cancer: Case-control study in general practice research database. BMJ 2000;320:1642–1646.
43 Akre K, Ekstrom AM, Signorello LB, Hansson LE, Nyren O: Aspirin and risk for gastric cancer: A population-based case-control study in Sweden. Br J Cancer 2001;84:965–968.
44 Sorensen HT, Friis S, Norgard B, Mellemkjær L, Blot WJ, McLaughlin JK, Ekbom A, Baron JA: Risk of cancer in a large cohort of non-aspirin NSAID users: A population-based study. Br J Cancer 2003;88:1687–1692.
45 IARC Working Group on the Evaluation of Carcinogenic Risks to Humans: Schistosomes, liver flukes and *Helicobacter pylori*, Lyon, June 7–14 1994. IARC Monogr Eval Carcinog Risks Hum 1994;61:1–241.
46 Uemura N, Okamoto S, Yamamoto S, Matsumura N, Yamaguchi S, Yamakido M, Taniyama K, Sasaki N, Schlemper RJ: *Helicobacter pylori* infection and the development of gastric cancer. N Engl J Med 2001;345:784–789.
47 Wong BC, Lam SK, Wong WM, Chen JS, Zheng TT, Feng RE, Lai KC, Hu WH, Yuen ST, Leung SY, Fong DY, Ho J, Ching CK, Chen JS, China Gastric Cancer Study Group: *Helicobacter pylori* eradication to prevent gastric cancer in a high-risk region of China: Randomized controlled trial. JAMA 2004;291: 187–194.
48 Sung JJ, Lin SR, Ching JY, Zhou LY, To KF, Wang RT, Leung WK, Ng EK, Lau JY, Lee YT, Yeung CK, Chao W, Chung SC: Atrophy and intestinal metaplasia one year after cure of *H. pylori* infection: A prospective, randomized study. Gastroenterology 2000;119: 7–14.
49 Tepes B, Kavcic B, Zaletel LK, Gubina M, Ihan A, Poljak M, Krizman I: Two- to four-year histological follow-up of gastric mucosa after *Helicobacter pylori* eradication. J Pathol 1999; 188:24–29.
50 Ito M, Haruma K, Kamada T, Mihara M, Kim S, Kitadai Y, Sumii M, Tanaka S, Yoshihara M, Chayama K: *Helicobacter pylori* eradication therapy improves atrophic gastritis and intestinal metaplasia: A 5-year prospective study of patients with atrophic gastritis. Aliment Pharmacol Ther 2002;16:1449–1456.
51 Genta RM, Franceschi F: Gastric markers of pre-malignancy are not reversible; in Hunt RH, Tytgut GNJ (eds): *Helicobacter pylori* – Basic Mechanisms to Clinical Cure 2000. Hamilton, Kluwer Academic, 2000, pp 524–534.
52 Franceschi F, Genta RM, Sepulveda AR: Gastric mucosa: Long-term outcome after cure of *Helicobacter pylori* infection. J Gastroenterol 2002;37:17–23.
53 Hojo M, Miwa H, Ohkusa T, Ohkura R, Kurosawa A, Sato N: Alteration of histological gastritis after cure of *Helicobacter pylori* infection. Aliment Pharmacol Ther 2002;16:1923–1932.
54 Nardone G, Rocco A, Malfertheiner P: Review article: *Helicobacter pylori* and molecular events in precancerous gastric lesions. Aliment Pharmacol Ther 2004;20:261–270.
55 Yamaguchi N, Kakizoe T: Synergistic interaction between *Helicobacter pylori* gastritis and diet in gastric cancer. Lancet Oncol 2001;2: 84–94.
56 Zullo A, Rinaldi V, Hassan C, Diana F, Winn S, Castagna G, Attili AF: Ascorbic acid and intestinal metaplasia in the stomach: A prospective, randomised study. Aliment Pharmacol Ther 2000;14:1303–1309.
57 Correa P, Fontham ET, Bravo JC, Bravo LE, Ruiz B, Zarama G, Realpe JL, Malcom GT, Li D, Johnson WD, Mera R: Chemoprevention of gastric dysplasia: randomized trial of antioxidant supplements and anti-*Helicobacter pylori* therapy. J Natl Cancer Inst 2000;92:1881–1888.
58 Weisburger JH, Chung FL, Weisburger JH, Chung FL: Mechanisms of chronic disease causation by nutritional factors and tobacco products and their prevention by tea polyphenols. Food Chem Toxicol 2002;40:1145–1154.
59 Ngoan LT, Mizoue T, Fujino Y, Tokui N, Yoshimura T: Dietary factors and stomach cancer mortality. Br J Cancer 2002;87:37.
60 Trichopoulos D, Ouranos G, Day NE, Tzonou A, Manousos O, Papadimitriou C, Trichopoulos A: Diet and cancer of the stomach: A case-control study in Greece. Int J Cancer 1985;36: 291–297.
61 Buiatti E, Palli D, Decarli A, Amadori D, Avellini C, Bianchi S, Biserni R, Cipriani F, Cocco P, Giacosa A, et al: A case-control study of gastric cancer and diet in Italy. Int J Cancer 1989; 44:611–661.
62 Kono S, Ikeda M, Tokudome S, Kuratsune M: A case-control study of gastric cancer and diet in northern Kyushu, Japan. Jpn J Cancer Res 1988;79:1067–1074.
63 Yu GP, Hsieh CC: Risk factors for stomach cancer: A population-based case-control study in Shanghai. Cancer Causes Control 1991;2: 169–174.
64 Fleischauer AT, Poole C, Arab L: Garlic consumption and cancer prevention: Meta-analyses of colorectal and stomach cancers. Am J Clin Nutr 2000;72:1047–1052.
65 Nagata C, Takatsuka N, Kawakami N, Shimizu H: A prospective cohort study of soy product intake and stomach cancer death. Br J Cancer 2002;87:31–36.
66 Kobayashi M, Tsubono Y, Sasazuki S, Sasaki S, Tsugane S: Vegetables, fruit and risk of gastric cancer in Japan: A 10-year follow-up of the JPHC study Cohort I. Int J Cancer 2002;102: 39–44.
67 Serafini M, Bellocco R, Wolk A, Ekstrom AM: Total antioxidant potential of fruit and vegetables and risk of gastric cancer. Gastroenterology 2002;123:985–991.
68 Blot WJ, Li JY, Taylor PR, Guo W, Dawsey S, Wang GQ, Yang CS, Zheng SF, Gail M, Li GY, et al: Nutrition intervention trials in Linxian, China: Supplementation with specific vitamin/mineral combinations, cancer incidence, and disease-specific mortality in the general population. J Natl Cancer Inst 1993;85:1483–1492.
69 Hennekens CH, Buring JE, Manson JE, Stampfer M, Rosner B, Cook NR, Belanger C, LaMotte F, Gaziano JM, Ridker PM, Willett W, Peto R: Lack of effect of long-term supplementation with β-carotene on the incidence of malignant neoplasms and cardiovascular disease. N Engl J Med 1996;334:1145–1149.
70 Xiao SD, Meng XJ, Shi Y, Hu JB, Zhu SS, Wang CW: Interventional study of high-dose folic acid in gastric carcinogenesis in beagles. Gut 2002;50:61–64.
71 Greenly RT, Hill-Harmon MB, Murray T, Thun M: Cancer statistics, 2001. CA Cancer J Clin 2001;51:15–36.

Review Article

Digestive Diseases

Dig Dis 2004;22:327–333
DOI: 10.1159/000083594

New Diagnostic Approaches for Early Detection of Gastric Cancer

Kentaro Sugano[a] Kiichi Sato[a] Kenshi Yao[b]

[a]Division of Gastroenterology, Department of Internal Medicine, Jichi Medical School and
[b]Department of Gastroenterology, Fukuoka University, Chikushi Hospital, Fukuoka, Japan

Key Words
Normal gastric mucosa, endoscopic features · Gastric cancer, early detection · Gastric cancer, endoscopic clues · Neoplastic lesion detection, new modalities

Abstract
Detection of gastric cancer in early stages is vitally important for ascertaining better prognosis and quality of life for the patients. Therefore, every endoscopist should be trained to master enough diagnostic skills to identify early gastric cancer that often shows minimal alteration from the surrounding mucosa, easily evading detection. For the first step, it is essential that endoscopists understand the normal gastric mucosa as well as the mucosal changes caused by chronic *H. pylori* infection, a high-risk condition for the development of gastric cancer. Once a suspicious lesion is identified, use of a dye-spraying method may be useful to clarify structural alteration caused by neoplastic changes and facilitate the biopsy sampling. Development of zoom (magnifying) endoscopy enabling 80 × magnification with a one-touch switch from conventional endoscopic observation helps to identify the detailed surface structure as well as the vascular architecture of the mucosa without tissue biopsy. Combined with chromoendoscopy, this powerful endoscopic method can be used to identify small cancer foci or delineate the margin of early gastric cancer that can be treatable by mucosal dissection. Other new modalities using a variety of optical devices have been developed but the real value of their utility still remains to be proven in the actual clinical settings.

Introduction

Gastric cancer remains a leading cause of mortality among all the gastrointestinal, hepatobiliary and pancreatic cancers in Japan. In an attempt to reduce the mortality, mass screening programs have been implemented by municipal governments across the country. As a result, many asymptomatic gastric cancer patients have been detected in the early stages, resulting in the better survival and reduction of gastric cancer mortality. In contrast, the majority of gastric cancer cases in Western countries are found in the advanced stages that are too late for operation and hence have very poor prognosis. Therefore, the first important lessen to be learned from experience in Japan is to reach out for the patients without alarming symptoms. However, in most Western countries where the incidence of gastric cancer has decreased, general mass screening programs as adopted in Japan are not feasible in terms of medical economy and resources. Therefore, an effective screening methodology must be developed.

The other difference between Japan and Western countries is on the definition of early gastric cancer [1, 2]. While the Japanese pathologists pay more attention to the cellular and structural abnormalities of the neoplastic tissue to diagnose cancer, Western pathologists, with rare exceptions, are more concerned about the infiltrative nature of the tumor, and the diagnosis of cancer is usually made based on the findings of submucosal invasion. Therefore, in Western countries, cancer confined to the mucosa has been diagnosed as dysplasia or carcinoma in situ. Logical weakness of the definition based on the submucosal invasion is obvious as a number of early gastric

KARGER

Fax +41 61 306 12 34
E-Mail karger@karger.ch
www.karger.com

0257–2753/04/0224–0327$21.00/0

Accessible online at:
www.karger.com/ddi

Kentaro Sugano
3311-1 Minamikawachi
Kawachi, Tochigi 329-0498 (Japan)
Tel. +81 285 587347, Fax +81 285 406598
E-Mail sugano@jichi.ac.jp

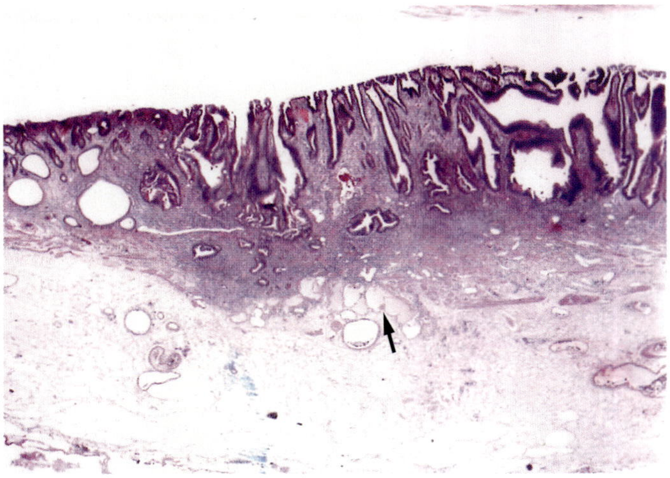

Fig. 1. Early gastric cancer showing invasion to submucosa (arrow). Only small foci in the entire cancer tissue showed invasion into the submucosa. If a biopsy sample is taken from the non-invasive area, it would be diagnosed as dysplasia according to Western criteria.

cancer tissues resected by endoscopic submucosal dissection (ESD) show evidence of infiltration in the limited area. As shown in figure 1, the majority of cancer tissues are confined to the mucosal layer in multiple sections, but if one looks carefully at the entire tissue sections, one notices a small part of the tumor cells with identical morphology to adjacent tumor cells that remain within the mucosa shows early invasion to the submucosa in a single section. With Western criteria, if one looks at the biopsy tissue taken from the tumors limited to the mucosa, it would be diagnosed as dysplasia because of no evidence of invasion to the submucosa. However, it turns out to be a cancer after pathological examination of the entire resected mucosal specimen in such a case. Since we encounter a number of early gastric cancers showing similar characteristics, we feel that the criteria used in Western countries should be dismissed. In recent years, however, the discrepancy between Western and Japanese pathologists

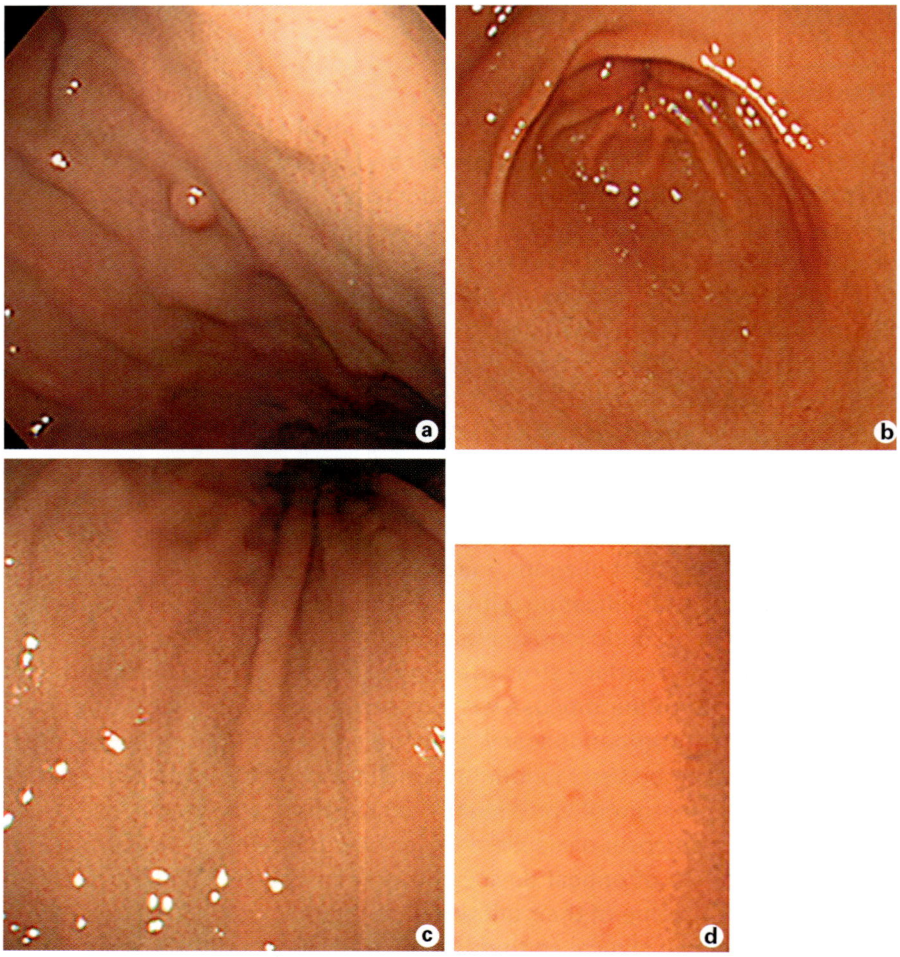

Fig. 2. Endoscopic features of the normal, *H. pylori*-negative gastric mucosa. **a** Fundic gland polyp. **b** Red streaks on the antral folds. Multiple streaks are usually present on the folds near the pylorus. **c** Regular arrangement of the collecting venules as observed by conventional endoscopy. Fine red spots arranged regularly on the mucosa. These red spots correspond to the collecting venules and can be clearly observed by conventional endoscopy at close-up view. **d** At close-up view with conventional endoscopy, these venules can be clearly recognized.

has been reconciled in part and the unified classification was proposed [3]. In this report, we adopt Japanese criteria for the definition of early gastric cancer that have erroneously been labeled as pseudo-disease [4].

Approach to Asymptomatic, but High-Risk Subjects

In order to provide a better chance to survive, gastric cancer should be detected as early as possible. Since early stage gastric cancer is generally asymptomatic, patients with early gastric cancer do not seek consultation, much less upper gastrointestinal endoscopic examination. Therefore, an efficient approach to screen and select high-risk patients who should be encouraged to receive examination by endoscopy must be established. One of the possible approaches would be the blood test using *Helicobacter pylori* antibody and pepsinogens. Since the *H. pylori* infection is a well-known risk factor of gastric cancer [5, 6], screening with a suitable serological test should reduce the target population. Serum pepsinogens that reflect the grade of inflammation and atrophy of the gastric mucosa may offer another convenient method to screen high-risk patients. Indeed, a screening program based on the pepsinogen method is used in Japan and is shown to be as effective as the radiological method [7]. Therefore, a systematic program that includes screening of asymptomatic subjects by such low-cost and non-invasive methods followed by endoscopic surveillance of high-risk subjects should be established to increase the chance of early detection of gastric cancer.

Endoscopic Features of Normal Gastric Mucosa

When one examines patients either from a health-screening program or from referral to pick up early gastric cancer, it is essential to understand what the normal gastric mucosa looks like by conventional endoscopy. Since there would be virtually no gastric cancer development without *H. pylori* infection, the features of the normal, uninfected gastric mucosal findings will rule out the diagnosis of gastric cancer. Although the correlation between endoscopic findings with *H. pylori* status has been considered to be poor, there are some features useful for judging *H. pylori* status. Fundic gland polyps (fig. 2a) are one of the examples of negative *H. pylori* status [8]. Except for a very rare case of familial adenomatous polyposis [9], gastric cancer does not develop from fundic gland polyps, or from the background mucosa. Linear hyperemic streaks on the ridge of the longitudinal folds in the antrum, resembling scratch marks by a comb (fig. 2b), are also a feature of the negative *H. pylori* status [10]. If one has access to magnifying endoscopy, regular arrangement of collective venules (RAC) is a cardinal feature of the normal appearance of the *H. pylori*-negative corpus mucosa [11], which can be identified by conventional high-resolution endoscopy (fig. 2c) viewed at a closer distance.

In contrast, these features of the normal gastric mucosa are lost when infected with *H. pylori*. Instead, sticky adherent mucus, turbidity of the gastric juice, and spotty erythemas on the mucosa indicate *H. pylori*-induced chronic gastritis (fig. 3a, b). In younger age groups, nodular gastritis presenting a goose-pimple-like appearance on the antral mucosa (fig. 3c) indicates *H. pylori* infection and may be a high-risk condition for undifferentiated gastric cancer [12]. Enlarged fold gastritis showing markedly enlarged hyperemic folds along the greater curvature of the corpus (fig. 3d) is also associated with *H. pylori* infection known to bear a higher risk to develop gastric cancer [13]. Xanthoma (fig. 3e) also indicates chronic *H. pylori* infection and is closely associated with atrophic changes [14]. It is also well known that atrophy and intestinal metaplasia (fig. 3f, g) are high-risk conditions of developing gastric cancer [15]. Although there is ample evidence that endoscopic findings and histology correlate poorly [16, 17], atrophy and intestinal metaplasia identified by endoscopy showed high specificity to predict histological diagnosis [18]. Therefore, if gastric atrophy extending to the corpus mucosa or the presence of intestinal metaplasia is noted by endoscopy, special attention to survey the presence of early gastric cancer should be exerted.

Endoscopic Clues to Detect Early Gastric Cancer

Early gastric cancers presenting as protruded, polypoid form (0-I[1]) or excavated type (0-III[1]) are obvious at endoscopic examination and no special consideration is necessary for the diagnosis. However, the majority of early gastric cancer cases assume slightly elevated, flat and slightly depressed lesions (0-IIa[1], 0-IIb[1], and 0-IIc[1] respectively) (fig. 4a–c). Full awareness of the features of these lesions as well as experienced technical skills is required

[1] The classification codes for early gastric cancer are adopted from the Japanese Classification of Gastric Carcinoma (1999).

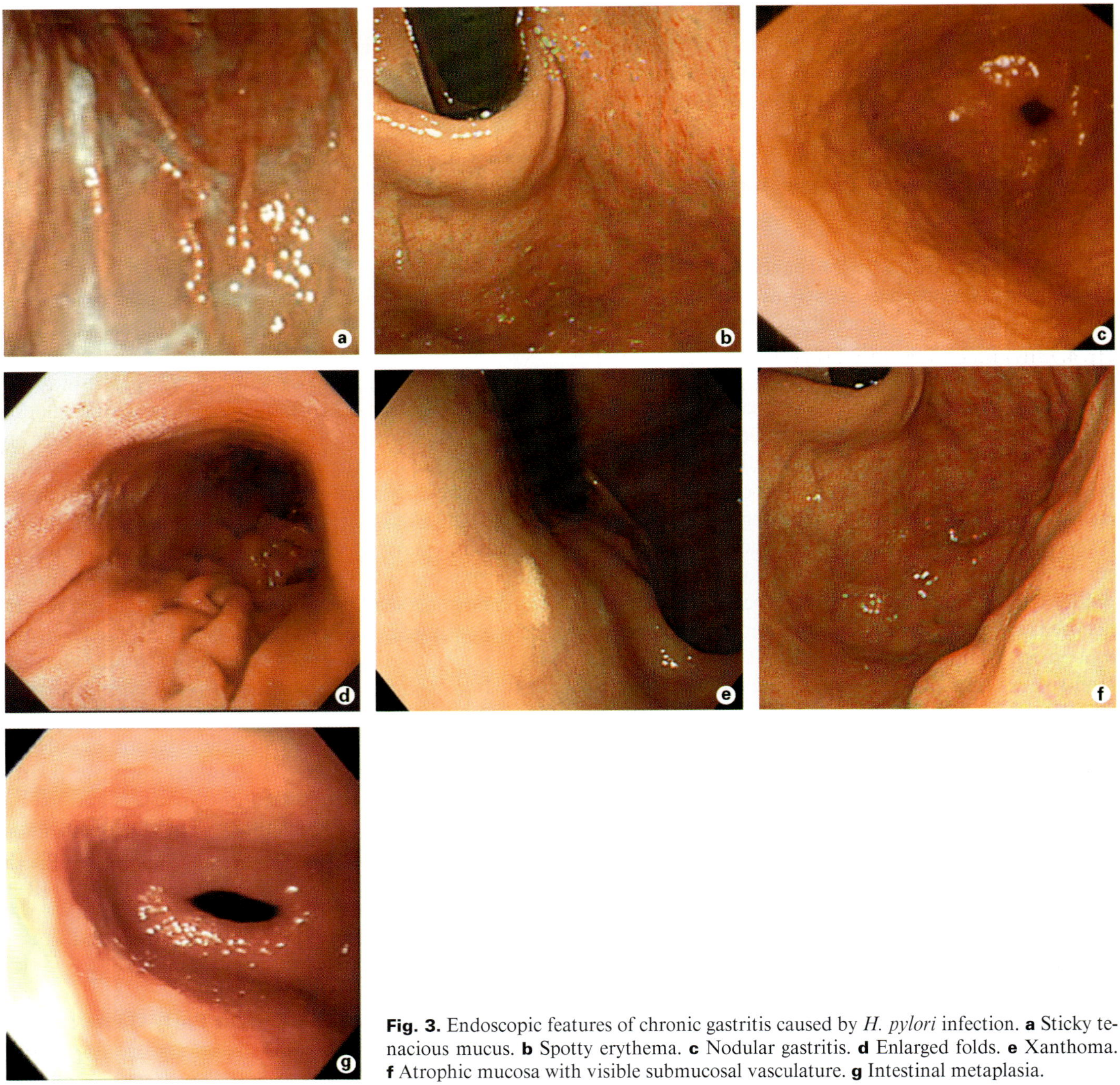

Fig. 3. Endoscopic features of chronic gastritis caused by *H. pylori* infection. **a** Sticky tenacious mucus. **b** Spotty erythema. **c** Nodular gastritis. **d** Enlarged folds. **e** Xanthoma. **f** Atrophic mucosa with visible submucosal vasculature. **g** Intestinal metaplasia.

to find them from the chronically inflamed background mucosa. Subtle discoloration or increased redness compared to the surrounding mucosa, minute changes in the fold calibers, discontinuity of the folds, abnormal friability of the mucosa as exemplified by spontaneous bleeding, and relative opacities of the mucosa have been proposed as endoscopic features indicative of early gastric cancer. In order to increase the detection of such lesions, endoscopic maneuvers, such as careful aspiration of the gastric juice, washing off the adherent mucus by water injection, and varying the amount of air insufflated, are mandatory. Once a lesion in question is recognized, spraying non-absorbable dye such as indigo carmine (chromoendoscopy) to enhance the subtle difference in the mucosal height and

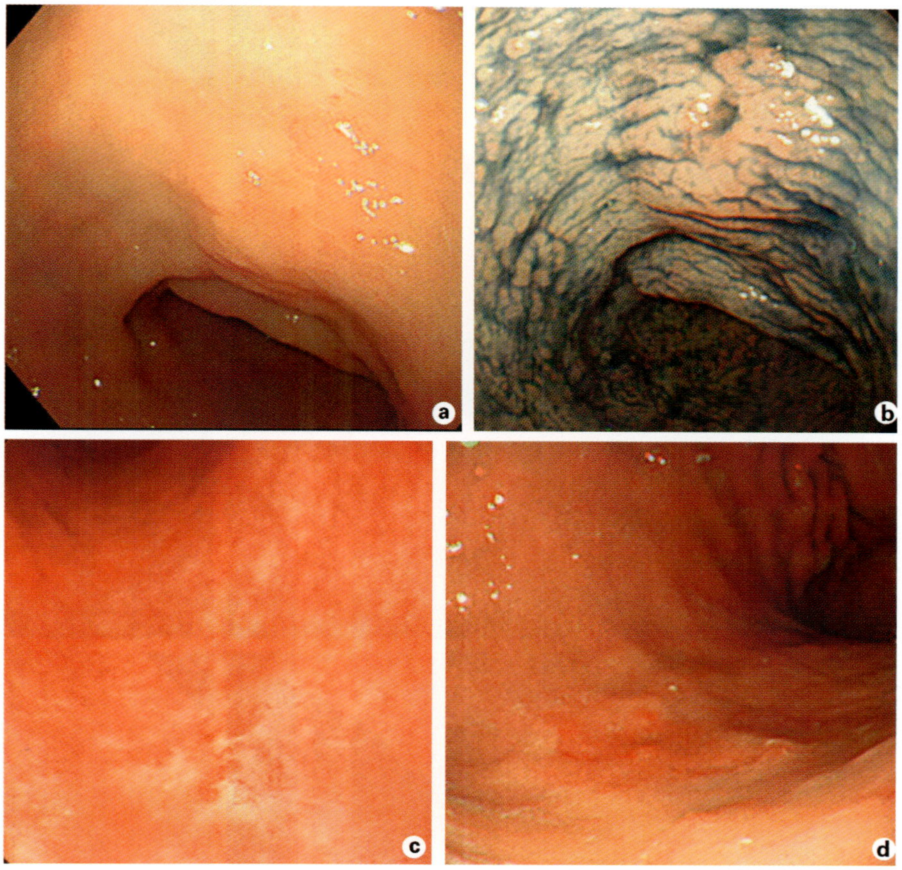

Fig. 4. Early gastric cancer detected by conventional endoscopy. **a** 0-IIa type of early gastric cancer. Slightly elevated area is noted on the lesser curvature of the oral side of the gastric angulus. **b** The tumor stands out after indigo carmine dye spraying. **c** 0-IIb type of early gastric cancer. Note the paler mucosa with abnormal tortuous vessel pattern. The margin of the lesion is unclear. **d** 0-IIc type of early gastric cancer (well-differentiated type). Well-differentiated adenocarcinoma in the early stage shows increased redness compared with the surrounding mucosa due to increased density of the capillary within the tumor tissue (see also magnifying images in fig. 5).

surface architectures can be utilized to demarcate the margin of the lesion for biopsy or mucosal resection. Multiple biopsy samples should be taken from the suspicious lesions which should be diagnosed according to the Vienna classification. If not, dysplasia may eventually be found as advanced cancer that is too late for mucosal resection. With the advent of magnifying endoscopy capable of magnifying about 80×, fine vascular as well as mucosal surface structures can be visualized and the analysis of these elements enabled the demarcation between normal mucosa and cancerous lesion as well as prediction of the histological nature of the cancer as differentiated or undifferentiated type [19, 20] (fig. 5). The magnifying endoscopy, however, is not suitable for surveying the entire mucosal surface of the stomach. Therefore, the best practical approach at present to improve the detection of early gastric cancer is to train endoscopists capable of recognizing the subtle mucosal changes presented by early cancer.

New Modalities of Detecting Neoplastic Lesions

Fluorescent endoscopy either using tissue autofluorescence or injecting fluorescence dye has been developed [21, 22]. These methods may have a potential to detect unrecognizable lesions by conventional endoscopy. At present, however, none of the methods have been used routinely in practical clinical settings.

Recently, endocytoscopy or confocal endoscopy that is based on the confocal imaging technology has been developed. With this technology, images of tissue autofluorescence at cellular levels with a scale of magnification of 1,000× can be acquired. The in vivo use of this new imaging system has already been published [23, 24] for colonic neoplasms, and the cellular and ductal architecture can be clearly captured. This revolutionary method may enable in vivo real-time pathological diagnosis (virtual biopsy) with the reservation that the lesion is identified beforehand by a conventional method.

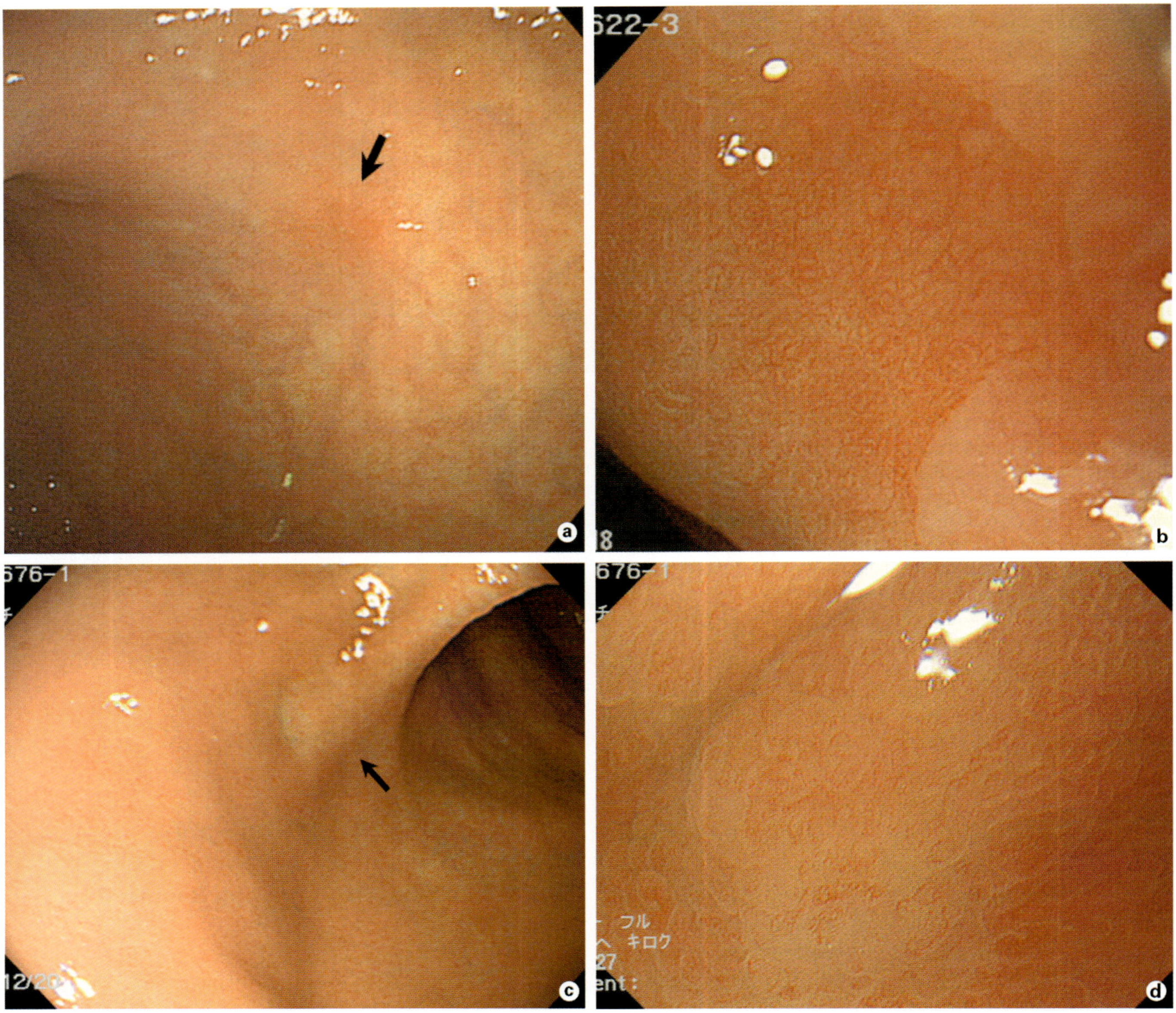

Fig. 5. Comparative images of standard and magnifying endoscopy. **a** Standard endoscopic image of an early gastric cancer of superficial depressed type (0-IIc, well-differentiated adenocarcinoma involving the mucosal layer). A slightly depressed lesion with faint redness was noted in the posterior wall of the antrum (arrow). The size of the carcinoma was measured as 6 mm in diameter. **b** Magnified endoscopic findings of the early gastric cancer are shown in figure 5a. When magnified the reddened mucosa (as shown by an arrow in figure 5a), microvessels which were irregular in size and arrangement proliferating within the depressed reddened part (irregular microvascular pattern) became evident. The presence of this irregular microvascular pattern as visualized by magnified endoscopy indicates a differentiated type of early gastric cancer which mimics gastritis by standard endoscopic examination. **c** Standard endoscopic findings of an early gastric cancer of superficial depressed type (0-IIc). A small pale mucosal lesion was noted on the anterior wall of the gastric angle. The diameter of the lesion was 8 mm. Histopathological investigation demonstrated undifferentiated carcinoma (signet-ring cell carcinoma) which was limited to the mucosal layer. **d** Magnified endoscopic photo of the cancer as shown in figure 5c. By magnification, density of regular subepithelial capillary network had reduced in the cancerous mucosa that is characteristic for early gastric cancer of undifferentiated type.

Promising new advancement of imaging such as laser Raman spectroscopy is ongoing [25] and we may be able to detect early neoplastic lesions in the stomach without experienced training in the future.

Conclusion

In order to improve the prognosis of gastric cancer, a systematic program enabling early detection by selecting high-risk subjects and recommending endoscopic examination is mandatory. A 'wait-and-check' policy does not work for early detection of gastric cancer. Secondly, full awareness on the endoscopic features of normal and pathological mucosa as well as careful observation by the endoscopists is important to diagnose early gastric cancer. Although chromoendoscopy and magnifying endoscopy help to identify the neoplastic lesions detected by conventional endoscopy, their utility to detect the lesion is limited. Future technical advancement may compliment the current limitation of endoscopic diagnosis, but at present, early detection of gastric cancer depends on motivated well-trained hands of endoscopists who understand the normal gastric anatomy, physiology and gastric carcinogenesis.

References

1 Shlemper RJ, Itabashi M, Kato Y, Lewin KJ, Riddell RH, Shimoda T, Sipponen P, Stolte M, Watanabe H, Takahashi H, Fujita R: Difference in diagnostic criteria for gastric carcinoma between Japanese and Western pathologists. Lancet 1997;349:1725–1729.

2 Schlemper RJ, Kato Y, Stolete M: Review of histological classification of gastrointestinal epithelial neoplasia: Difference in diagnosis of early carcinomas between Japanese and Western pathologists. J Gastroenterol 2001;36: 445–456.

3 Schlemper RJ, Riddell RH, Kato Y, Borchard F, Cooper HS, Dawsey SM, Dixon MF, Fenoglio-Preiser CM, Flejou JF, Geboes K, Hattori T, Hirota T, Itabashi M, Iwafuchi M, Iwashita A, Kim YI, Kirchner T, Klimpfinger M, Koike M, Lauwers GY, Lewein KJ, Oberhuber G, Offner F, Price AB, Rubio CA, Shimizu M, Shimoda T, Sipponen R, Solcia E, Stolte M, Watanabe H, Yamabe H: The Vienna classification of gastrointestinal epithelial neoplasia. Gut 2000;47:251–255.

4 Everett SM, Axon ATR: Early gastric cancer: Disease or pseudo-disease? Lancet 1998;351: 1350–1352.

5 Huang JQ, Sridhar S, Chen Y, Hunt RH: Meta-analysis of the relationship between *Helicobacter pylori* seropositivity and gastric cancer. Gastroenterology 1998;114:1169–1179.

6 Helicobacter and Cancer Collaborative Group: Gastric cancer and *Helicobacter pylori*: A combined analysis of 12 case-control studies nested within prospective cohorts. Gut 2001;49:347–353.

7 Miki K, Morita M, Sasajima M, Hoshina R, Kanda E, Urita Y: Usefulness of gastric cancer screening using the serum pepsinogen test method. Am J Gastroenterol 2003;98:735–739.

8 Sakai N, Tatsuta M, Hirasawa R, Iishi H, Baba M, Yokota Y, Ikeda F: Low prevalence of *Helicobacter pylori* infection in patients with hamartomatous fundic polyp. Dig Dis Sci 1998;43:766–772.

9 Hofgartner WT, Thorp M, Ramus MW, Delorefice G, Chey WY, Ryan CK, Takahashi GW, Lobitz JR: Gastric adenocarcinoma associated with fundic gland polyps in a patient with attenuated familial adenomatous polyposis. Am J Gastroenterol 1999;94:2275–2281.

10 Kawabe T, Maeda S, Ogura K, Yamaji Y, Okamoto M, Yoshida H, Shiratori Y, Omata M: Antral red streaking is a negative endoscopic sign for *Helicobacter pylori* infection. Dig Endosc 2002;14:87–92.

11 Yagi K, Nakamura A, Sekine A: Comparison between magnifying endoscopy and histological, culture and urease test findings from the gastric mucosa of the corpus. Endoscopy 2002; 34:376–381.

12 Miyamoto M, Haruma K, Yoshihara M, Hiyama T, Sumioka M, Nishisaka T, Tanaka S, Chayama K: Nodular gastritis in adults is caused by *Helicobacter pylori* infection. Dig Dis Sci 2003;48:968–975.

13 Nishibayashi H, Kanayama S, Kiyohara T, Yamamoto K, Miyazaki Y, Yasunaga Y, Shinomura Y, Takeshita T, Takeuchi T, Morimoto K, Matsuzawa Y: *Helicobacter pylori*-induced enlarged-fold gastritis is associated with increased mutagenicity of gastric juice, increased oxidative DNA damage and an increased risk of gastric carcinoma. J Gastroenterol Hepatol 2003;18:1384–1391.

14 Isomoto H, Mizuta Y, Inoue K, Matsuo T, Hayakawa T, Miyazaki M, Onita K, Takeshima F, Murase K, Shimokawa I, Kohno S: A close relationship between *Helicobacter pylori* infection and gastric xanthoma. Scand J Gastroenterol 1999;34:346–352.

15 Uemura N, Okamoto S, Yamamoto S, Matsumura N, Yamaguch S, Yamakido M, Taniyama K, Sasaki N, Schlemper RJ: *Helicobacter pylori* infection and the development of gastric cancer. N Engl J Med 2001;345:784–789.

16 Carpenter HA, Talley NJ: Gastroscopy is incomplete without biopsy: Clinical relevance of distinguishing gastropathy from gastritis. Gastroenterology 1995;108:917–924.

17 Redeen S, Petrsson F, Johsson KA, Borch K: Relationship of gastroscopic features to histological findings in gastritis and *Helicobacter pylori* infection in a general population sample. Endoscopy 2003;35:946–950.

18 Kaminishi M, Yamaguchi H, Nomura S, Oohara T, Sakai S, Fukutomi H, Nakahara A, Kashimura H, Oda M, Kitahara T, Ichikawa H, Yabana T, Yagawa Y, Sugiyama T, Itabashi M, Unakami M, Oguro Y, Sakita T: Endoscopic classification of chronic gastritis based on a pilot study by the research society for gastritis. Dig Endosc 2002;14:138–151.

19 Yao K, Oishi T, Matsui T, Yao T, Iwashita A: Novel magnified endoscopic findings of microvascular architecture in intramucosal gastric cancer. Gastrointest Endosc 2002;56:279–284.

20 Otsuka Y, Niwa Y, Ohmiya N, Ando N, Ohashi A, Hirooka Y, Goto H: Usefulness of magnifying endoscopy in the diagnosis of early gastric cancer. Endoscopy 2004;36:165–169.

21 Kobayashi M, Tajiri H, Seike E, Shitaya M, Tounou S, Mine M, Oba K: Detection of early gastric cancer by a real-time autofluorescence imaging system. Cancer Lett 2001;165:155–159.

22 Ohkawa A, Miwa H, Namihisa A, Kobayashi O, Nakaniwa N, Ohkusa T, Ogihara T, Sato N: Diagnostic performance of light-induced fluorescence endoscopy for gastric neoplasms. Endoscopy 2004;36:515–521.

23 Sakashita M, Inoue H, Kashida H, Tanaka J, Cho JY, Satodate H, Hidaka E, Yoshida T, Fukami N, Tamegai Y, Shiokawa A, Kudo S: Virtual histology of colorectal lesions using laser-scanning confocal microscopy. Endoscopy 2003;35:1033–1038.

24 Kiesslich R, Burg J, Vieth M, Gnaendiger J, Enders M, Delaney P, Poglase A, McLaren W, Janell D, Thomas S, Nafe B, Galle PR, Neurath MF: Confocal laser endoscopy for diagnosing intraepithelial neoplasias and colorectal cancer in vivo. Gastroenterology 2004;127:706–713.

25 Dacosta RS, Wilson BC, Marcon NE: New optical technologies for earlier endoscopic diagnosis of premalignant gastrointestinal lesions. J Gastroenterol Hepatol 2002;17(suppl):S85–S104.

Review Article

Digestive Diseases

Dig Dis 2004;22:334–337
DOI: 10.1159/000083595

Novel Endoscopic Imaging Techniques toward in vivo Observation of Living Cancer Cells in the Gastrointestinal Tract

Haruhiro Inoue[a] Shin-ei Kudo[a] Akira Shiokawa[b]

[a]Digestive Disease Center and [b]Department of Pathology, Showa University Northern Yokohama Hospital, Yokohama, Japan

Key Words
Endomicroscopy · Endocytoscopy · Confocal microscopy system · Laser-scanning confocal microscopy

Abstract
Recent advances in endoscopic imaging technology have enabled the visualization of cellular-level microstructures of early-stage cancer and its precursors. Chromoendoscopy, magnifying endoscopy, endoscopic optical coherent tomography (EOCT) spectroscopy, and various combinations of these technologies, are all important for the recognition of small and unclear lesions. In order to observe cancer cells in vivo two types of ultra-high magnifying endoscope – 'laser-scanning confocal laser-scanning endoscopy series' and 'contact endoscopy series' – that have a maximum of >1,000 times magnifying power have been developed. The use of these endoscopes has allowed the generation of high quality images of both living cancer cells and normal cells in the gastrointestinal tract. In particular, clear images of cells and their nuclei, equivalent to the high quality that is possible with conventional cytology, have been produced. These novel imaging technologies may make in vivo histological diagnosis by virtual histology possible.

Introduction

Recent advancements in endoscopic imaging technology enable visualization of early stages of cancer or preneoplastic lesions. Chromoendoscopy, magnifying endoscopy, spectroscopy and the combination of these techniques play important roles in the identification of small and unclear lesions. Two types of ultrahigh magnifying endoscopes have been developed which allow the magnification of these lesions with a more than 1,000-fold magnifying power. Thereby, living cancer cells and normal cells in the gastrointestinal tract were successfully observed in high-quality images. 'Endomicroscopy' is an application of laser-scanning confocal technology. 'Endocytoscopy' is an application of contact light microscopic technology. By utilizing these imaging technologies, living cells in both normal mucosa and cancer tissue were clearly demonstrated in the gastrointestinal tract. In particular cell and nuclei were clearly demonstrated with high-quality images which are comparable to conventional cytology. This novel technology may be regarded as the opening of the in vivo histological diagnosis by virtual biopsy and virtual histology. Further developments of this interesting technology are expected.

KARGER

Fax +41 61 306 12 34
E-Mail karger@karger.ch
www.karger.com

0257–2753/04/0224–0334$21.00/0

Accessible online at:
www.karger.com/ddi

Haruhiro Inoue, MD
Digestive Disease Center
Showa University Northern Yokohama Hospital
Chigasaki Chuo 35-1, Tsuzuki-ku, Yokohama 224-8503 (Japan)
Tel. +81 45 9497641/7000, Fax +81 45 9497265, E-Mail haru.inoue@juno.ocn.ne.jp

Confocal Microscopy System

Laser-scanning confocal microscopy is a novel optical technology which provides microscopy-level images without obtaining biopsy specimen. This technology was first used to investigate superficially exposed organs such as skin, eye and the oral cavity.

In order to use this technology, micromachine technology was developed using a thin catheter probe equipped a with laser-scanning confocal microscopy system. A catheter probe with 3.4 mm outer diameter and 250 cm longitudinal length which can pass through the instrumental channel of the endoscope was developed (Endo-Microscopy, Prototype, Olympus). A miniaturized sensor is mounted on the distal end of this probe. A digitalized image is acquired by counting the reflective light of the laser beam. The light source is a 405-nm wavelength diode laser beam, and the spatial resolution is around 1 μm. No vital staining process is required in the endomicroscopy system. This avoids a possible allergic reaction to vital staining dye [1–3].

At almost the same time, another team independently tried to develop a confocal microscopic imaging system. Optiscan is laser-scanning confocal microscopy mounted onto a colonoscope. A high-quality image is obtained in combination with fluorescent injection [4].

Endocytoscopy

Endocytoscopy is based on the technology of light contact microscopy. In the field of otolaryngology, rigid endoscopes (contact endoscopy, Karl Storz, Germany) were introduced to observe the cellular abnormality of the mucosa. The tip of the rigid endoscope is in direct contact with the dye-stained surface mucosa, and the target mucosa is scanned with condensed normal white light. Cellular-level images were clearly demonstrated by this method. Ooue et al. first reported the application of this rigid endoscope to the diagnosis of colorectal cancer during open surgery. Kumagai et al. [5] also reported ex vivo application of a contact endoscopy to the esophageal squamous cell carcinoma. These achievements indicated that the direct observation of the living cell in vivo is theoretically feasible, and in order to achieve in vivo observation of a living gastrointestinal mucosa, the further development of a flexible catheter-type contact endoscope is mandatory.

In the era of the fiberoptic scope, the ultra-high magnifying contact endoscope was once designed as a prototype endoscope. An approximately 500× magnifying view was successfully achieved, but the acquired images were not satisfactorily translated and were not generally accepted until the development of videoendoscope monitoring.

The 'Endo-Cytoscopy system' (Prototype, Olympus) is a new development in this field. Two sets of the prototype are available. In the prototype I, 450× magnification is achieved, and in the prototype II, 1,100× magnification is achieved (fig. 1). The outer diameter of the 'Endo-Cytoscope' is 3.4 mm and the total length is 250 cm. Any endoscope with a 3.7-mm working channel may serve as a mother endoscope, which then allows the insertion of the baby scope 'Endo-Cytoscope'. Under topical pharyngeal anesthesia, a therapeutic endoscope (GIF-1T, Olympus) is first introduced to the upper gastrointestinal tract [5, 6]. In case of assessment of the colon, a colonoscope is introduced into the site. 1% methylene blue solution is then sprayed onto the lesion through a spraying catheter. Just after dye spraying, the stained mucosal surface is flushed with water. The 'Endo-Cytoscope' is introduced through the working channel and then touches softly the lesion surface. The magnified image is continuously observed as long as the tip of 'Endo-Cytoscope' is in contact with the mucosal surface. After staining of the surface mucosa with methylene blue, the nuclei and cell bodies were successfully demonstrated in vivo in the esophagus, stomach and colon (fig. 1, 2). In the esophagus, nucleoli were also frequently observed inside the cell. The image is clear enough to be evaluated regarding the subcellular microstructures. The 'Endo-Cytoscopy' images from cancer tissue exhibited characteristic features such as blurred and irregularly enlarged nuclei. These high-quality images can be compared to conventional cytology or histology images. The authors applied 'Endo-Cytoscopy' for 87 cases (38 cases in the esophagus, 18 cases in the stomach, 35 cases in the colon). High-quality images were acquired in 83 cases (95.4%). In 4 cases of the stomach lesions, images of cellular level were not acquired because the gastric mucous secretion does not allow staining nucleus with methylene blue. However, in the esophagus and colon, high-quality images were obtained in all cases. Contact bleeding from the cancer lesion occurred in 8 cases (9.2%) and stopped without intervention. No major bleeding was experienced.

Endocytoscopy images are of high quality using methylene blue staining, but vital staining has been associated with a risk for tissue and DNA damage [7]. Endomicroscopy does not require vital staining although endomicroscopy images are still of less quality compared to endocy-

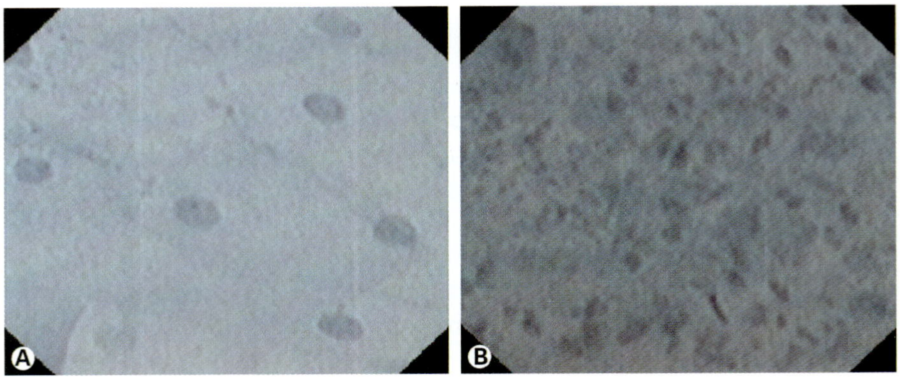

Fig. 1. Endo-Cytoscopy. **A** Normal squamous cell in the esophagus. **B** Squamous cell carcinoma in the esophagus. ×1,100.

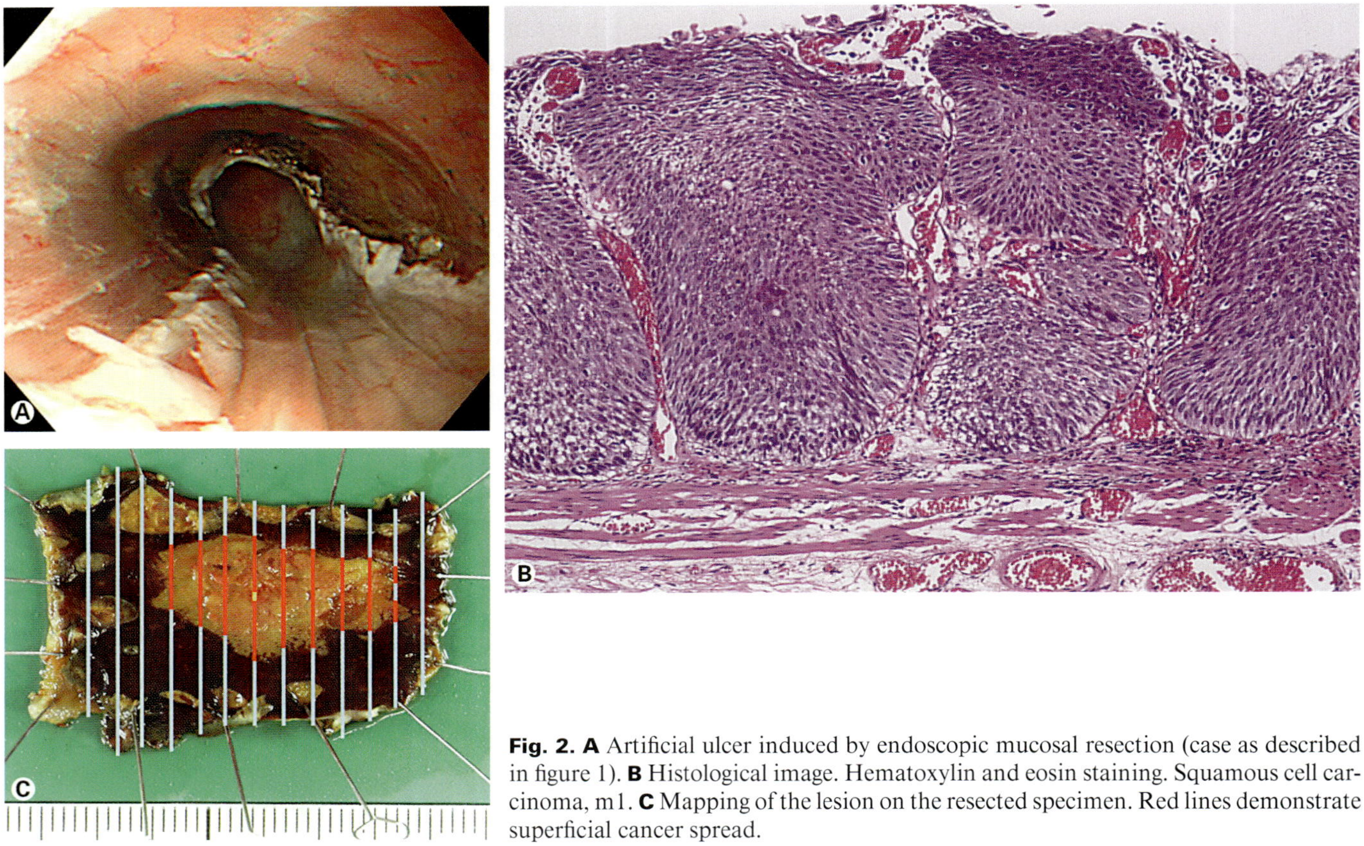

Fig. 2. A Artificial ulcer induced by endoscopic mucosal resection (case as described in figure 1). **B** Histological image. Hematoxylin and eosin staining. Squamous cell carcinoma, m1. **C** Mapping of the lesion on the resected specimen. Red lines demonstrate superficial cancer spread.

toscopy. Another advantage of endomicroscopy is the digitalization of images and the scanning at various depths of the tissue, which may allow cross-sectional analysis of the tissues. In contrast, endocytoscopy scans at a fixed depth of the tissue, and does not allow cross-sectional analysis.

These cellular-level microscopic imaging technologies will potentially reduce the number of biopsies required for diagnosis by offering as simultaneous endoscopical and virtual microscopic image. The endomicroscopes may also reduce the time delay in acquiring histological diagnosis and will allow the targeted examination of lesions in the gastrointestinal tract [8].

Conclusions

Endoscopic imaging of the microstructure of living cells from both normal mucosa and cancer tissue of the gastrointestinal tract is possible. In endomicroscopy, cell and nuclei were demonstrated without vital staining. In endocytoscopy, nuclei, cell bodies, and even nucleoli were clearly demonstrated with methylene blue staining. These novel technologies potentially enable in vivo histological diagnosis during endoscopic examination.

References

1 Inoue H, Igari T, Nishikage T, et al: A novel method of virtual histology utilizing laser-scanning confocal microscopy for untreated fresh specimens of the gastrointestinal mucosa. Endoscopy 2000;32:439–443.

2 Inoue H, Cho JY, Satodate H, et al: Development of virtual histology and virtual biopsy using laser-scanning confocal microscopy. Scand J Gastroenterol 2003;38:37–39.

3 Sakashita M, Inoue H, Kashida H, et al: Virtual histology of colorectal lesions using laser-scanning confocal microscopy. Endoscopy 2003;35:1–6.

4 Kiesslich R, Burg J, Vieth M, et al: Confocal laser endoscopy for diagnosing intraepithelial neoplasias and colorectal cancer in vivo. Gastroenterology 2004;127:706–713.

5 Kumagai Y, Monma K, Kawada K: Magnifying chromoendoscopy of the esophagus: In-vivo pathological diagnosis using an endocytoscopy system. Endoscopy 2004; 36: 590–594.

6 Inoue H, Kazawa T, Sato Y, et al: In vivo observation of living cancer cells in the esophagus, stomach, and colon using catheter-type contact endoscope, 'Endo-Cytoscopy system'. Gastrointest Endosc Clin N Am 2004;14:589–594.

7 Olliver JR, Wild CP, Sahay P, et al: Chromoendoscopy with methylene blue and associated DNA damage in Barrett's oesophagus. Lancet 2003;362:373–374.

8 Inoue H, Kudo S, Shiokawa A: Technology insight: laser-scanning confocal microscopy and endocytoscopy for cellular observation of the gastrointestinal tract. Nat Clin Pract Gastroenterol Hepatol 2005;2:31–37.

Review Article

Digestive Diseases

Dig Dis 2004;22:338–344
DOI: 10.1159/000083596

Update on Surgery of Gastric Cancer: New Procedures versus Standard Technique

Hitoshi Katai Takeshi Sano Mitsuru Sasako Takeo Fukagawa Makoto Saka

Department of Surgical Oncology, National Cancer Center Hospital, Tokyo, Japan

Key Words
Gastric cancer · Early gastric cancer, surgery · Node dissection

Abstract
D2 lymphadenectomy has been the mainstay of treatment for every stage of gastric cancer including early gastric cancer in Japan. However, the use of conventional D2 nodal dissection is being challenged. There was a recent improvement in techniques for preoperative diagnosis and perioperative diagnosis. Less extensive surgeries to maintain patients' quality of life have been introduced as standard treatment for some forms of early gastric cancer in the Gastric Cancer Treatment Guidelines 2001 (The Japanese Gastric Cancer Association). Superextended dissection (more than D2) for non-early gastric cancer is set at investigational treatment. Japanese surgeons are now aiming at wide variations of surgical treatment according to the stage of disease based on new procedures. Further evaluations are proceeding to prove superior to standard techniques.

Introduction

D2 lymphadenectomy has been the mainstay of treatment for every stage of gastric cancer including early gastric cancer [1, 2]. However, the use of conventional D2 nodal dissection is being challenged, especially for early gastric cancer.

The Japanese Gastric Cancer Association issued the first version of Gastric Cancer Treatment Guidelines in March 2001 and a revised version appeared in 2004 [3]. The aim of this article is to introduce an outline of treatment guidelines for doctors' reference. The guidelines aim to provide a standard indication for doctors to select the proper treatments of gastric cancer according to the clinical stages of patients.

Although gastrectomy of at least two-thirds of the stomach with D2 node dissection was assigned as a standard treatment for most stages of advanced gastric cancer, modified surgeries were also described as standard or investigational treatments in the guidelines. Less extensive gastrectomy, which is widely performed in Japan at present for 'presumed mucosal cancers', is authorized. More extensive dissection (D3) is set at investigational treatment.

In this article we report the background of modified treatments and describe the details of every treatment.

Less Extensive Surgery for Early Gastric Cancer

Background

D2 lymphadenectomy and detailed histopathologic studies of the resected specimens have resulted in an accumulation of a vast amount of knowledge of the extent

KARGER

Fax +41 61 306 12 34
E-Mail karger@karger.ch
www.karger.com

0257–2753/04/0224–0338$21.00/0

Accessible online at:
www.karger.com/ddi

Hitoshi Katai, MD
Department of Surgical Oncology
National Cancer Center Hospital
5-1-1 Tsukiji, Chuo-ku, Tokyo 104-0045 (Japan)
Tel. +81 3 3542 2511, Fax +81 3 3542 3815, E-Mail hkatai@ncc.go.jp

Table 1. Incidence of nodal metastasis by depth of invasion (surgical T) from databases of major Japanese hospitals [data taken from 3]

Mucosal cancer	pN0	pN1	pN2	total	95% CI
Differentiated type	496 (98.0%)	9 (1.8%)	1 (0.2%)	10/506 (2.0%)	1.0–3.6%
Undifferentiated type	320 (93.6%)	20 (5.8%)	2 (0.6%)	22/342 (6.4%)	4.1–9.6%
Submucosal cancer	**pN0**	**pN1**	**pN2**		
Differentiated type					
Tumor size					
<1.5 cm	232/242 (95.9%)	10/242 (4.1%)	0/242 (0%)		
1.6–2.0 cm	147/164 (89.6%)	12/164 (7.3%)	5/164 (3.0%)		
>2.1 cm	431/513 (84.0%)	57/513 (11.1%)	25/513 (4.9%)		
Total	810/919 (88.1%)	79/919 (8.6%)	30/919 (3.3%)		

Depth of invasion was decided by inspection and palpation during operation.

of nodal metastasis observed for various types and stages of gastric carcinoma. As a result, it is now widely accepted by Japanese surgeons that such an extended lymphadenectomy (D2) is not inevitable for certain subsets of early gastric cancer with a very rare chance of nodal involvement [4–7] (table 1).

The detection rate of early gastric cancer has also increased in recent times due to the development of diagnostic methods and widespread use of mass screening [8, 9]. The incidence of aged patients has increased due to a prolonged lifespan [10]. Therefore, recent trends in the management of EGC show that Japanese surgeons have been increasingly adopting more conservative methods to preserve the quality of life while at the same time maintaining a high level of radicality, such as endoscopic mucosal resection (EMR) or function-preserving gastrectomies for EGC.

Lymph Node Metastasis from EGC

Distant metastasis from EGC is extremely rare, and peritoneal seeding is unlikely because the tumor is completely confined to the gastric wall. The only possible local spread is via the lymphatic route. The incidence and extent of nodal metastasis from EGC is closely related to the depth of tumor invasion [11]. Mucosal cancers rarely metastasize (3% or less), while nearly 20% of EGC invading the submucosa metastasize to the regional nodes, and the incidence approaches 50% in T2 tumors [12].

Treatment Guidelines for EGC

A patient with early gastric cancer is usually assigned as stage IA (T1N0), stage IB (T1N1) or stage II (T1N2). Less extensive surgeries are advocated for stage IA and stage IB in the guidelines (table 2). Since T2 tumor has a high incidence of nodal metastasis, the accuracy of preoperative diagnosis is the key to perform less extensive treatment, since understaged patients will have insufficient treatment.

Less extensive resection is defined as modified gastrectomy (table 3) in the guidelines according to the Japanese Classification of Gastric Carcinoma [13]. The guidelines also introduced optional treatment methods, such as pylorus-preserving, vagal nerve-preserving, and laparoscopic assistance.

Stage IA (T1N0). EMR or modified gastrectomy (MG) is indicated for this stage according to table 4. EMR should be indicated for patients with small mucosal cancer with no lymph node metastasis. Vigorous retrospective studies have been made in Japan. Databases containing several hundreds or even thousands of patients with EGC who have undergone surgery with lymphadenectomy have been analyzed to identify the specific features of EGC without lymph node metastasis [6, 7, 14].

It is now accepted that a tumor satisfying all the following conditions is suitable for EMR: (1) tumor confined to the mucosal layer; (2) tumor of elevated type (I or IIa), or depressed type (IIc) without ulcer or ulcer scar (endoscopically no fold convergence); (3) well or moderately differentiated adenocarcinoma; (4) tumor <2.0 cm [15].

Table 2. Japanese treatment guidelines [data taken from 3]

T	N			
	N0	N1	N2	N3
T1 (M)	IA EMR (wel or mod, ≤2 cm, ul (–)) MGA (else)	IB MGB (≤2 cm) D2 (>2 cm)	II D2	IV D3
T1 (SM)	IA MGA (wel or mod, ≤1.5 cm) MGB (else)	IB MGB (≤2 cm) D2 (>2 cm)	II D2	IV D3
T2	IB D2	II D2	IIIA D2	IV D3
T3	II D2	IIIA D2	IIIB D2 (D3)	IV D3
T4	IIIA D2 extended	IIIB D2 extended	IV D2 extended	IV D3 extended

Table 3. Type of gastrectomy [data taken from 3]

Gastrectomy	Area of resection	Dissection	Option
Modified A	<2/3	D1 + No.7[1]	Vagus-preserving
Modified B	<2/3	D1+No.7, 8a, 9	Pylorus-preserving
Laparoscopic			
Standard	≥2/3	D2	
Extended	≥2/3 Combined resection	D2	D3

[1] No. 7 nodes along the left gastric artery; No. 8a nodes along the common hepatic artery (antero-superior group), and No. 9 nodes around the celiac artery.

In case of lower third cancer, No. 8a nodes should be dissected. Standard gastrectomy includes proximal, distal or total gastrectomy associated with D2 according to the size and location of the tumor (Japanese Classification of Gastric Carcinoma issue by Japanese Gastric Cancer Association).

Table 4. Treatment methods for stage IA [data taken from 3]

Depth of invasion	Histology	Size	Methods
Mucosa (M)	Differentiated	≤2 cm	EMR
Mucosa (M)	Else		MG A
Submucosa (SM)	Differentiated	≤1.5 cm	MG A
Submucosa (SM)	Else		MG B

Conditions 2–4 are diagnosed by endoscopy and biopsy. The EMR is then performed and the resected specimen retrieved. When the histological examination confirms condition 1 for the specimen, the procedure is considered curative.

Mucosal cancer that does not meet this condition should be treated by MG A. MG A is also indicated for the differentiated submucosal cancer <1.5 cm in diameter. Submucosal cancer that does not meet this condition should be treated by MG B.

Stage IB (T1N1). As shown in table 4, MG B or standard gastrectomy is indicated for stage IB cancer according to the T and N categories. If the T1N1 tumor is <2.0 cm in diameter, MG B is indicated, and the T1N1 tumor >2.1 cm or T2N0 tumor is treated by standard gastrectomy.

Treatment Details

Endoscopic Mucosal Resection

Endoscopic treatment mainly using laser therapy was primarily employed as a palliative treatment for patients with high operative risks or incurable disease [16]. Tada et al. [17] first described the technique of 'strip biopsy' in

1984 and developed it into a method for the cure of mucosal gastric cancer. The revolutionary point of this technique is that not only a polypoid but also a depressed mucosal lesion can be removed along with the surrounding normal mucosa, which provides sufficient material for histological confirmation of tumor cell infiltration.

After successful EMR, however, close follow-up of the patient by endoscopy is mandatory, because multifocal lesions, either synchronous or metachronous, are not uncommon in the stomach [18]. A second or third lesion will again be removed by EMR if it satisfies the above criteria.

EMR has already become an essential tool for treatment in Japan [19]. Large series of up to 400 EMRs in a single institution are presented at congresses [20]. Various techniques, such as endoscopic submucosal resection, are being tested for safer and wider resection and expansion of inclusion criteria [19, 21, 22]. Although no prospective study has been published in the English literature, a prospective, nationwide collection of EMR cases will be performed in the future, and the above criteria will no doubt undergo modifications.

D2 Gastrectomy for EGC

Gastrectomy with D2 lymphadenectomy has long been the standard treatment for gastric cancer in Japan as already mentioned. Recently, European surgeons have also advocated it as treatment of choice for EGC [23–25], because of excellent outcomes of retrospective series comparable to Japanese results. Although modified gastrectomies are described in the guidelines in Japan, gastrectomy with D2 dissection is considered reasonable for 'seemingly early gastric cancer', firstly because N2 nodes can be involved from submucosal EGC, though the incidence is low, and secondly because the diagnosis of EGC is not always accurate [26], leaving the possibility of the tumor being T2 or deeper.

Modified Gastrectomy for EGC

Various modified gastrectomies for EGC have been devised in Japan, aimed at preserving the function of the stomach. All these operations are employed after careful patient selection, again based on the guidelines defined by lymph node studies, so as not to decrease the survival rate. The published studies are classified as phase II or pilot, and the functional comparison with conventional counterparts is a retrospective one, with historical controls. Then, accuracy of a diagnosis of depth of invasion is most important to perform surgery with limited nodal dissection.

Total Gastrectomy without Splenectomy. For EGC in the proximal stomach, total or proximal gastrectomy is performed. According to the Japanese Classification of Gastric Carcinoma, D2 for proximal tumors includes dissection of the splenic hilar nodes. However, metastasis to this area from EGC is extremely rare [17, 27]. Even in T2 tumors, the splenic hilar metastasis is seldom seen unless the primary tumor is located on the greater curvature. Therefore, the spleen should be preserved in these tumors, especially in view of the additional morbidity associated with splenectomy.

Proximal Gastrectomy. At least for early gastric cancer, the benefit of a total gastrectomy with splenectomy has not been seen and is limited. Therefore, for EGC in the proximal third of the stomach, proximal gastrectomy is being tested in some institutions with or without preservation of the vagal nerves [27–29]. Proximal gastrectomy is currently indicated for EGC only when we can preserve at least half of the stomach to keep radicality of operation and capacity of the remnant stomach.

All regional nodes except for the splenic hilum nodes (No. 10) and distal splenic nodes (No. 11d) can be dissected as in the standard D2 operation, although the dissection of the lesser curvature nodes (No. 3) was incomplete at the distal part. An antireflux procedure such as jejunal interposition (physiological sphincter) and new gastric fundus formation is routinely added.

Proximal gastrectomy was prospectively evaluated in the one arm study in our institution and the survival data was almost identical to that after total gastrectomy, and was satisfactory [27]. The literature reported that improved post-operative absorption [30, 31] and body weight recovery is good as compared to total gastrectomy. Pylorus function is also preserved with this method by preserving vagus nerves including hepatic and pyloric branches, which is the same as pylorus-preserving gastrectomy. Reflux esophagitis may be a possible sequela.

Simple esophagogastrostomy produced a higher incidence of reflux esophagitis [32, 33], despite several modifications. Minimizing the incidence of esophagitis has been required for routine use of this gastrectomy. Recent efforts including the jejunal interposition method produced good results [27, 34].

Pylorus-Preserving Gastrectomy (PPG). PPG was originally applied for peptic ulcers [35] and has also been applied for early gastric cancer [36–40]. The distal two-thirds of the stomach are resected but a pyloric cuff of about 2 cm is preserved. A recent report showed the benefit of a longer cuff for gastric motility. Infrapyloric vessels are occasionally preserved to maintain the blood supply of a longer pyloric cuff. The result of infrapyloric node dissection preserving these vessels should be evaluated. Vagal nerves are identified and preserved to maintain pylorus function. Furthermore, preservation of the celiac branch of the posterior vagal trunk has also been done in combination with a PPG by several Japanese surgeons.

All regional nodes, except suprapyloric nodes (No. 5), can be dissected as in the standard D2 operation. PPG is currently indicated for EGC in the middle stomach from which nodal metastasis to No. 5 is extremely uncommon [39]. Since a pyloric cuff is retained, PPG is not desirable for lesions located in the distal antrum.

The literature reports that the incidence of post-gastrectomy dumping syndrome, bile regurgitation, and gall bladder stone formation is decreased, and body weight recovery is good as compared to Billroth-I reconstruction [37–39]. However, these benefits have not been proven by a prospective randomized trial. Emptying disturbance may be a possible sequela.

Segmental Gastrectomy. A gastrectomy with a more limited resection of the stomach body is the segmental gastrectomy. This is indicated for mucosal tumor in the mid-gastric body. A segment of the stomach containing the tumor is resected with [41] or without preservation of the Latarjet branch of the vagal nerve [42]. The hepatic and pyloric branches are preserved. Lymphadenectomy is limited to the perigastric regions close to the resected segment, but for lesser curve tumors the nodes along the left gastric artery can also be dissected. Functional results are generally satisfactory.

Wedge Resection. An attempt at local wedge resection with regional lymphadenectomy was reported [43]. Several reports showed the possibilities for developing sentinel node-guided surgery for gastric cancer [44, 45].

Laparoscopic Surgery. Laparoscopic surgery for gastric cancer is underway in some institutions. Laparoscopy-assisted gastrectomy with nodal dissection was performed and was being evaluated in some reports. The evaluation of survival should be very strict, since the survival rate of open surgery operation is quite good. The literature reported faster recovery, less pain, and shorter hospital stay. However, the benefit of quality of life might be only better cosmesis. A multicenter randomized controlled trial will be needed in the near future [46].

Laparoscopic local resection of the stomach: Two types of laparoscopic local resection, laparoscopic wedge resection by the lesion-lifting method [47] and intragastric mucosal resection [48], have been performed in Japan for early gastric cancer. Since the target of laparoscopic local resection is early gastric cancer without lymph node metastasis, expansion of inclusion criteria of endoscopic treatment may cause a decrease in the number of patients treated by this method. The lesion-lifting method is carried out by retracting the metal rod, piercing the lesion through the abdominal and gastric wall, and wedge resection is carried out with endoscopic staplers [47]. Intragastric mucosal resection is performed through trocars, which are placed in the gastric lumen [48].

A survey by the Japanese Society for Endoscopic Surgery [49] showed low perioperative morbidity and zero mortality, and possibly shorter hospital stay. There is a report of local recurrence [47].

Laparoscopy-assisted distal gastrectomy: Laparoscopy-assisted Billroth-I gastrectomy for early gastric cancer was first performed in 1991 by Kitano et al. [50], and the Billroth-II gastrectomy was reported in 1992 by Goh and Kum [51]. Laparoscopy-assisted gastrectomy is still in the developmental phase around the world, while the number of patients with early gastric cancer treated by LADG has increased significantly in Japan.

The guidelines described LADG as one of the optional treatments in MG. Even D2 gastrectomy can be attempted safely at the proper time [52]. LADG is still performed in only a limited number of hospitals in Japan.

The survey of the Japan Society for Endoscopic Surgery showed low morbidity-mortality rates of LADG, similar to open distal gastrectomy [49]. A small randomized study showed some advantages including less pain and less impaired pulmonary function after LADG to open distal gastrectomy [53]. A multicenter randomized controlled trial is needed to confirm the clinical advantages of LADG including medical expenses.

Investigational Treatment for Non-Early Cancer

Superextended Para-Aortic Lymphadenectomy

Since 1980, more extended lymphadenectomy than D2 procedures have been practiced in many Japanese specialized centers. The literature reported that 20–30% of patients with non-early gastric cancer had microscopic metastasis present in the para-aortic nodes [54–57]. The 5-year survival for these patients has reached 14–30% after superextended systematic dissection.

In addition to D2 lymphadenectomy, lymph nodes around the upper abdominal aorta were dissected, primarily for ultimate local tumor control. However, this dissection may not only increase operative morbidity but also may affect the function of other abdominal organs. To evaluate the survival benefit and operative complications of D2 gastrectomy and extended para-aortic dissection in gastric cancer surgery, a multi-institutional randomized controlled trial was conducted on behalf of the Japan Clinical Oncology Group. Although the morbidity for the superextended surgery group was slightly higher, the hospital mortality rate was as low as 0.8% in each group [58].

Total Gastrectomy with Spleen Preservation

Japanese retrospective studies revealed that 15–20% of patients with non-early carcinoma in the proximal stomach have nodal metastasis in the splenic hilum [59] and the 5-year survival rate after dissection is 20–25% [60, 61], and therefore pancreas-preserving splenectomy [62] is part of the standard operation in specialized centers. However, even in Japan, there are several studies that report on the lack of benefit of splenectomy [63–66]. Recent European clinical trials of gastrectomy showed that splenectomy is an important risk factor for post-operative morbidity and mortality [67, 68].

To evaluate the role of splenectomy in potentially curative total gastrectomy for proximal gastric carcinoma in terms of survival benefit and post-operative morbidity, a multi-institutional randomized controlled trial was conducted on behalf of the Japan Clinical Oncology Group [69]. Since metastasis in the splenic hilum is frequently found for the tumor invading the greater curvature, the tumor invading greater curvature will be excluded [70].

Conclusion

The latest developments in surgery for gastric cancer could be described as wide variations of surgical treatment according to the stage of disease based on new procedures. Further evaluation is required to prove the superiority to standard techniques.

References

1 Sawai K, Takahashi T, Suzuki H: New trends in surgery for gastric cancer in Japan. J Surg Oncol 1994;56:221–226.

2 Maruyama K, Okabayashi K, Kinoshita T: Progress in gastric cancer surgery in Japan and its limits of radicality. World J Surg 1987;11:418–425.

3 Nakajima T: Gastric cancer treatment guidelines in Japan. Gastric Cancer 2002;5:1–5.

4 Tsujitani S, Oka S, Saito H, Kondo A, Ikeguchi M, Maeta M, Kaibara N: Less invasive surgery for early gastric cancer based on the low probability of lymph node metastasis. Surgery 1999;125:148–154.

5 Nakamura K, Morisaki T, Sugitani A, Ogawa T, Uchiyama A, Kinukawa N, Tanaka M: An early gastric carcinoma treatment strategy based on analysis of lymph node metastasis. Cancer 1999;85:1500–1505.

6 Yamao T, Shirao K, Ono H, et al: Risk factors for lymph node metastasis from intramucosal gastric carcinoma. Cancer 1996;77:602–606.

7 Gotoda T, Yanagisawa A, Sasako M, et al: Incidence of lymph node metastasis from early gastric cancer: Estimation with a large number of cases at two large centers. Gastric Cancer 2000;3:219–25.

8 Hisamichi S, Sugawara N: Mass screening for gastric cancer by X-ray examination. Jpn J Clin Oncol 1984;14:11–23.

9 Shiratori Y, Nakagawa S, Kikuchi A, et al: Significance of a gastric mass screening survey. Am J Gastroenterol 1985;80:831–834.

10 Abridged Life Table for Japan, 2003. Tokyo, Statistics and Information Department, Minister's Secretariat, Ministry of Health, Labor and Welfare, 2004.

11 Yasuda K, Shiraishi N, Suematsu T: Rate of detection of lymph node metastasis is correlated with the depth of submucosal invasion in early stage gastric carcinoma. Cancer 1999;85:19–23.

12 Sasako M, Sano T, Katai H, Maruyama K: Radical surgery; in Sugimura T, Sasako M (eds): Gastric Cancer. Oxford, Oxford University Press, 1997, pp 223–248.

13 Japanese Gastric Cancer Association: Japanese Classification of Gastric Carcinoma, 2nd Engl ed. Gastric Cancer 1998;1:10–24.

14 Sano T, Kobori O, Muto T: Lymph node metastasis from early gastric cancer: Endoscopic resection of tumour. Br J Surg 1992;79:241–244.

15 Yoshida S: Endoscopic treatment; in Sugimura T, Sasako M (eds): Gastric Cancer. Oxford, Oxford University Press, 1997, pp 252–262.

16 Tajiri H, Oguro Y: Contact Nd:YAG laser treatment of gastrointestinal cancer; in Joffee SN, Oguro Y (eds): Advances in Nd:YAG Laser Surgery. New York, Springer, 1978, pp 74–78.

17 Tada M, Karita M, Yanai H, Takemoto T: Endoscopic therapy of early gastric cancer by strip biopsy. Gan To Kagaku Ryoho 1988;15:1460–1465.

18 Takeshita K, Tani M, Honda T: Treatment of primary multiple early gastric cancer: From the viewpoint of clinicopathologic features. World J Surg 1997;21:832–836.

19 Makuuchi H, Kise Y, Shirnada H, et al: Endoscopic mucosal resection for early gastric cancer. Semin Surg Oncol 1999;17:108–116.

20 Nakajima T, Ochiai T, Ogawa M, et al: Meeting report of the 7lst Japanese Gastric Cancer Congress. Gastric Cancer 1999;2:145–150.

21 Takeshita K, Tani M, Inoue H, et al: A new method of endoscopic mucosal resection of neoplastic lesions in the stomach: Its technical features and results. Hepatogastroenterology 1997;44:602–611.

22 Gotoda T, Kondoh H, Ono H, et al: A new endoscopic mucosal resection procedure using insulated tipped diathermic knife for rectal lesions. Gastrointest Endosc 1999;51:560–563.

23 Sue-Ling HM, Martin I, Griffith J, et al: Early gastric cancer: 46 cases treated in one surgical department. Gut 1992;33:1318–1322.

24 Hayes N, Karat D, Scott DJ, et al: Radical lymphadenectomy in the management of early gastric cancer. Br J Surg 1996;83:1421–1423.

25 Whiting JL, Fielding WL: Radical surgery for early gastric cancer. Eur J Surg Oncol 1998;24:263-266.

26 Sano T, Okuyama Y, Kobori O, et al: Early gastric cancer: Endoscopic diagnosis of depth of invasion. Dig Dis Sci 1990;35:1340–1344.

27 Katai H, Sano T, Fukagawa T, Shinohara H, Sasako M: Prospective study of proximal gastrectomy for early gastric cancer in the upper third of the stomach. Br J Surg 2003;90:850–853.

28 Furukawa H, Hiratsuka M, Imaoka S: Limited surgery for early gastric cancer in cardia. Ann Surg Oncol 1998;5:338–341.
29 Takeshita K, Saito N, Saeki I: Proximal gastrectomy and jejunal pouch interposition for the treatment of early cancer in the upper third of the stomach: Surgical techniques and evaluation of postoperative function. Surgery 1997;121:278–286.
30 Harada K, Misumi A, Misumi K, Basa K, Atobe Y, Kondo H, Maeno M, Honmyo U, Kanemitsu T, Akagi M: Comparative studies between proximal and total gastrectomies for cardiac cancer of the stomach with special reference to long-term postoperative course. Jap J Surg Gastroenterol 1987;20:965–969.
31 Mizumoto K, Furumoto T, Nosaka K, Kono K, Odachi T, Nishimura O, Kaibara N, Koga S: Significance of proximal gastrectomy for carcinoma of the upper portion of the stomach, with special reference to operative curability and postoperative gastrointestinal hormones. Jap J Surg Gastroenterol 1987;20:970–974.
32 Sato T, Kameyama J, Sasaki I, Imamura M: Post-gastrectomy symptoms: Studies for various types of gastrectomy based on postoperative complaints. Gastroenterol Surg 1980;3:1663–1669.
33 Matsushiro T, Hariu T, Nagashima H, Yamamoto K, Imaoka Y, Yamagata K, Okuyama S, Mishina H: Valvuloplasty plus fundoplasty to prevent esophageal regurgitation in esophagogastrostomy after proximal gastrectomy. Am J Surg 1986;152:314–319.
34 Merendino KA, Dillard DH: The concept of sphincteric substitution by an interposed jejunal segment for anatomic and physiologic abnormalities at the esophagogastric junction. Ann Surg 1955;142:486–509.
35 Maki T, Shiratori T, Hatafuku T, et al: Pylorus-preserving gastrectomy as an improved operation for gastric ulcer. Surgery 1967;61:838–845.
36 Kodama M, Koyama K, Chida T, Arakawa A, Tur G: Early postoperative evaluation of pylorus-preserving gastrectomy for gastric cancer. World J Surg 1995;19:456–461.
37 Sawai K, Takahashi T, Fujioka T, et al: Pylorus-preserving gastrectomy with radical lymph node dissection based on anatomical variations of the intrapyloric artery. Am J Surg 1995;170:285–288.
38 Isozaki H, Okajima K, Momura E, et al: Postoperative evaluation of pylorus-preserving gastrectomy for early gastric cancer. Br J Surg 1996;83:266–269.
39 Kodama M, Koyama K: Indications for pylorus-preserving gastrectomy for early gastric cancer located in the middle third of the stomach. World J Surg 1991;15:628–634.
40 Kodera Y, Yamamura Y, Kanemitsu Y, et al: Lymph node metastasis in cancer of the middle-third stomach: Criteria for treatment with a pylorus-preserving gastrectomy. Surg Today 2001;31:196–203.
41 Furukawa H, Hiratsuka M, Imaoka S: Phase 11 study of limited surgery for early gastric cancer: Segmental gastric resection. Ann Surg Oncol 1999;6:166–170.
42 Ohwada S, Nakamura S, Ogawa T: Segmental gastrectomy for early cancer in the mid-stomach. Hepatogastroenterology 1991;46:1229–1233.
43 Seto Y, Nagawa H, Muto Y: Preliminary report on local resection with lymphadenectomy for early gastric cancer. Br J Surg 1999;86:526–528.
44 Isozaki H, Kimura T, Tanaka N, Satoh K, Matsumoto S, Ninomiya M, Ohsaki T, Mori M: Esophagus gastrointestinal surgical treatment study: An assessment of the feasibility of sentinel lymph node-guided surgery for gastric cancer. Gastric Cancer 2004;7:149–153.
45 Kitagawa Y, Fujii H, Mukai M, et al: Radioguided sentinel node detection for gastric cancer. Br J Surg 2002;89:604–608.
46 Kitano S, Shiraishi N: Current status of laparoscopic gastrectomy for cancer in Japan. Surg Endosc 2004;18:182–185.
47 Ohgami M, Otani Y, Kumai K, et al: Curative laparoscopic surgery for early gastric cancer: Five years' experience. World J Surg 1999;23:187–192.
48 Ohashi S: Laparoscopic intraluminal (intragastric) surgery for early gastric cancer. Surg Endosc 1995;9:169–171.
49 Kitano S, Bandoh T, Kawano K: Endoscopic surgery in Japan. Minim Invasive Ther Allied Technol 2001;10:215–219.
50 Kitano S, Iso Y, Moriyama M, et al: Laparoscopy-assisted Billroth-I gastrectomy. Surg Laparosc Endosc 1994;4:146–148.
51 Goh P, Kum CK: Laparoscopic Billroth-II gastrectomy: A review. Surg Oncol 1993;2:S13–S18.
52 Kitano S, Shiraishi N, Fujii K, et al: A randomized controlled trial comparing an open versus a laparoscopy-assisted distal gastrectomy for the treatment of early gastric cancer: An interim report. Surgery 2002;131:S306–S311.
53 Uyama I, Sugioka A, Fujita J, et al: Completely laparoscopic extraperigastric lymph node dissection for gastric malignancies located in the middle or lower third of the stomach. Gastric Cancer 1999;2:186–190.
54 Takahashi S: Study of para-aortic lymph node metastasis of gastric cancer subjected to superextensive lymph node dissection. Nippon Geka Gakkai Zasshi 1999;91:29–35.
55 Kitamura M, Arai K, Iwasaki Y: Clinico-pathological studies and problems on para-aortic lymph node dissection: D4 dissection. Nippon Geka Gakkai Zasshi 1996;97:302–307.
56 Isozaki H, Okajima K, Fujii K, et al: Effectiveness of para-aortic lymph node dissection for advanced gastric cancer. Hepatogastroenterology 1999;46:549–554.
57 Baba M, Hokita S, Natsugoe S, et al: Paraaortic lymphadenectomy in patients with advanced carcinoma of the upper third of the stomach. Hepatogastroenterology 2000;47:893–896.
58 Sano T, Sasako M, Yamamoto S, et al: Gastric cancer surgery: Morbidity and mortality results from a prospective randomized controlled trial comparing D2 and extended para-aortic lymphadenectomy – Japan Clinical Oncology Group Study 9501. J Clin Oncol 2004;14:2767–2773.
59 Sasako M, McCulloch P, Kinoshita T, Maruyama K: New method to evaluate the therapeutic value of lymph node dissection for gastric cancer. Br J Surg 1995;82:346–351.
60 Sasako M, et al: Surgical treatment; in Sugimura Tl, Sasako M (eds): Gastric Cancer. London, Oxford University Press, 1997.
61 Okajima K, Isozaki H: Splenectomy for treatment of gastric cancer: Japanese experience. World J Surg 1995;19:537–540.
62 Maruyama K, Sasako M, Kinoshita T, Sano T, Katai H, Okajima K: Pancreas-preserving total gastrectomy for proximal gastric cancer. World J Surg 1995;19:532–536.
63 Brady MS, Rogatko A, Dent LL, Shiu MH: Effect of splenectomy on morbidity and survival following curative gastrectomy for carcinoma. Arch Surg 1991;126:359–364.
64 Wanebo HJ, Kennedy BJ, Winchester DP, Stewart AK, Fremgen AM: Role of splenectomy in gastric cancer surgery: Adverse effect of elective splenectomy on long-term survival. J Am Coll Surg 1997;185:177–184.
65 Kodera Y, Yamamura Y, Shimizu Y, Torii A, Hirai T, Yasui K, Morimoto T, Kato T, Kito T: Lack of benefit of combined pancreaticosplenectomy in D2 resection for proximal-third gastric carcinoma. World J Surg 1997;21:622–628.
66 Maehara Y, Moriguchi S, Yoshida M, Takahashi I, Korenaga D, Sugimachi K: Splenectomy does not correlate with length of survival in patients undergoing curative total gastrectomy for gastric cancer. Cancer 1991;67:3006–3009.
67 Bonenkamp JJ, Hermans J, Sasako M, van de Velde CJ: Extended lymph-node dissection for gastric cancer. Dutch Gastric Cancer Group. N Engl J Med 1999;340:908–914.
68 Cuschieri A, Weeden S, Fielding J, Bancewicz J, Craven J, Joypaul V, Sydes M, Fayers P: Patient survival after D1 and D2 resections for gastric cancer: Long-term results of the MRC randomized surgical trial. Surgical Cooperative Group. Br J Cancer 1999;79:1522–1530.
69 Japan Clinical Oncology Group Study: Study randomized controlled trial to evaluate splenectomy in total gastrectomy for proximal gastric carcinoma. Japan Clinical Oncology Group Study JCOG 0110-MF.
70 Nomura T, et al: Indication for dissection of splenic hilar lymph nodes for upper gastric cancer located in lesser curvature. Jpn J Gastroenterol Surg 2000;33:1609–1614.

Review Article

Digestive Diseases

Dig Dis 2004;22:345–350
DOI: 10.1159/000083597

(Neo)adjuvant Strategies of Advanced Gastric Carcinoma: Time for a Change?

Markus Moehler[a] Carl C. Schimanski[a] Ines Gockel[b] Theodor Junginger[b]
Peter R. Galle[a]

[a]First Department of Internal Medicine and [b]Institute of Surgery, Johannes Gutenberg University of Mainz, Mainz, Germany

Key Words
Gastric cancer · Chemotherapy · Adjuvant/neoadjuvant therapy · Chemoradiation · Taxanes · Irinotecan · Oxaliplatin · Docetaxel

Abstract
Despite surgical R0 resections, patients with gastric cancer stage UICC II–III have a high risk of recurrence and metachronic metastases. Preliminary evidence exists that adjuvant chemotherapy or neoadjuvant chemo(radio)therapy protocols may improve the prognosis of these patients undergoing surgery of gastric cancer with curative intention. As for palliative regimens, 5-fluorouracil and cisplatin are integral components of such (neo)adjuvant strategies. Upcoming cytostatic agents, i.e. irinotecan, docetaxel, oxaliplatin, and oral fluoropyridines are currently under investigation in new multimodality treatment regimens and may further increase R0 resection rates and may prolong disease-free and overall survival in the treatment of advanced localized gastric cancer.

Introduction

Despite the improvements of surgical resection as primary curative treatment for gastric cancer in Japanese and Western countries, between 50 and 70% of patients with T3–4 tumors undergoing radical primary tumor resection relapse and die within 5 years (table 1). Therefore, there is an urgent need to further improve the treatment for gastric cancer.

Table 1. Biological behavior of gastric cancer: incidence of metastasis and survival rate after resection according to Sasako [49]

Tumor depth	JCGC stage	Tumors	Lymph node, %	Liver %	Peritoneum, %	5-year survival rate, %
T1	M	1,063	3.3	0.0	0.0	93.3
	SM	881	17.4	0.1	0.0	88.9
T2	MP	436	46.4	1.1	0.5	81.3
	SS	325	63.7	3.4	2.2	65.8
T3	SE	1,232	78.9	6.3	17.8	35.5
T4	SI	724	89.8	15.5	41.6	10.1
Overall		4,683	47.8	4.5	11.5	60.3

JCGC = Japanese classification of gastric cancer; M = mucosal; SM = submucosal; MP = muscularis propria; SS = subserosa; SE = serosa exposed; SI = serosa infiltrating (neighboring organ or organs involved).

KARGER

Fax +41 61 306 12 34
E-Mail karger@karger.ch
www.karger.com

0257–2753/04/0224–0345$21.00/0

Accessible online at:
www.karger.com/ddi

PD Dr. Markus Moehler
First Department of Internal Medicine, Johannes Gutenberg University of Mainz
Langenbeckstrasse 1
DE–55101 Mainz (Germany)
Tel. +49 6131 177134, Fax +49 6131 173438, E-Mail moehler@mail.uni-mainz.de

Since 1960, chemotherapy has increasingly justified its role in the treatment of metastatic disease, as the survival of treated patients was significantly better compared with patients under best supportive care [1, 2]. Up to now, 5-fluorouracil (5-FU) combined with cisplatin have been approved to be the most useful standards of palliative chemotherapy, most often additionally modulated by combinations with other anticancer drugs, such as epirubicin or leucovorin (folinic acid, FA) [2]. Since these protocols allow response rates of more than 40%, they have the potential to reduce the local recurrence rate and to increase survival of patients with advanced localized gastric cancer in an adjuvant or neoadjuvant setting.

Currently, three main strategies are under development to improve the clinical outcome of patients with advanced gastric cancer: (1) adjuvant treatment, given as postoperative chemotherapy or chemoradiation; (2) neoadjuvant treatment, combined with or without radiation, and (3) perioperative therapy, as a combination of neoadjuvant and adjuvant protocols.

Extended Lymph Node Dissection and/or Adjuvant Therapy?

Since 1993, different meta-analyses have compared adjuvant treatment protocols versus surgery alone [3–5]. In the early meta-analyses mostly studies with only 5-FU were included and no significant difference over surgery alone was found. However, in a recent meta-analysis comparing combination regimens such as ELF, 5-FU plus mitomycin- or cisplatin-based regimens [6], the 5-year survival results suggested a moderate improvement of 5% for the use of adjuvant treatment. In contrast, such an improvement has not been demonstrated in any single randomized, large phase III study.

This discussion was further stimulated by the study presentation of the SWOG 9008-INT 0116 group, with the combination of radiochemotherapy in resected stage IB–IV gastric cancers (table 2) [7]. After randomization of 566 patients to either observation or to two cycles of FA/5-FU followed by radiation + FA/5-FU and another two cycles of FA/5-FU, a statistically significant difference for disease-free and overall survival in favor of the chemoradiation was shown. Additionally, the local relapse rate was reduced from 90 to 29% in the multimodality arm.

However, there was no difference for the risk of distant metastasis for either group. Despite the positive data, several concerns have been raised: (1) The survival rates in the surgery-only arm were significantly lower compared to European patients in different studies. (2) The survival benefit with chemoradiation was comparable to European patients after surgery without adjuvant treatment. This can be explained by a limited resection (54% of below D1) and raised the possibility that suboptimal surgery was counterbalanced by adjuvant chemoradiation. (3) Only 76% of patients received a full dose of radiation in the SWOG trial, possibly demonstrating a high level of toxicity.

Table 2. Protocol of adjuvant radiochemotherapy according to Macdonald et al. [7]

Bolus 5-FU	425 mg/m^2, days 1–5
Folinic acid	20 mg/m^2, days 1–5
radiation 45 Gy tumor bed and 1,8 Gy/d regionally (days 26–63) plus	
Bolus 5-FU	400 mg/m^2, days 1–5
Folinic acid	20 mg/m^2, days 1–5
on days 1–4 and the last 3 days of radiation	
Repeat chemo in weeks 13 and 17 (days 1–5)	

To analyze the role of extended lymphadenectomy and the extent of gastrectomy, several prospective randomized trials were performed in Western countries. Two large trials were performed comparing D1 with D2 dissection, one of which in the Netherlands by the Dutch Gastric Cancer Group (DGCG), and the other one in the UK by the Medical Research Council (MRC) [8, 9]. Both trials demonstrated that extended lymphadenectomy is associated with significantly higher morbidity and mortality rates as compared with limited lymphadenectomy [10, 11]. Likewise, splenectomy and pancreatectomy were significantly associated with an increased risk of operative mortality. Interestingly however, no significant survival difference was found for both groups in the final results of the DGCG study after 11 years' follow-up [12].

In contrast, a retrospective multicenter observation study in Germany found a significant survival advantage in patients undergoing extended lymphadenectomy [13]. Very recently, the Japan Clinical Oncology Group (JCOG) presented an ambitious trial of D2 lymph node dissection as compared with more extensive lymphadenectomy. Here, the extended lymphadenectomy included the lymph node tissue along the aorta within a D2 dissection [14]. In this study, the mortality rate was less than 1%, which is remarkably low compared to a large population-based study of US patients, where the operative mortality

Table 3. Comparison of results to trials 0116 and JCOG [49]

	0116	JCOG
Patients treated with surgery, %		
D0	54	–
D1	36	–
D2	10	50
D4	–	50
Adjuvant treatment		
Radiation	45 Gy	None
Chemotherapy	Fluorouracil and leucovorin	None
Patients	281	523
Tumor localisation		
Antrum	53	–
Gastric body	24	–
Gastric cardia	21	–
Multiple lesions	2	–
Lower third	–	41
Middle third	–	39
Upper third	–	19
Tumor stage		
I	14	23
II	74	257
III	175	230
IV	18	13
Tumor-related deaths	3 (1.1%)	4 (0.8%)
Survival, %		
3 years	50	–
5 years	42	71.4

Table 4. Recent randomized phase III studies in advanced gastric cancer

Group (first author)	Protocol	Patients n	RR %	Median survival, months	p value
Webb [50]	FAMTX	130	21	5.8	0.0009
	ECF	126	45	8.9	
Ross [51]	MCF		44	8.7	
	ECF		42	9.4	
Vanhoefer [52]	FUP	134	20	7.2	NS
	ELF	132	9	7.2	
	FAMTX	133	12	6.7	
Ajani ASCO 2003	DCF	111	39	10.2	0.0064
	CF	112	23	8.5	

C or P = cisplatin; F = 5-fluorouracil; M = mitomycin; E = epirubicin; ELF = etoposide/leucovorin/5-fluorouracil.

reached approximately 9% [15]. However, the median patient age was only 61 years, with no patient being older than 75 years, which is lower compared to most 'Western' studies. Secondly, the surgeons were highly experienced in performing the procedure. All participating hospitals treated more than 50 cases of gastric resections per year strongly arguing for the role of high volume centers, which has also been shown for other countries [16]. Additionally, the JCOG surgeons rarely employed splenectomy and vigorously avoided pancreatectomy, with 36.5 and 4.2% respectively [14].

In addition to the above-mentioned SWOG trial, Park et al. [17] and Italian colleagues investigated a similar protocol in 290 patients, all of whom were curatively resected with extensive D2 lymph node dissection. After a median follow-up of 49 months, 43% of patients relapsed, with 67% local relapses and 36% distant metastases. The 5-year overall and relapse-free survival rates were 60 and 57% – better than in the SWOG trail – respectively [17]. Therefore, it is still questionable whether Japanese or European patients undergoing D2 resection may benefit of postoperative chemoradiation (table 3).

On the other hand, the availability of new substances more effective than the 5-FU/FA Mayo Clinic protocol, as used in the SWOG and Italian trials, promise to be superior compared to former standard chemotherapy. In the near future, prospective randomized phase III trials will be presented to elute these questions.

Neoadjuvant Multimodality Treatment: Chemotherapy or Chemoradiation?

Although a number of randomized studies have suggested a clinical benefit with improved survival for neoadjuvant chemotherapy as compared to historical controls, randomized trial evidence is yet missing [18–21]. Again, a recently reported randomized study of preoperative chemotherapy compared with surgery alone in 56 patients showed no benefit with chemotherapy [22].

As there is little doubt that gastric cancer is a chemosensitive tumor and a response rate can be achieved in at least 40%, the use of new adjuvant protocols is interesting for locally advanced tumors [6, 23, 24]. Ongoing trials have shown improvement of survival with palliative ECF, PLF, irinotecan plus the AIO regimen, and docetaxel plus cisplatin/5-FU (DCF). The duration of response is still short (table 4) [2].The value of preoperative FAMTX (5-FU, doxorubicin and methotrexate) is currently under investigation in the Netherlands, and in

Table 5. Possible advantages of neoadjuvant therapy

Better tumor vascularization results in higher therapeutic efficacy and downstaging
Excision of chemoradiated areas may result in lower long-term toxicity
Early systemic therapy may allow better control of tumor micrometastases
Operation may not be compromised with higher morbidity and mortality

a joined MRC study with ECF (epirubicin, cisplatin and 5-FU).

Neoadjuvant chemotherapy was particularly interesting as short-term therapy (i.e. two cycles of 6–8 weeks) simultaneously given or/and sequentially given with chemoradiation (table 5) [25]. Furthermore, patients responding to neoadjuvant treatment presented with a better performance status during their remission without compromising the later operation with a higher morbidity and mortality [26].

While the incidence of distal gastric cancer is decreasing, cancers of the proximal stomach and the gastroesophageal junction, including the Barrett's carcinoma, are a dramatically increasing challenge [27]. Meanwhile, adenocarcinomas of the gastroesophageal junction have been categorized as an important group with its own pathological and treatment characteristics, counted neither among the patterns of esophagus nor of gastric cancer [27].

Very recently, Ajani et al. [28] demonstrated a substantially high R0 resection of 70%, pathologic complete and partial response rates of 30 and 24%, respectively, and resulting in durable overall survival time of 33.7 months in a multi-institutional trial of preoperative chemoradiotherapy, mainly for 'proximal' gastric tumors. To extrapolate the neoadjuvant data of the gastroesophageal junction, three main randomized studies for esophagus cancer included high percentages of adenocarcinomas of the lower esophagus or even the cardia region [29–31]. In contrast to one large negative phase III trail with chemotherapy/surgery versus surgery alone [29], two studies showed a significant survival benefit and a trend for benefit in 3-year survival for the chemoradiation arm, respectively [30, 31]. Additionally, a recent MRC trial randomized 802 patients comparing two cycles of preoperative cisplatin/5-FU against surgery alone and demonstrated a survival benefit for the chemotherapy-treated group revealing no difference in the number of perioperative deaths or the rate of postoperative complications [25]. Thus, it is reasonable to continue to use surgery as standard of care, as well as to continue investigation of potentially more effective multimodality regimens. However, it has still to be determined whether chemotherapy alone or chemoradiation is of more benefit for these tumors [32–36].

Perioperative Chemotherapy

So far, the recently published MAGIC trial is the only large randomized study of perioperative chemotherapy conducted with an adequate follow-up period. It was initiated to compare surgery alone (S) with perioperative chemotherapy in which patients received three preoperative and three postoperative cycles of ECF (CS). After enrolment of 503 patients with resectable gastric (74%) or lower esophageal cancer (26%), the proportion of patients with curative resection was greater in the CS arm (79 vs. 69%, $p = 0.018$). After 5 years, the progression-free survival favored the CS arm over the S arm (hazard ratio 0.70, 95% CI 0.56–0.88, $p = 0.092$) and a potential improvement in overall survival, although this failed to reach statistical significance (hazard ratio 0.80, 95% CI 0.68–1.01, $p = 0.063$). However, there is still considerable hope that the continued follow-up of the MAGIC trail will allow definitive conclusions with regards to the implications of such a perioperative strategy on the survival in advanced gastric cancer.

Conclusions

In the adjuvant setting, meta-analyses suggest that systemic treatment may achieve a small but significant reduction in the risk of death. Preoperative chemotherapy alone however, generally well tolerated, did not yet decrease the incidence of local failure beyond the level achieved with surgery alone. Preoperative radiotherapy alone enhanced local control, but failed to improve overall survival. Thus, only neoadjuvant radiochemotherapy with better anticancer drugs may improve survival, especially after reaching high pathological complete and partial remission rates. Additionally, the neoadjuvant approach may be worth a direct comparison with postoperative adjuvant chemoradiotherapy. The MAGIC trial – a combination of both as perioperative chemotherapy – already demonstrated an improvement in progression-free survival and a slight improvement in overall survival.

In recent years, new anticancer drugs such as irinotecan, taxanes and oxaliplatin reported even higher objective response rates of up to 70% and an improvement of overall median survival of up to 12 months in palliative treatment [2, 37–39]. These new chemotherapy regimens may be additional treatment options for localized resectable or unresectable advanced disease to further decrease incomplete resection rates as well as morbidity and mortality rates. Ongoing and upcoming adjuvant, neoadjuvant or perioperative studies with these new promising compounds will define their definitive role.

Furthermore, new diagnostic techniques, such as endoscopic sonography, (mini)laparoscopy, magnetic resonance tomography and position emission tomography allow better pre- or postoperative staging [40, 41]. In this regard, endosonography with its high sensitivity in the assessment of tumor size and local lymph node involvement has increasingly been accepted for preoperative staging [42–44]. In addition, (mini)laparoscopy allows detection of peritoneal carcinosis, which is being found in ~20–30% of gastric cancer patients at primary diagnosis [45–48]. As the position emission tomography scan has been additionally proven to effectively predict the clinical response in esophageal and gastric cancer, such diagnostic procedures will allow better allocations and adjustments for an individualized and optimized treatment strategy.

References

1 Glimelius B, et al: Randomized comparison between chemotherapy plus best supportive care with best supportive care in advanced gastric cancer. Ann Oncol 1997;8:163–168.
2 Hohler T, Moehler M: New chemotherapeutic options in advanced gastric cancer (in German). Onkologie 2003;26(suppl 7):54–59.
3 Kim R, Toge T: Clinical relevance of meta-analysis of survival benefit when deciding treatment of adjuvant chemotherapy in gastric cancer. Anticancer Res 2003;23:1843–1846.
4 Mari E, Floriani I, Tinazzi A, et al: Efficacy of adjuvant chemotherapy after curative resection for gastric cancer: A meta-analysis of published randomised trials. A study of the GISCAD (Gruppo Italiano per lo Studio dei Carcinomi dell'Apparato Digerente). Ann Oncol 2000;11:837–843.
5 Panzini I, Gianni L, Fattori PP, et al: Adjuvant chemotherapy in gastric cancer: A meta-analysis of randomized trials and a comparison with previous meta-analyses. Tumori 2002;88:21–27.
6 Falcone A: Future strategies and adjuvant treatment of gastric cancer. Ann Oncol 2003; 14(suppl 2):45–47.
7 Macdonald JS, et al: Chemoradiotherapy after surgery compared with surgery alone for adenocarcinoma of the stomach or gastroesophageal junction. N Engl J Med 2001;345:725–730.
8 Cuschieri A, et al: Patient survival after D1 and D2 resections for gastric cancer: Long-term results of the MRC randomized surgical trial. Surgical Co-operative Group. Br J Cancer 1999;79:1522–1530.
9 Bonenkamp JJ, et al: Comparison of factors influencing the prognosis of Japanese, German, and Dutch gastric cancer patients. World J Surg 1993;17:410–415.
10 Bonenkamp JJ, et al: Randomised comparison of morbidity after D1 and D2 dissection for gastric cancer in 996 Dutch patients. Lancet 1995;345:745–748.
11 Cuschieri A, et al: Postoperative morbidity and mortality after D1 and D2 resections for gastric cancer: Preliminary results of the MRC randomised controlled surgical trial. The Surgical Cooperative Group. Lancet 1996;347:995–999.
12 Hartgrink HH, et al: Extended lymph node dissection for gastric cancer: Who may benefit? Final results of the randomized Dutch gastric cancer group trial. J Clin Oncol 2004;22:2069–2077.
13 Siewert JR, Bottcher K, Stein HJ, Roder JD: Relevant prognostic factors in gastric cancer: Ten-year results of the German Gastric Cancer Study. Ann Surg 1998;228:449–461.
14 Sano T, et al: Gastric cancer surgery: Morbidity and mortality results from a prospective randomized controlled trial comparing D2 and extended para-aortic lymphadenectomy – Japan Clinical Oncology Group Study 9501. J Clin Oncol 2004;22:2767–2773.
15 Wanebo HJ, Kennedy BJ, Winchester DP, Stewart AK, Fremgen AM: Role of splenectomy in gastric cancer surgery: Adverse effect of elective splenectomy on long-term survival. J Am Coll Surg 1997;185:177–184.
16 Bottcher K, et al: Risk of surgical therapy of stomach cancer in Germany. Results of the German 1992 Stomach Cancer Study. German Stomach Cancer Study Group ('92) (in German). Chirurg 1994;65:298–306.
17 Park SH, Kim DY, Heo JS, et al: Postoperative chemoradiotherapy for gastric cancer. Ann Oncol 2003;14:1373–1377.
18 Fink U, Stein HJ, Siewert JR: Multimodal therapy of tumors of the upper gastrointestinal tract (in German). Chirurg 1998;69:349–359.
19 Fink U, Stein HJ, Schuhmacher C, Wilke HJ: Neoadjuvant chemotherapy for gastric cancer: Update. World J Surg 1995;19:509–516.
20 Janunger KG, Hafstrom L, Glimelius B: Chemotherapy in gastric cancer: A review and updated meta-analysis. Eur J Surg 2002;168: 597–608.
21 Schipper DL, Wagener DJ: Chemotherapy of gastric cancer. Anticancer Drugs 1996;7:137–149.
22 Songun I, et al: Chemotherapy for operable gastric cancer: results of the Dutch randomised FAMTX trial. The Dutch Gastric Cancer Group (DGCG). Eur J Cancer 1999;35:558–562.
23 Gallardo-Rincon D, Onate-Ocana LF, Calderillo-Ruiz G: Neoadjuvant chemotherapy with P-ELF (cisplatin, etoposide, leucovorin, 5-fluorouracil) followed by radical resection in patients with initially unresectable gastric adenocarcinoma: A phase II study. Ann Surg Oncol 2000;7:45–50.
24 Geh JI, et al: Preoperative ECF chemotherapy in gastro-oesophageal adenocarcinoma. Clin Oncol (R Coll Radiol) 2000;12:182–187.
25 Medical Research Council Oesophageal Cancer Working Group: Surgical resection with or without preoperative chemotherapy in oesophageal cancer: A randomised controlled trial. Lancet 2002;359:1727–1733.
26 Kelsen D: Neoadjuvant therapy for upper gastrointestinal tract cancers. Curr Opin Oncol 1996;8:321–328.
27 Siewert JR, Stein HJ: Classification of adenocarcinoma of the oesophagogastric junction. Br J Surg 1998;85:1457–1459.
28 Ajani JA, Mansfield PF, Janjan N, et al: Multi-institutional trial of preoperative chemoradiotherapy in patients with potentially resectable gastric carcinoma. J Clin Oncol 2004;22: 2774–2780.

29 Kelsen DP, et al: Chemotherapy followed by surgery compared with surgery alone for localized esophageal cancer. N Engl J Med 1998; 339:1979–1984.

30 Walsh TN, et al: A comparison of multimodal therapy and surgery for esophageal adenocarcinoma. N Engl J Med 1996;335:462–467.

31 Urba SG, et al: Randomized trial of preoperative chemoradiation versus surgery alone in patients with locoregional esophageal carcinoma. J Clin Oncol 2001;19:305–313.

32 Geh JI, Crellin AM, Glynne-Jones R: Preoperative (neoadjuvant) chemoradiotherapy in oesophageal cancer. Br J Surg 2001;88:338–356.

33 Samel S, et al: Neoadjuvant radio-chemotherapy of adenocarcinoma of the oesophagogastric junction. Onkologie 2001;24:278–282.

34 Lordick F, Stein HJ, Peschel C, Siewert JR: Neoadjuvant therapy for oesophagogastric cancer. Br J Surg 2004;91:540–551.

35 Stewart JR, et al: Improved survival with neoadjuvant therapy and resection for adenocarcinoma of the esophagus. Ann Surg 1993;218: 571–578.

36 Jones DR, et al: Induction chemoradiotherapy followed by esophagectomy in patients with carcinoma of the esophagus. Ann Thorac Surg 1997;64:185–192.

37 Haller DG, Misset JL: Docetaxel in advanced gastric cancer. Anticancer Drugs 2002;13: 451–460.

38 Ajani JA: Docetaxel for gastric and esophageal carcinomas. Oncology (Huntingt) 2002;16:89–96.

39 Kohne CH, Wils JA, Wilke HJ: Developments in the treatment of gastric cancer in Europe. Oncology (Huntingt) 2000;14:22–25.

40 Ott K, et al: Prediction of response to preoperative chemotherapy in gastric carcinoma by metabolic imaging: Results of a prospective trial. J Clin Oncol 2003;21:4604–4610.

41 Ott K, et al: Fluorodeoxyglucose-positron emission tomography in adenocarcinomas of the distal esophagus and cardia. World J Surg 2003;27:1035–1039.

42 Wakelin SJ, et al: A comparison of computerised tomography, laparoscopic ultrasound and endoscopic ultrasound in the preoperative staging of oesophagogastric carcinoma. Eur J Radiol 2002;41:161–167.

43 Pfau PR, Chak A: Endoscopic ultrasonography. Endoscopy 2002;34:21–28.

44 Chen CH, Yang CC, Yeh YH: Preoperative staging of gastric cancer by endoscopic ultrasound: The prognostic usefulness of ascites detected by endoscopic ultrasound. J Clin Gastroenterol 2002;35:321–327.

45 Ozmen MM, et al: Staging laparoscopy for gastric cancer. Surg Laparosc Endosc Percutan Tech 2003;13:241–244.

46 Feussner H, Omote K, Fink U, Walker SJ, Siewert JR: Pretherapeutic laparoscopic staging in advanced gastric carcinoma. Endoscopy 1999;31:342–347.

47 Denzer U, et al: Minilaparoscopy in the diagnosis of peritoneal tumor spread: Prospective controlled comparison with computed tomography. Surg Endosc 2004;18:1067–1070.

48 Denzer U, et al: Mini-laparoscopically guided percutaneous gastrostomy and jejunostomy. Gastrointest Endosc 2003;58:434–438.

49 Sasako M: Principles of surgical treatment for curable gastric cancer. J Clin Oncol 2003;21: 274S–275S.

50 Webb A, et al: Randomized trial comparing epirubicin, cisplatin, and fluorouracil versus fluorouracil, doxorubicin, and methotrexate in advanced esophagogastric cancer. J Clin Oncol 1997;15:261–267.

51 Ross P, et al: Prospective randomized trial comparing mitomycin, cisplatin, and protracted venous-infusion fluorouracil (PVI 5-FU) with epirubicin, cisplatin, and PVI 5-FU in advanced esophagogastric cancer. J Clin Oncol 2002;20:1996–2004.

52 Vanhoefer U, et al: Final results of a randomized phase III trial of sequential high-dose methotrexate, fluorouracil, and doxorubicin versus etoposide, leucovorin, and fluorouracil versus infusional fluorouracil and cisplatin in advanced gastric cancer: A trial of the European Organization for Research and Treatment of Cancer Gastrointestinal Tract Cancer Cooperative Group. J Clin Oncol 2000;18: 2648–2657.

Review Article

Digestive Diseases

Dig Dis 2004;22:351–359
DOI: 10.1159/000083598

Endoscopic Palliation and Nutritional Support in Advanced Gastric Cancer

A.J. Dormann

Department of Medicine, Krankenhaus Holwelde, Köln, Germany

Key Words
Gastric outlet obstruction · Self-expanding metal stents · Malignant stricture · Gastrointestinal stents · Percutaneous endoscopic gastrostomy · Enteral nutrition · Introducer long-term nutrition · Skin jejunal nutrition · Nasoenteral tube · Cachexia

Abstract
Most of the patients with advanced gastric cancer have incurable disease at presentation and require palliative treatment to reduce symptoms as vomiting, nausea and inability to eat. Treatment options are palliative surgery and endoscopic techniques. Insertion of self-expanding metal stents is nowadays a well-established method of treating biliary and esophageal strictures and is also effective in gastric tumors. The indication and application technique are described in this review. In addition, enteral nutrition is indicated if the gastrointestinal tract functions but swallowing or mastication is compromised by disease or if it is needed to pass an obstructed area, especially in gastric tumor patients. This article reviews the enteral nutrition techniques and their clinical value for patients with advanced gastric cancer.

Introduction

More than 50% of patients with advanced gastric cancer have incurable disease at presentation and require palliative treatment for dysphagia, motility problems and gastric outlet stenoses [1]. Patients presenting with high-grade gastric outlet obstruction are difficult to treat due to the underlying disease. They often exhibit intractable vomiting, nausea and inability to eat. The consequences are gastric distension, weight loss, and dehydration requiring treatment with additional fluid and nutritional support [1]. Furthermore, the patients are at a risk of aspiration with consecutive pneumonia. Therefore, rapid palliation of obstructions is mandatory.

The aim of this review is to demonstrate endoscopic therapeutic options for palliation in these groups of patients and to summarize the rationale for nutritional support in patients with advanced gastric cancer.

Treatment Options

Surgery versus Endoscopy

Palliative surgical management of patients with advanced gastric cancer is considered of high risk and limited effect due to the poor condition of the patient on presentation [2]. The classical treatment for these patients has been surgical open gastrectomy or gastroenterostomy, sometimes combined with choledochojejunostomy with high primary success rates up to 90% [3].

KARGER

Fax +41 61 306 12 34
E-Mail karger@karger.ch
www.karger.com

0257–2753/04/0224–0351$21.00/0

Accessible online at:
www.karger.com/ddi

PD Dr. med. A.J. Dormann
Kliniken der Stadt Köln GmbH, Krankenhaus Holwelde, Medizinische Klinik
Neufelder Strasse 32, DE–51058 Köln (Germany)
Tel. +49 221 89 07 26 02, Fax +49 221 89 07 27 99
E-Mail dormanna@kliniken-koeln.de

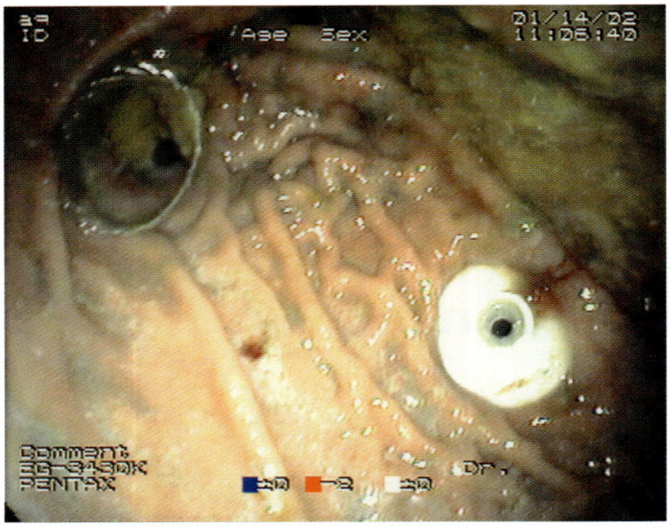

Fig. 1. Enteral stent in gastroenterostomy with PEG in place.

The major shortcomings of these surgical procedures are: (1) their relative high risk of mortality and morbidity, estimated as high as 8–33% and 20–60% respectively, in patients with advanced disease and poor general status; (2) a lengthy hospital stay for bowl transit recovery, and (3) digestive dysfunction, such as persistent symptoms of delayed gastric emptying, which develops in about 10–26% of all patients [4–6].

The use of minimally invasive operative techniques has been applied recently to the management of palliation of gastric outlet obstruction. Initial trials have shown that laparoscopic gastroenterostomy associated with cholecystojejunostomy offers a less invasive alternative than open surgery with a shorter hospital stay and a more rapid return to normal activity [7, 8].

Two recently published randomized trials comparing the open or laparoscopic surgical approach with the endoscopic stenting for antropyloric stricture palliation have shown that placement of metal stents is an effective alternative to surgical palliation [9, 10]. Both studies revealed a lower complication rate and significant reduced hospitalization rate. Therefore, the surgical approach is a valid option in patients fit for laparotomy with the intention of curative resection. Patients who present intraoperative criteria for non-resectability and patients with a good prognosis and an expected survival of more than 6 months are also candidates for surgery [11, 12]. Today there is an ongoing debate about the best therapeutic approach in these patients, as patient selection is crucial [12, 13].

Endoscopy

Alternative non-surgical endoscopic modalities are balloon dilatation or periodic bougienage, laser ablation, and placement of feeding tubes. APC has had only limited use for imminent gastric outlet obstruction [14]. The main disadvantage of these tools are that they are often ineffective or produce only a transient effect on symptoms allowing the patients to consume adequate oral intake [15–18].

To palliate gastrointestinal bleeding, Nd:YAG laser has been used. In 18 patients with bleeding esophageal and gastric cancer, hemostasis with Nd:YAG laser was achieved in 94.5%. This effect was persistent for 77.8% of patients [19]. Oguro et al. [20] noted successful hemostasis in 75% of their patients with upper gastrointestinal cancer bleeding. One study has shown that the cessation of hemorrhage with Nd:YAG laser can be only temporary, with all patients rebleeding within several days [21]. APC has also been used infrequently to treat diffuse gastric cancer hemorrhage [14]. In general, APC treatment for upper gastrointestinal cancer bleeding is safe but not very effective in long-term follow-up.

Stenting

Insertion of self-expanding metal stents (SEMS) is nowadays a well-established method of treating biliary and esophageal strictures. More recently, enteral SEMS have been used to palliate malignant gastric outlet stenosis and gastroduodenal obstructions after Truong et al. [22] published their first stent procedure in 1992. Today it is accepted that placement of a SEMS for gastric outlet obstruction has the potential of providing immediate and more durable relief than other non-surgical modalities [12].

Indication

Because most of the patients are in a state of advanced disease at the time when they present with signs of gastric outlet obstruction, indications for stenting in patients are mainly given in tumors of the antropyloric region [12]. In some cases, stent placement in pericardial tumors can be useful but the necrosis of gastric wall tissue due to the mechanical damage of the metal stent often reduces the overall success rate of this approach. Furthermore, stent placement can support a non-functioning surgical gastroenterostomy in a minimally invasive way (fig. 1) and is sometimes very helpful after primary surgical intervention [23].

Enteral Stenting

Beside a CT scan, an upper gastrointestinal series and endoscopy can be performed prior to stent placement to estimate the character and length of the stenosis. Distal obstruction in the small bowl which could compromise passage and gastric hypomotility due to diffuse tumor infiltration should also be excluded. If this can be diagnosed, the post-interventional clinical success rate deteriorates and the indication for enteral stenting should be proven again by discussing other treatment options (e.g. total parenteral nutrition via Port-A-Cath).

SEMS placement for gastric tumors can sometimes be very difficult due to the anatomical angulation of the stomach and gastroduodenal lumen, leading to difficulties in stent deployment, and is therefore not very widely used [24]. Stent placement was initially performed via gastrostomy or by using esophageal SEMS or biliary Wallstents with a small diameter [25]. However, in order not to subject the patient to an additional procedure and risk, the peroral route of stent implantation should be chosen. All esophageal SEMS have shortcomings related to their large size (Z-stent) and limited length (Endocoil, Ultraflex) of the delivery system [25, 26].

After introducing newly designed enteral stents, the approach is now divided between through-the-scope placement, fluoroscopy with endoscopic control and fluoroscopy only. In a recently published systematic review on SEMS in gastroduodenal obstruction, we could evaluate that in 606 patients the endoscopic approach was favored in 73% of the users. Through-the-scope placement was performed in 39%, fluoroscopy with endoscopic control in 34% and fluoroscopy only in 27% of all [12]. In the minority, stents had been placed using fluoroscopy alone because the tortuosity of the access route and dilatation of the stomach makes manipulation of the catheters and stent difficult [27]. Endoscopy alone gives an inaccurate assessment of the lesion and shows only the proximal margin of the stricture well. In addition, endoscopy alone requires blind cannulation of the lesion and blind predilatation of the stricture for endoscopic assessment of the distal extent of the lesion. In our experience the combined approach with endoscopy and fluoroscopy is most effective.

Several different stents are available which are suitable for the use in the gastrointestinal tract. Stent types which were used in 606 analyzed procedures were Enteral Wallstent™ (Boston Scientific, Natwick, Mass., USA) in 51%, other Wallstent™ (Boston Scientific) in 23%, InStent™ (InStent Inc., Eden Prairie, Minn., USA) in 8%, Ultraflex™ (Boston Scientific) in 8%, Choo/Song™ (MI Tech Ltd, Korea) in 3% and several other types in 7% of all cases.

The main stent used in the more recently published papers was the enteral Wallstent™. It is currently available in lengths of 60 and 90 mm and in diameters of 18, 20, and 22 mm. The enteral Wallstent™ originally designed for colonic stenting furthermore offers the advantage of a small delivery system (10 Fr) and a long working shaft (230 cm). The stent has a good radial force, which is particularly useful when sited across the pylorus or along the curve of the duodenum. To place the stent through-the-scope, a 'therapeutic channel' endoscope (channel size minimum 3.6 mm) is needed.

After being kept on a nil-per-os regimen for 8–12 h, patients are placed in the left lateral position. Following intravenous sedation (e.g. 50 mg pethidine i.v., 5 mg midazolam i.v.) the endoscope is advanced to the proximal end of the stenosis. Proximal and distal margins of the stricture can be assessed by contrast injection with fluoroscopical control. Sometimes it is helpful to mark the margin with a submucosal injection of contrast (e.g. 1 ml lipiodol). A stiff guide wire (0.035 or 0.038 inch with a soft tip) is then advanced as deep as possible across the stenosis with fluoroscopic control (fig. 2a). The choice of the guide wire is important in negotiating the often irregular and tortuous strictures and sometimes a hydrophilic wire is needed and can later be changed into a stiff wire which reduces buckling of the insertion shaft. A dilatation with a balloon or a bougienage prior to stent insertion it not recommended and only necessary if the stent device does not pass the stricture. The stent is then advanced over the wire through-the-scope and placed by keeping the endoscope stationed adjacent to the stricture (fig. 2b). Pushing forward the stent can be assisted by pulling the wire a little backward especially in very tortuous and tight strictures. Wallstents shorten during expansion, which must be taken into consideration when positioning the introduction system.

Deployment of the stents should be performed under both fluoroscopic and endoscopic control. Pulling back the restraining sheath is normally easy to perform. In cases with strong angulated tumors it can be more difficult and needs time. The stent should always be selected at least 2–3 cm longer than the treated stricture and placed with a minimum distance of 2–3 cm proximally or distally at an angulation to reduce intestinal obstruction. During stent deployment, continuous, gentle upward traction should be applied on the catheter to prevent distal stent migration. An advantage of the Wallstent™ is that it can be recaptured (if not expanded over more than 75%) by advancing the constraining sheath and repositioning the entire stent. Dilatation after stent deployment

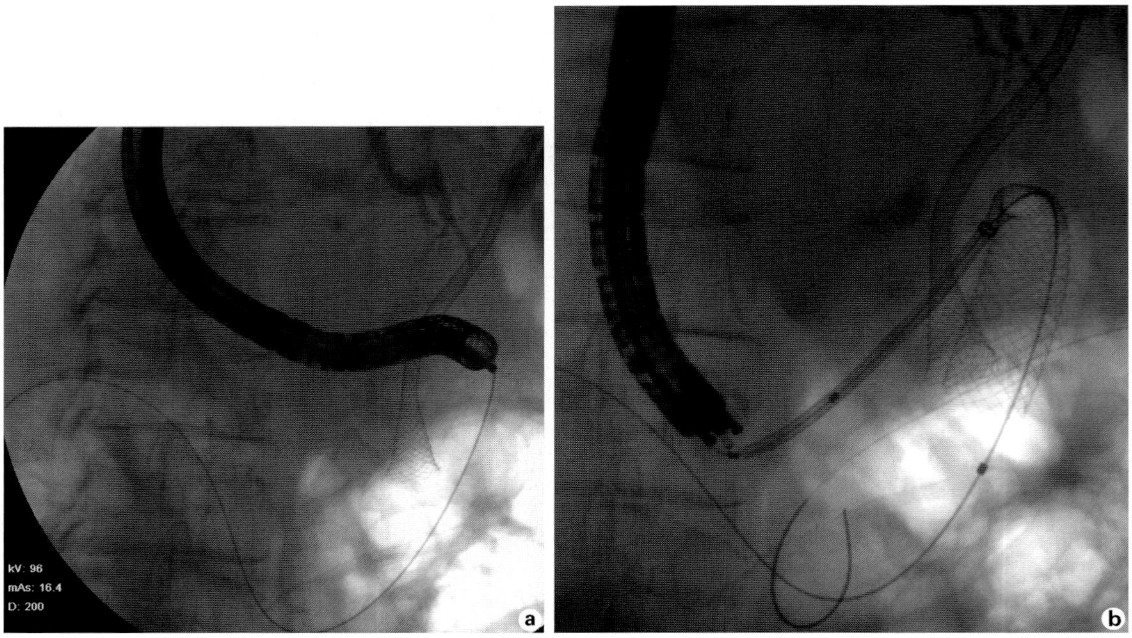

Fig. 2. **a** Guide wire in position. **b** Stent in position during release.

is rarely needed, as these stents tend to self-expand within the next 24–48 h after deployment.

Endoscopic evaluation without passage through the stent followed by Gastrografin contrast-enhanced upper gastrointestinal radiography should immediately be carried out to assess the patency and location of the stent (fig. 3a). The next day, contrast images should be performed to ensure stent passage (fig. 3b).

Follow-Up

Technical success defined as successful stent placement and deployment can be achieved in 97% of all patients [12]. In less than 5%, technical failure occurs mainly due to failure to gain access through the obstruction – complicated anatomy or severe obstruction. Sometimes failures are caused by stent positioning and deployment issues. Clinical success defined as relief of symptoms and/or improvement of oral intake can be achieved in 89% of the technically successful stented patients.

Clinical improvement of gastric emptying can be measured on the pooled population in accordance with the Gastric Outlet Score (no oral intake = 0, liquids only = 1, soft solids = 2, full diet = 3) [28]. At baseline, the score of the 606 review patients was 0.4 and reached 2.4 after the intervention [12]. Post-procedure oral intake improved for all clinically successful patients. 48% of them were on full diet, 39% on soft solids and 13% on liquids only. 11% of the group did not experience symptom relief and/or improvement of food intake. The majority of these failures (61%) were due to progression of the disease, 20% to early migrations, and 15% to procedure-related reasons such as a stent deployed too proximally or too distally, a stent not expanded fully or a prosthesis not correctly placed.

It is important for the clinical management that final resolution of symptoms is attained within a mean of 4 days and a broad range of 1–7 days. So after the procedure the patients can be started on clear liquid diet within 24 h, progressing to full diet as tolerated. These outcomes are strong indicators of patient comfort, and therefore quality of life after the intervention. To improve clinical efficacy, a standardized enteral feeding protocol should be followed within the first 3–5 days after stent insertion [12]. Because the survival time of patients after palliative enteral stenting is limited with a mean of 12.1 weeks, patient description is a major but difficult issue.

Complications

The stent procedure is in general safe and no procedural mortality has been reported up to now in the literature [12]. Severe complications including perforation and bleeding are rare, occurring in less than 1.2% of all interventions. Non-severe complications occur in 27% of the stent population. Obstruction of the stent represents the

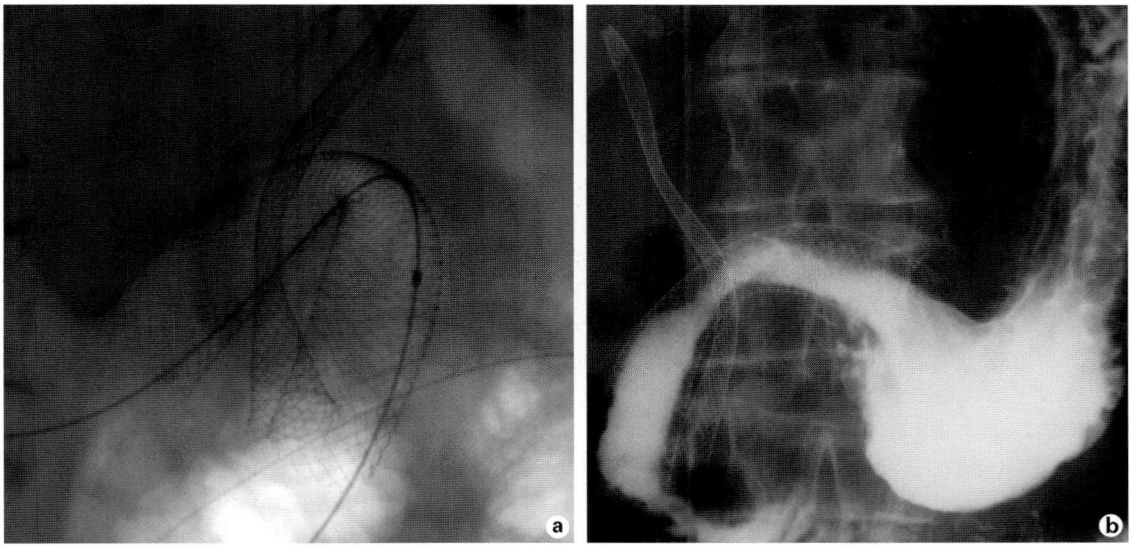

Fig. 3. **a** Stent after release. **b** Contrast study after 24 h.

majority of events with 18%. The causes of obstruction were mainly due to the progression of the disease: tumor in- or overgrowth and obstruction at other sites. Some obstructions are due to stent and technical reasons (generally implantation issues, such as insufficient stenosis coverage, stent fracture or broken struts, and collapse of the stent etc.). Obstruction of SEMS remains a problem especially when utilizing non-covered devices in patients for long-term palliation. New stent designs with greater diameter and the efficacy to prevent tumor ingrowth may solve this problem in the future [29, 30].

Rarely, obstructions due to the migration of the stent, food impaction or mucosal prolapse occur. The migration rate of enteral stents is about 5%. In the majority of patients, stent migration can be managed by insertion of an additional stent; some patients do not need another intervention or must undergo surgery.

Post-procedural biliary problems due to stent-induced obstruction of the papilla major rarely occur and can be managed by placement of a biliary stent. There is still discussion regarding primary biliary drainage before antroduodenal stenting. Some authors have reported high biliary intervention rates due to secondary biliary obstruction following duodenal stent insertion [28]. This data may support a recommendation for primary biliary evaluation and SEMS stent placement in patients with distal tumor involvement of the papilla or expected stent application across the papilla to prevent secondary biliary obstruction.

Nutritional Support in Gastric Cancer Patients

Nutritional support in patients with upper gastrointestinal cancer is often difficult to achieve for several reasons. Obstruction caused by the tumor may preclude oral ingestion, and odynophagia, and anorexia may compound the problem. Although the variety of palliative methods described above are often effective, failures do occur. Furthermore, many studies have shown that even when luminal patency is achieved, dysphagia persists because of functional difficulties with swallowing that may be related to tumor invasion of neuromuscular structures [31].

There are four primary perspectives in the nutritional care of cancer patients [32]. First, nutritional care should always be considered supportive, whether the oncologic aim is cure or palliation. The goal of nutrition care is always to support nutritional status, body composition, functional status, and quality of life.

Second, nutritional intervention in end-stage malnutrition is potentially more successful than chemotherapeutic approaches in end-stage malignancy. In both cases, early diagnosis and intervention offer the best chance for success [33]. Hospital malnutrition is well known and the incidence in hospitalized tumor patients ranged from 30 to 55% [34]. Malnutrition has an economic impact and is associated with longer hospital stays, higher costs and increased mortality and morbidity [35].

Third, reduced caloric and protein intake serve as the primary basis for clinically evident nutritional deterioration in malignancy. Anorexia is the most common symptom contributing to poor nutrient intake in many of the tumor patients. In addition, inadequate oral intake is caused by numerous gastrointestinal symptoms (e.g. nausea, vomiting, stomatitis, mucositis, diarrhea, obstipation), sensory changes and pain. In cancer, high inflammatory stress is usual and the tumor cell-initiated inflammation process has a paradoxical effect [32]. The inflammatory response is as effective as invading pathogens. However, while the inflammatory process may be effective in dealing with single malignant cells, once cancer is established the inflammatory process becomes a cause of the patient's demise, rather than a means of destroying the tumor. In addition to stimulating the cytokine mediated and hormonal aspects of the inflammatory response, tumor-specific products also add to the level of inflammatory stress in the patient. There is a different quality of tissue depletion in the syndrome of cancer cachexia to that seen during starvation. While starvation results primarily in fat loss, with secondary loss in protein mass, cachexia results almost equally in fat and protein loss.

Fourth, a standardized, easily performed, cost-effective and predictive assessment tool is absolutely necessary to judge the success or failure of any nutritional regimen (e.g. subjective global assessment (SGA)). This assessment instrument formalizes standard available information obtained as part of a patient database in a manner similar to the subjective evaluation of performance status [32].

Enteral Nutrition

Enteral nutrition is indicated if the gastrointestinal tract functions but swallowing or mastication is compromised by disease or neurological disorders, or if it is needed to pass an obstructed area, especially in gastric tumor patients. It is important that the decisions about tube feeding be made after a proper evaluation of the patient. This will avoid initiating enteral nutrition in instances where a more conservative approach may be successful [36]. Decisions in tumor patients need to be individualized, however, because many patients will do well if instructed and helped from the onset of therapy by a skilled dietician. In some cases with anorexia, food supplements and appetite enhancers can be quite effective and are less risky, and certainly much less expensive than tube feeding [36].

The advantage of tube feeding is that it is like oral feeding and relies on the absorption of nutrients or specific solutions providing supplemental or complete nutrition through the intestinal mucosa. Enteral nutrition support can be achieved by the use of transnasally and percutaneous endoscopically placed tubes in the stomach or the jejunum. The types of tubes have different indications, advantages and complications. Specific details of insertion have been described before [38].

Tube Feeding

Nasoenteral Tube Feeding

Nasogastral and nasoenteric feeding tubes are available for short-term (<4 weeks) use in cancer patients. The advantage is that no endoscopic access is necessary to place nasogastric tubes. In gastric tumors, nasogastric feeding is often ineffective and the risk of aspiration pneumonia is high in patients with delayed gastric emptying [37]. The indication for nasoenteral feeding should primarily be given in cases with malignant outlet stenoses [38, 39]. In these patients, two or three lumen tubes should be preferred because they increase the tolerance of enteral feeding by simultaneous gastric decompression [39]. Endoscopic or fluoroscopic guidance are essential to place nasoenteric tubes and both techniques are often combined [40, 41]. Endoscopic positioning can be achieved by pulling the tube into the jejunum beneath the scope (BTS) or pushing it over a wire (OTW) which was initially placed under endoscopical control [38] (fig. 4).

Percutaneous Tube Feeding

Since its clinical introduction by Gauderer et al. [42], percutaneous endoscopic gastrostomy (PEG) has been widely used to maintain long-term (>4 weeks) enteral nutrition and is currently the standard method for enteral feeding in patients with swallowing disorders [38]. Studies have shown good long-term success of PEGs in supplying nutrition and preventing aspiration in patients with cancer [43]. It is today evident from these studies that percutaneous endoscopically placed tubes for enteral nutrition are safe to insert and are effective in providing long-term nutrition for patients with dysphagia, gastric outlet obstruction, or recurrent aspiration [38].

In patients with advanced tumors and ascites the problem of leakage after PEG occurs in up to 25% [44]. Di Lorenzo et al. [45] reported a significant risk of leakage and subsequent peritonitis due to displacement of the stomach from the abdominal wall. However, Lee et al. [46] could demonstrate a favorable result of the pull-through PEG in patients with ascites after preinterventional paracentesis. Ryan et al. [47] performed percutaneous radiological gastrostomy placement using the T-fastener technique in patients with malignant ascites with a

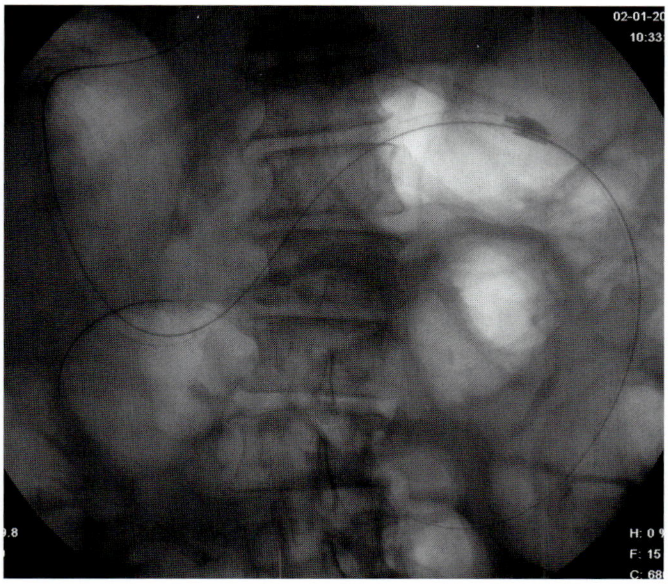

Fig. 4. Multiple lumen nasoenteral tube in position – the tip of the tube is behind the ligament of Treitz.

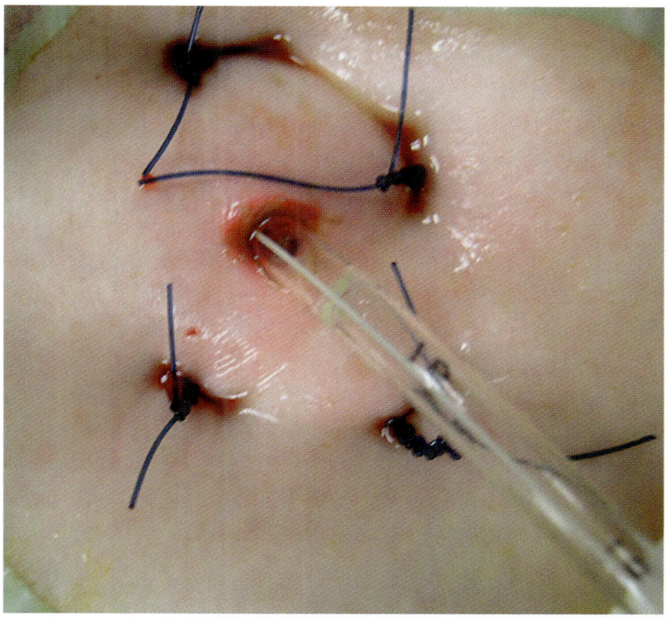

Fig. 5. Pull-through PEG in a patient with ascites combined with four gastropexy sutures.

complication rate of 15.6%. The combination of endoscopic suture gastropexy with the PEG pull-through technique can be very effective in patients with ascites [48]. Due to our experience with the gastropexy technique, we think that three or four sutures are needed to have a safe attachment of the anterior gastric to the abdominal wall (fig. 5). PEG tubes may be required for purposes of gastric decompression in patients with malignant ascites. We think that this new technique can be a helpful tool in these cases.

Patients with malignant gastric or gastroduodenal outlet obstructions often suffer from gastric distension and vomiting. The jejunal enteral tube through the PEG (PEG-J) can be very helpful to give gastric decompression via PEG and simultaneous jejunal nutrition. The tube can be placed by pushing a jejunal feeding tube through the previously placed PEG using a BTS or OTW technique. An initial positioning of the tube behind the ligament of Treitz is essential to reduce the retrograde migration rate [49]. Although the efficacy to reduce tube feeding-related aspiration has not been proven definitively in many patients, the gastric decompression via PEG and simultaneous jejunal nutrition shows clinical benefit in many patients [50, 51].

For long-term jejunal feeding, direct percutaneous endoscopic jejunostomy (D-EPJ), a modification of the pull PEG technique, is the ideal procedure. D-EPJ can normally placed without problems in patients with partial or post-gastrectomy and is considerably more difficult prior to surgery [52–54].

No guidelines are available for selecting patients for either PEG-J or D-PEJ. Although it is evident that patients with partial (Billroth I or II resection) or total gastrectomy are ideal candidates for D-EPJ. The decision to use PEG-J or D-EPJ depends on the individual situation of the patients [55]. In patients with gastroparesis and a history of aspiration or reflux we prefer D-EPJ, and also in those with gastric outlet stenosis and vomiting PEG-J [38].

In experienced centers, endoscopic tube placement is not successful in less than 2% of all patients. There are different techniques to create a surgical gastro- or jejunostomy but also laparoscopic techniques are available now. Needle catheter jejunostomy can always be applied in surgical interventions in cancer patients and carries fewer complications than a formal tube jejunostomy [56].

An important aspect of long-term enteral access are minor or major complications. The main complications are leakage, bad odor from the stoma, skin irritation and granulation tissue. To reduce these problems and to increase patient's quality of life, skin-level devices were introduced. Skin-level gastrostomy tubes provide an easy and comfortable approach for enteral nutrition and are well established. These systems (e.g. button, skin-level conversion system, one-step button) should not be primarily used in cases with advanced gastric tumors [38].

Total Parenteral Nutrition (TPE)

Cancer is the most common indication for the use of TPE as a method used for the delivery of nutrients directly into the blood, bypassing the decreased food intake and dysfunction of the gastrointestinal tract [57]. TPE has been shown to be appropriate for malnourished cancer patients receiving aggressive anticancer treatment, and to have a permissive role in those patients who cannot be given oncologic therapy because of a poor nutritional status.

TPE should be reserved for patients with gastrointestinal tract dysfunction due to an obstruction, peritoneal carcinomatosis, surgery, high output fistula, fibrosis or major intestinal resections, who have a reasonable prognosis and cannot tolerate enteral feeding [57]. This category of patients can benefit from long-term TPE at home, with TPE-related complications comparable to those seen in benign diseases. The use of TPN in advanced cancer with gastrointestinal obstruction or severe dysfunction should be carefully considered with reference to several factors. It is predicated on the expectation of demonstrable benefit for the patient. The efficacy depends on whether it improves the quality of life rather than simply lengthening survival. In different studies mean survival ranging from 17 days to 3.7 months from appearance of bowel obstruction has been reported in advanced cancer patients treated by medical management. Unfortunately, poor candidates for TPN are evident retrospectively and the routine use of TPN should be avoided when it takes the form of prolongation of life. Only those patients who strongly support this decision after explanation should be offered this regimen.

References

1 Siersema PD, Marcon N, Vakil N: Metal stents for tumors of the distal esophagus and gastric cardia. Endoscopy 2003;35:79–85.

2 Doberneck RC, Berndt GA: Delayed gastric emptying after palliative gastrojejunostomy for carcinoma of the pancreas. Arch Surg 1987;102:608–613.

3 Kikuchi S, Tsutsumi O, Kobayashi N, et al: Does gastrojejunostomy for unresectable cancer of the gastric antrum offer satisfactory palliation? Hepatogastroenterology 1999;46:584–587.

4 Sarr MG, Cameron JL: Surgical palliation of unresectable carcinoma of the pancreas. World J Surg 1984;8:906–918.

5 Weaver D, Winczek R, Bowemian H, et al: Gastrojejunostomy: Is it helpful for patients with pancreatic cancer? Surgery 1987;107:608–613.

6 Fujino Y, Suzuki Y, Kamigaki T, et al: Evaluation of gastroenteric bypass for unresectable pancreatic cancer. Hepatogastroenterology 2001;48:563–568.

7 Choi YB: Laparoscopic gastrojejunostomy for palliation of gastric outlet obstruction in unresecable gastric cancer. Surg Endosc 2002;16:1620–1626.

8 Röthlin MA, Schöb O, Weber M: Laparoscopic gastro-hepaticojejunostomy for palliation of pancreatic cancer. Surg Endosc 1999;13:1065–1069.

9 Mittal A, Windsor J, Woodfield J, Casey P, Lane M: Matched study of three methods for palliation of malignant pyloroduodenal obstruction. Br J Surg 2004;91:205–209.

10 Fiori E, Lamazza A, Volpino P, Burza A, Paparelli C, Cavallaro G, Schillaci A, Cangemi V: Palliative management of malignant antro-pyloric strictures: gastroenterostomy vs. endoscopic stenting. A randomized prospective trial. Anticancer Res 2004;24:269–272.

11 Van Heek NT, van Geenen RC, Bush OR, et al: Palliative treatment in 'peri'-pancreatic carcinoma: Stenting or surgical therapy? Acta Gastroenterol Belg 2002;65:171–175.

12 Dormann A, Meisner S, Verin N, Wenk Lang A: Self-expanding metal stents for gastroduodenal malignancies: Systematic review of their clinical effectiveness. Endoscopy 2004;36:543–550.

13 Bergamaschi R, Marvik R, Thorensen JE, et al: Open versus laparoscopic gastrojejunostomy for palliation in advanced pancreatic cancer. Surg Laparosc Endosc 1998;8:92–96.

14 Akhtar K, Byrne JP, Bancewicz J, et al: Argon beam plasma coagulation in the management of cancers of the esophagus and stomach. Surg Endosc 2000;14:1127–1130.

15 Riemann JF, Ell C, Lux G, Demling L: Combined therapy of malignant stenoses of the upper gastrointestinal tract by means of laser beam and bougienage. Endoscopy 1985;17:43–48.

16 Watson JP, Bennett MK, Griffin SM, Matthewson K: The tissue effect of argon plasma coagulation on esophageal and gastric mucosa. Gastrointest Endosc 2000;52:342–345.

17 Tendler DA: Malignant gastric outlet obstruction: Bridging another divide. Am J Gastroenterol 2002;97:4–6.

18 Norberto L, Ranzato R, Marino S, Angriman I, Erroi F, Donadi M, Vella V, D'Erminio A, D'Amico DF: Endoscopic palliation of esophageal and cardial cancer: Neodymium-yttrium aluminum garnet laser therapy. Dis Esophagus 1999;12:294–296.

19 Schwesinger WH, Chumley DL: Laser palliation for gastrointestinal malignancy. Am Surg 2001;54:100–104.

20 Oguro Y, Tajiri H, Takenoto T, et al: Present status of laser endoscopic treatment of cancers of the gastrointestinal tract in Japan. Prog Dig Endosc 1986;29:94.

21 Takemoto T, Okazaki Y, Otani T, et al: Palliative laser therapy. Endoscopy 1987;19:12–15.

22 Truong S, Bohndorf V, Geller H, et al: Self-expanding metal stents for palliation of malignant gastric outlet obstruction. Endoscopy 1992;24:433–435.

23 Zollikofer CL, Jost R, Schoch E, Decurtins M: Gastrointestinal stenting. Eur Radiol 2000;10:329–341.

24 Keymling M, Wagner H, Vakil N, Knyrim R: Relief of malignant duodenal obstruction by percutaneous insertion of a metal stent. Gastrointest Endosc 1993;39:439–441.

25 Wigginghaus B, Dormann AJ, Grünewald T: Self-expandable metallic stents in malignant gastric outlet obstructions – An alternative approach using modified techniques. Z Gastroenterol 1999;11:1093–2000.

26 Kozarek RA, Ball TJ, Patterson DJ: Metallic self-expanding stent application in the upper gastrointestinal tract: Caveats and concerns. Gastrointest Endosc 1992;38:1–6.

27 Profili S, Meloni GB, Bifulco V, et al: Self-expandable metal stents in the treatment of antropyloric and/or duodenal strictures. Acta Radiol 2001;42:176–180.

28 Adler DG, Baron TH: Endoscopic palliation of malignant gastric outlet obstruction using self-expanding metal stents: Experience in 36 patients. Am J Gastroenterol 2002;97:72–78.

29 Kaw M, Singh S, Gagneja H, et al: Role of self-expandable metal stents in the palliation of malignant duodenal obstruction. Surg Endosc 2003;17:646–650.

30 Dormann AJ, Eisendrath P, Wigginghaus B, Huchzermeyer H, Deviere J: Palliation of esophageal carcinoma with a new self-expanding plastic stent. Endoscopy 2003;35:207–211.

31 Kubba AK, Krasner N: An update in the palliative management of malignant dysphagia. Eur J Surg Oncol 2000;26:116–129.

32 Ottery FD: Supportive nutrition to prevent cachexia and improve quality of life. Semin Oncol 1995;22:98–111.
33 Elia M, Stratton RJ: How much undernutrition is there in hospitals. Br J Nutr 2000;84: 325–335.
34 Senkal M, Dormann A, Suchner U, Shang E, Stehle P: Survey on structure and performance of nutrition-support teams in Germany. Clin Nutr 2002;21:329–335.
35 Bettany GE, Powell-Tuck J: Malnutrition: Incidence, diagnosis, causes, effects and indications for nutritional support. Eur J Gastroenterol Hepatol 1995;7:494–500.
36 Tchekmedyian NS: Costs and benefits of nutrition support in cancer. Oncology 1995;9(suppl):79–84.
37 Olivares L, Segovia A, Revuelta R: Tube feeding and lethal aspiration in neurological patients: A review of 720 autopsy cases. Stroke 1974;5:654–657.
38 Dormann AJ, Huchzermeyer H: Endoscopic techniques for enteral nutrition: Standards and innovations. Dig Dis 2002;20:145–153.
39 Shang E, Kähler G, Meier-Hellmann A, Scheele J: Advantages of endoscopic therapy of gastrojejunal dissociation in critical care patients. Intensive Care Med 1999;25:162–165.
40 Külling D, Bauerfeind P, Fried M: Transnasal versus transoral endoscopy for placement of nasoenteral feeding tubes in critically ill patients. Gastrointest Endosoc 2000;52:506–510.
41 Montecalvo MA, Steger KA, Farber HW, Smith BF, Dennis RC, Fitzpatrick GF, Pollack SD, Korsberg TZ, Birkett DH, Hirsh EF, Craven DE: Nutritional outcome and pneumonia in critical care patients randomized to gastric versus jejunal feedings. Crit Care Med 1992; 20:1377–1387.
42 Gauderer MWL, Ponsky JL, Izant RJ Jr: Gastrostomy without laparotomy: A percutaneous technique. J Pediatr Surg 1980;15:872–875.
43 Shike M, Berner YN, Gerdes H, et al: Percutaneous endoscopic gastrostomy and jejunostomy for long-term feeding in patients with cancer of the head and neck. Otolarygology Head Neck Surg 1989;101:549–554.
44 Keeffe O, Carrasco CH, Charsangavej C: Percutaneous drainage and feeding gastrostomies in 100 patients. Radiology 1989;172:341–343.
45 Di Lorenzo J, Dalton B, Miskovitz P: PEG: What are their benefits, what are the risks? Postgrad Med 1992;91:277–281.
46 Lee MJ, Saini S, Brink JA: Malignant small bowel obstruction and ascites: Not a contraindication to percutaneous gastrostomy. Clin Radiol 1991;44:332–334.
47 Ryan JM, Hahn, PF, Mueller PR Performing radiologic gastrostomy or gastrojejunostomy in patients with malignant ascites. AJR 1998; 171:1003–1006.
48 Dormann AJ, Glosemeyer R, Leistner U, Deppe H, Roggel R, Wigginghaus B, Huchzermeyer H: Modified percutaneous endoscopic gastrostomy with gastropexy – Early experience with a new introducer technique. Z Gastroenterol 2000;38:933–938.
49 De Legge MH, Duckworth PF, McHenry L: Percutaneous endscopic gastrojejunostomy: A dual center safety and efficacy trial. JPEN 1995;19:239–243.
50 Lazarus BA, Murphy JB, Culpepper L: Aspiration associated with long-term gastric versus jejunal feeding: A critical analysis of the literature. Arch Physiol Med Rehabil 1990;71:46–53.
51 Lien HC, Chand CS, Chen GH: Can percutaneous endoscopic jejunostomy prevent gastroesophageal reflux in patients with preexisting esophagitis?. Am J Gastroenterol 2000;95:34–39–43.
52 Shike M, Latkany L: Direct percutaneous endoscopic jejunostomy. Gastrointest Endosoc Clin N Am 1998;8:569–580.
53 Mellert J, Naruhn MB, Grund KE, Becker HD: Direct endoscopic percutaneous jejunostomy. Clinical results. Surg Endsoc 1994;8:867–870.
54 Rumalla G, Baron TH: Results of direct percutaneous endoscopic jejunostomy, an alternative method for providing jejunal feeding. Mayo Clin Proc 2000:75:807–810.
55 Kadakia SC, Sullivan HO, Stames E: Percutaneous endoscopic gastrostomy or jejunostomy and the incidence of aspiration in 79 patients. Am J Surg 1992;164:114–118.
56 Sarr MG: Appropriate use, complications and advantages demonstrated in 500 consecutive needle catheter jejunostomies. Br J Surg 1999; 86:557–561.
57 Mercadante S: Parenteral versus enteral nutrition in cancer patients: Indications and practice. Support Care Cancer 1998;6:85–93.

Review Article

Digestive Diseases

Dig Dis 2004;22:360–365
DOI: 10.1159/000083599

Recent Developments in Chemotherapy of Advanced Gastric Cancer

Tobias Götze[a] Kerstin Schütte[a] Christoph Röcken[b] Peter Malfertheiner[a] Matthias P.A. Ebert[a]

[a]Department of Gastroenterology, Hepatology and Infectious Diseases, and
[b]Institute of Pathology, Otto von Guericke University Magdeburg, Magdeburg, Germany

Key Words
Gastric cancer · Gastric cancer, palliative treatment · Taxane · Irinotecan · Oxaliplatin · Capecitabine

Abstract
Approximately 1 million individuals develop gastric cancer every year and the mortality of gastric cancer is only second to lung cancer. The poor prognosis is caused by late diagnosis of most cancers in advanced stages and the limited therapeutic options in these stages. Apart from the elucidation of underlying molecular and genetic changes in the development and progression of gastric cancers, the development of new treatment strategies is critical for the improvement of the treatment and prognosis of these patients. In this review we have summarized and critically assessed recent studies dealing with the chemotherapy of advanced gastric cancer. While the efficacy of most treatment regimens is only limited, new developments may indicate that treatment with chemotherapy may confer some benefit in the future.

Introduction

In Germany, gastric cancer is diagnosed in approximately 20,000 individuals every year. Most patients suffer from advanced disease either due to local invasion or the presence of lymph node and/or distant metastases. In this stage, a curative resection is impossible and palliative treatment, besides palliative surgery or endoscopical procedures, is the only option for these patients with a poor prognosis. Therefore, the development of effective and well-tolerated systemic palliative chemotherapy regimens is very important for the clinical management of these patients. Here we review the latest results from clinical studies assessing the role of palliative chemotherapy of advanced gastric cancer.

Treatment Regimens[1]

5-FU and Combination Chemotherapy

5-FU is a pyrimidine antagonist that is similar in structure to the pyrimidine base thymine and inhibits DNA synthesis by blocking the formation of normal pyrimidine nucleotides through enzyme inhibition and by interfering with DNA synthesis after incorporation into a replicating cell. Furthermore, 5-FU is also able to block the production of RNA, thereby contributing to cell death. Since the therapy of gastric cancers with 5-FU alone only achieves

KARGER
Fax +41 61 306 12 34
E-Mail karger@karger.ch
www.karger.com

0257–2753/04/0224–0360$21.00/0

Accessible online at:
www.karger.com/ddi

Matthias Ebert, MD
Department of Gastroenterology, Hepatology and Infectious Diseases
Otto von Guericke University, Leipziger Strasse 44, DE–39120 Magdeburg (Germany)
Tel. +49 391 6721520, Fax +49 391 67290054
E-Mail Matthias.Ebert@medizin.uni-magdeburg.de

low response rates, recently, new combinations with other drugs were tested and compared to the standard ECF protocol. ECF consists of Epirubicin, Cisplatin and 5-FU and has been demonstrated to be of high efficacy in at least two large phase III studies in which results were significantly better than Fluorouracil/Doxorubicin/Methotrexate (FAMTX) and mitomycin plus cisplatin plus 5-FU (MCF) [1, 2]. ECF is not preferred in some countries because it requires a central intravenous line, therefore, other treatment regimens have been developed. A phase III study of the EORTC tested ELF (Etoposide/Leucovorin/Fluorouracil) against cisplatin/5-FU (FUP) and against FAMTX. The overall response rates were disappointing, cisplatin/5-FU achieved only a response rate of 20%. The median time of survival was between 6.7 months (FAMTX) and 7.2 months (cisplatin/5-FU and ELF) [3]. In Europe, cisplatin and 5-FU combinations are mainly used. In Germany, PLF is used frequently, a combination consisting of cisplatin, and weekly 24-hour continuous infusion of 5-FU. To this date, a controlled randomized comparison of PLF against ECF has not been performed, but based on phase II studies it seems that PLF may be superior to ECF.

In conclusion, treatment with 5-FU-based combination therapy shows some survival benefit for patients with advanced gastric cancer, therefore, it has become a basic strategy in the past decade for the palliative treatment of gastric cancer. However, 5-FU is rapidly degraded by dihydropyrimidine dehydrogenase (DPD), and the expression of DPD seems to be of considerable importance for the efficacy of 5-FU-based therapy. Recently, combinations using oral fluoropyrimidine co-administered orally with inhibitors of this enzyme have been developed. An oral compound with DIF (DPD inhibitory fluoropyrimidine) activity, named S1, has been evaluated in several clinical studies. Two earlier phase II clinical studies showed a combined response rate of 44.6% [4, 5]. In 2003, Koizumi et al. [6] published a new phase I/II study with a combination of S1 combined with cisplatin (CDDP). The phase II study consisted of 19 patients with advanced gastric cancer that where treated with this regimen. The overall response rate was 74% with a median survival time of 12.6 months. Hematological and non-hematological side effects were observed in 15.8 and 26.3%, respectively.

UFT, a combination of the oral accessible fluoropyrimidines uracil and tegafur, is frequently used in patients with advanced gastric cancer in Japan. Takiuchi and Ajani [7] tested UFT in a trial with patients suffering from advanced gastric cancer and achieved response rates of 42% for UFT alone, and of 50% for the combination with cisplatin and/or epirubicin. Capecitabine is a recently developed prodrug of 5-FU that is metabolized to active 5-FU after enteral uptake. Capecitabine is activated to 5-FU by the enzyme thymidine phosphorylase, which is highly expressed in the cancer cells. This 5-FU prodrug has been studied in several trials with patients suffering from gastric or colon cancer. Kim et al. [8] conducted a phase II study of capecitabine in combination with cisplatin. The overall response rate was 55% with a median survival time of 10.1 months. Grade 3 and 4 toxicity, according to WHO guidelines, was observed in approximately one third of patients (neutropenia 32.5%). However, its oral application and selective activation in cancer cells makes it an interesting option for the palliative treatment of gastric cancer patients.

Platinum and Derivatives

Platinum is an alkylating agent inhibiting DNA replication by forming adducts between two adjacent gua-

[1] *Summary of the abbreviations of treatment regimens*

5-FU	5-Fluorouracil
CAC	Capecitabine + Cisplatin
CAD	Capecitabine + Docetaxel
CDDPS1	Cisplatin + S1
CF	Cisplatin + 5-FU
CFSFU	Cisplatin + Folinic acid + 5-FU
CG	Cisplatin + Gemcitabine
DC	Docetaxel + Cisplatin
DCF	Docetaxel + Cisplatin + 5-FU
DFUE	Docetaxel + 5-FU + Epirubicin
DG	Docetaxel + G-CSF
ECF	Epirubicin + Cisplatin + 5-FU
EDP	Epirubicin + Docetaxel + Cisplatin
ELF	Etoposide + Leucovorin + 5-FU
FAM	Fluorouracil + Doxorubicin + Mitomycin
FAMTX	Fluorouracil + Doxorubicin + Methotrexate
FS	Folinic acid
FUP	Cisplatin + 5-FU
I	Irinotecan
IC	Irinotecan + Cisplatin
IFU	Irinotecan + 5-FU
IFSFU	Irinotecan + Folinic acid + 5-FU
IFUL	Irinotecan + 5-FU + Leucovorin
IOP	Irinotecan [CPT-11] + Oxaliplatin [L-OHP]
MCF	Mitomycin + Cisplatin + 5-FU
OFSFU	Oxaliplatin + Folinic acid + 5-FU 24 h
PELF	Cisplatin + Epidoxorubicin + Leucovorin + Fluorouracil
PLF	Cisplatin + 5-FU + Leucovorin
UFT	Uracil + Tegafur
UFT + C/E	Uracil + Tegafur + Cisplatin and/or Epirubicin

nines or between guanine and adenine molecules. Recently a study using a new cisplatin-based combination was published by De Lange et al. [9] in 2004. They used cisplatin with gemcitabine and tested it in 24 patients with advanced gastric cancer. Gemcitabine itself showed no significant antitumor activity in gastric cancer, despite the fact that this drug has been demonstrated to be effective in various gastrointestinal cancers and was even approved as first-line therapy for advanced pancreatic cancer. The overall response rate in this study was 30%. Interestingly, the median time of survival was 11 months, which was considered a positive result. Aside from cisplatin, other platin derivatives have also been studied in gastric cancer. Oxaliplatin, another alkylating agent, appears to be more effective than cisplatin regarding the inhibition of DNA synthesis. This drug along with folinic acid and fluorouracil was recently tested in a phase II study in 41 patients. Al-Batran et al. [10] reported an overall response rate of 43% and a median time of survival of 9.6 months. While these results are comparable to other chemotherapy regimens, their patients experienced significantly less toxicity, mainly consisting of WHO grade 1 and 2 nausea (73.1%), vomiting (41.5%) and diarrhea (36.6%). Grade 3 and 4 toxicities were anemia (7.3%) and neutropenia (4.9%). A treatment regimen including a platin derivative called PELF (Cisplatin/Epidoxorubicin/Leucovorin/Fluorouracil) was tested by Cocconi et al. [11] against fluorouracil and doxorubicin/mitomycin (FAM) in a controlled randomized trial in patients with gastric cancer. PELF proved to be superior with an overall response rate of 38% and a median time of survival of 7.7 months (table 1).

Taxanes

Taxane-based drugs interfere with mitosis and cell replication by binding to a subunit of tubulins. Mainly two taxane-based drugs are used for the treatment of advanced gastric cancer: paclitaxel (Taxol) and docetaxel (Taxotere). Several phase II studies have been performed over the last decades to evaluate the efficacy of these drugs for the control of gastric cancer growth. Among others, Kim et al. [12] used a regimen consisting of Taxol, cisplatin and 5-FU in 41 patients with advanced gastric cancer. The overall response rate was 51%, but the overall survival was just 6 months. In the same year, Chun et al. [13] reported the results of their study using the same regimen in 37 patients. In this study, the overall response rate was higher with 64%, however overall survival was again poor with 7 months. Kollmannsberger et al. [14] took a different approach and combined paclitaxel with cisplatin and 5-FU. They treated 45 patients and the overall response rate was 51% with an overall survival time of an impressive 14 months.

Since docetaxel (Taxotere) is considered to be more potent in tumor growth control compared to Taxol, several groups used this drug for the therapy of gastric cancer. In 2000, Roth et al. [15] used Taxotere and cisplatin as a combination therapy in 48 patients with advanced gastric cancer, gaining an overall response rate of 56% and an overall median survival time of 9 months. Four years later the same group [16] tested a combination of Taxotere, cisplatin and 5-FU in 52 patients, but the result was not superior to the two-drug regimen (RR 50%; overall survival time 9.3 months). The group of Ajani et al. [17] also tested docetaxel, cisplatin and 5-FU (DCF) in a phase III study and compared their results to the combination of cisplatin und 5-FU (CF). While DCF was superior to CF with a response rate of 39% compared to 23% and an overall median survival of 10.2 months compared to 8.5 months, it was not superior compared to other docetaxel-based studies. Even worse, the rate of WHO grade 3 and 4 neutropenia increased to 80% for the DCF regimen. In 2001, Ridwelski et al. [18] also tested docetaxel and cisplatin in 39 patients. The overall response rate was 37% and the median survival was 10.4 months in their study population. In a further phase II study reported by Lee et al. [19], docetaxel was combined with cisplatin and epirubicin. 30 patients were treated, the overall response rate was 47% and the median survival was 11 months. Mavroudis et al. [20] published a phase II study with 30 patients who were treated with docetaxel and granulocyte colony-stimulating factor. The response rate was only 20% und the median survival 7 months. Interestingly, the combination of docetaxel with capecitabine, an oral fluoropyrimidine, proved to be more successful. Park et al. [21] enrolled 42 patients in a phase II study between 2001 and 2003. Of these patients, 38 were available for evaluation of tumor response, the overall response rate was 60% with a median survival time of 10.5 months (table 1).

Irinotecan

Irinotecan is a DNA topoisomerase I inhibitor that interferes with DNA replication and cell division. Recently, a significant survival advantage for the single agent in patients with colorectal cancer, who failed in a first-line therapy with 5-FU, has been reported [22]. Chun et al. [23] used a similar approach and conducted a phase II study in 37 patients with advanced gastric cancer, who failed in the first-line therapy with cisplatin. The result was an overall tumor control rate of 42.9% but the overall

Table 1. Overview of recent chemotherapy studies for the treatment of gastric cancer

Group (first author)	Year	Protocol	Design	Patients	Overall response rate, %	Median time of survival months
Platinum and combinations						
Cocconi	2001	FAMTX	RCT	97	21	6.9
		PELF		98	38	7.7
Koizumi	2003	CDDPS1	Phase II	19	74	12.5
De Lange	2003	CG	Phase II	23	30	11.0
Al-Batran	2004	OFSFU	Phase II	41	43	9.6
Taxanes						
Kim	1999	Taxol + Cisplatin + 5-FU		41	51	6.0
Chun	1999	Taxol + Cisplatin + 5-FU		37	64	7.0
Mavroudis	2000	DG	Phase II	30	20	7.0
Roth	2000	Taxotere + Cisplatin		48	56	9.0
Kollmannsberger	2000	Paclitaxel + Cisplatin + 5-FU	Phase II	45	51	14.0
Ridwelski	2001	DC	Phase II	39	37	10.4
Ajani	2003	DCF	Randomised phase III		39	10.2
		CF			23	8.5
Lee	2004	EDP	Phase II	30	47	11.0
Park	2004	CAD	Phase II	38	60	10.5
Roth	2004	Taxotere + Cisplatin + 5-FU	Phase II	52	50	9.3
Irinotecan based						
Boku	1999	IC		44	48	10.1
Pozzo	2001	IFSFU	Randomized phase II	74	34	10.7
		IC		72	26	6.9
Ajani	2002	IC		38	58	9.0
Köhne	2003	I	Phase II	40	20	7.1
Bouche	2003	LFU	Randomized phase II	45	14	6.8
		PLF		44	27	9.5
		IFUL		45	40	11.3
Bugat	2003	I			17–23	
Louvet	2004	IFSFU	Phase II		40	11.3
		CFSFU			27	9.5
Assersohn	2004	IFUL	Phase II	38	29	6.4
Chun	2004	I		37	20	5.2
Souglakos	2004	IOP	Phase II	32	50	8.5

response rate was just 20% with a median time of survival of 5.2 months. Main complications were neutropenia and diarrhea. Those findings were confirmed by Bugat [24] who used irinotecan as a single agent in patients with gastric cancer and reported response rates between 17 and 23%. Assersohn et al. [25] combined irinotecan with 5-FU/leucovorin in a phase II study with patients with primary refractory or relapsed advanced esophageal and gastric carcinomas; 38 patients were treated in this study. The overall response rate was 29% and the median time of survival was 6.4 months. In 2003, Koehne et al. [26] studied the efficacy of irinotecan as a single agent in 40 patients with metastatic gastric cancer, but the response rate was only 20%, with a median survival of 7.1 months. More promising results were achieved through the combination of irinotecan (CPT-11) with oxaliplatin as a first-line treatment. Souglakos et al. [27] analyzed 32 patients who received this regimen. The overall response rate was 50% and the median time of survival 8.5 months. Bouche et al. [28] conducted a randomized phase II trial using leucovorin and 5-FU. This treatment was then combined with either cisplatin or irinotecan in their study. The combination with irinotecan achieved the best result in this study with a response rate of 40% (14% for single infusion, 27% for the cisplatin combination) and a median time of survival of 11.3 months (6.8 single; 9.5 for cisplatin combination). Recently, very promising results were reported from the group of Ajani et al. [29], who used the combination of irinotecan with cisplatin in 38 patients with gastric cancer. The response rate was 58% with a median time of survival of 9 months. Boku et al. [30] also combined irinotecan and cisplatin and tested this regimen in 44 patients. The overall response rate was 48% and, thus, lower compared to the study reported by Ajani et al. [29], however the median time of survival was increased (10.1 months). In contrast, other groups have reported less promising results for the combination of irinotecan with other chemotherapeutic agents for the treatment of gastric cancer. In a phase II study conducted by Pozzo et al. [31] the combination of irinotecan/cisplatin was tested against irinotecan/folinic acid/5-FU. The two-agent regimen achieved a response rate of 26%, whereas the triple therapy achieved a response rate of 34%. Overall median time of survival was 6.9 months for irinotecan and cisplatin compared to 10.7 months for irinotecan/folinic acid/5-FU. This triple therapy was tested again in 2003 by Moehler et al. [32], who tested the irinotecan-based therapy against a therapy with etoposide and 5-FU (ELF). The response rate in the irinotecan-based therapy was 43%. Furthermore, Louvet et al. [34] conducted a study in which the treatment with irinotecan/folinic acid/5-FU was tested against cisplatin/folinic acid/5-FU. The response rate for the irinotecan-based therapy was very similar with 40% (compared to 27% for the cisplatin-based therapy) and the overall median time of survival was 11.3 months [33–35]. Altogether, irinotecan improved the median time of survival in a subgroup of patients with gastric cancer.

Conclusion

Despite recent developments in the assessment of new therapeutic reagents for the therapy of advanced gastric cancer, the impact on survival has been limited. The development of prodrugs and orally available drugs are interesting new approaches which need to be studied in larger patient series. Nonetheless, a significant subgroup of patients with advanced gastric cancer benefit from the therapy with taxanes and/or irinotecan. For the future it will be important to (1) further elucidate the pathology of gastric cancer(s) on transcriptomic and proteomic levels to identify novel targets for a specific therapy (please also see the article related to advances in molecular therapy in this issue); (2) determine subgroups of patients with gastric cancer – based on clinical and/or molecular characteristics – that may benefit from patient-tailored chemotherapy; (3) determine the underlying molecular causes of chemotherapy resistance in gastric cancers and, finally (4) perform clinical studies with a significant number of patients in order to confirm the promising results obtained in smaller phase I or phase II studies using the new drugs irinotecan and/or taxanes.

References

1 Webb A, Cunningham D, Scarffe JH, Harper P, Norman A, Joffe JK, Hughes M, Mansi J, Findlay M, Hill A, Oates J, Nicolson M, Hickish T, O'Brien M, Iveson T, Watson M, Underhill C, Wardley A, Meehan M: Randomized trial comparing epirubicin, cisplatin, and fluorouracil versus fluorouracil, doxorubicin, and methotrexate in advanced esophagogastric cancer. J Clin Oncol 1997;15:261–267.

2 Ross P, Nicolson M, Cunningham D, Valle J, Seymour M, Harper P, Price T, Anderson H, Iveson T, Hickish T, Lofts F, Norman A: Prospective randomized trial comparing mitomycin, cisplatin, and protracted venous-infusion fluorouracil (PVI 5-FU) with epirubicin, cisplatin, and PVI 5-FU in advanced esophagogastric cancer. J Clin Oncol 2002;20:1996–2004.

3 Vanhoefer U, Rougier P, Wilke H, Ducreux MP, Lacave AJ, Van Cutsem E, Planker M, Santos JG, Piedbois P, Paillot B, Bodenstein H, Schmoll HJ, Bleiberg H, Nordlinger B, Couvreur ML, Baron B, Wils JA: Final results of a randomized phase III trial of sequential high-dose methotrexate, fluorouracil, and doxorubicin versus etoposide, leucovorin, and fluorouracil versus infusional fluorouracil and cisplatin in advanced gastric cancer: A trial of the European Organization for Research and Treatment of Cancer Gastrointestinal Tract Cancer Cooperative Group. J Clin Oncol 2000; 18:2648–2657.

4 Sakata Y, Ohtsu A, Horikoshi N, Sugimachi K, Mitachi Y, Taguchi T: Late phase II study of novel oral fluoropyrimidine anticancer drug S-1 (1 *M* tegafur-0.4 *M* gimestat 1 *M* otastat potassium) in advanced gastric cancer patients. Eur J Cancer 1998;34:1715–1720.

5 Koizumi W, Kurihara M, Nakano S, Hasegawa K, The S1 Cooperative Gastric Cancer Study Group: Phase II study of S-1, a novel oral derivative of 5-fluorouracil, in advanced gastric cancer. Oncology 2000;58:191–197.

6 Koizumi W, Tanabe S, Saigenji K, Ohtsu A, Boku N, Nagashima F, Shirao K, Matsumura Y, Gotoh M: Phase I/II study of S-1 combined with cisplatin in patients with advanced gastric cancer. Br J Cancer 2003;89:2207–2212.

7 Takiuchi H, Ajani JA: Uracil-tegafur in gastric carcinoma: A comprehensive review. J Clin Oncol 1998;16:2877–2885.

8 Kim TW, Kang YK, Ahn JH, Chang HM, Yook JH, Oh ST, Kim BS, Lee JS: Phase II study of capecitabine plus cisplatin as first-line chemotherapy in advanced gastric cancer. Ann Oncol 2002;13:1893–1898.

9 De Lange SM, van Groeningen CJ, Kroep JR, Van Bochove A, Snijders JF, Peters GJ, Pinedo HM, Giaccone G: Phase II trial of cisplatin and gemcitabine in patients with advanced gastric cancer. Ann Oncol 2004;15:484–488.

10 Al-Batran SE, Atmaca A, Hegewisch-Becker S, Jaeger D, Hahnfeld S, Rummel MJ, Seipelt G, Rost A, Orth J, Knuth A, Jaeger E: Phase II trial of biweekly infusional fluorouracil, folinic acid, and oxaliplatin in patients with advanced gastric cancer. J Clin Oncol 2004;15:658–663.

11 Cocconi G, Carlini P, Gamboni A, et al: PELF is more active than FAMTX in metastatic gastric carcinoma. Proc Am Soc Clin Oncol 2001; 20:A501.

12 Kim YH, Shin SW, Kim BS, Kim JH, Kim JG, Mok YJ, Kim CS, Rhyu HS, Hyun JH, Kim JS: Paclitaxel, 5- Fluorouracil, and cisplatin combination chemotherapy for the treatment of advanced gastric carcinoma. Cancer 1999; 85:295–301.

13 Chun H, Olson C, Mittelman A, Puccio C, Kang M, Ahmed T: Chemotherapy with cisplatin, fluorouracil and paclitaxel for adenocarcinoma of the stomach and gastrooesophageal junction. Proc Am Soc Clin Oncol 1999; 18:A280.

14 Kollmannsberger C, Quietzsch D, Haag C, Lingenfelser T, Schroeder M, Hartmann JT, Baronius W, Hempel V, Clemens M, Kanz L: A phase II study of paclitaxel, weekly, 24-hour continuous infusion 5-fluorouracil, folinic acid and cisplatin in patients with advanced gastric cancer. Br J Cancer 2000;83:458–462.

15 Roth AD, Maibach R, Martinelli G, Fazio N, Aapro MS, Pagani O, Morant R, Borner MM, Herrmann R, Honegger H, Cavalli F, Alberto P, Castiglione M, Goldhirsch A: Docetaxel (Taxotere)-cisplatin (TC): An effective drug combination in gastric carcinoma. Swiss Group for Clinical Cancer Research (SAKK) and the European Institute of Oncology (EIO). Ann Oncol 2000;11:301–306.

16 Roth AD, Maibach R, Fazio N, Sessa C, Stupp R, Morant R, Herrmann R, Borner MM, Goldhirsch A, de Braud F: 5-Fluorouracil as protracted continuous intravenous infusion can be added to full-dose docetaxel (Taxotere)-cisplatin in advanced gastric carcinoma: A phase I–II trial. Ann Oncol 2004;15:759–764.

17 Ajani J, Moiseyenko V, Tjulandin S, Fodor M, Majlis A, Boni C, Zuber E, Blattmann: Docetaxel, cisplatin, 5-fluorouracil for chemonaive patients with metastasic or locally recurrent, unresectable gastric carcinoma: Interim results of a randomized phase III trial. Proc Am Soc Clin Oncol 2003;22:A258.

18 Ridwelski K, Gebauer T, Fahlke J, Kroning H, Kettner E, Meyer F, Eichelmann K, Lippert H: Combination chemotherapy with docetaxel and cisplatin for locally advanced and metastatic gastric cancer. Ann Oncol 2001;12:47–51.

19 Lee SH, Kang WK, Park J, Kim HY, Kim JH, Lee SI, Park JO, Kim K, Jung CW, Park YS, Im YH, Lee MH, Park K: Combination chemotherapy with epirubicin, docetaxel and cisplatin in metastatic or recurrent, unresectable gastric cancer. Br J Cancer 2004;91:18–22.

20 Mavroudis D, Kourousis C, Androulakis N, Kalbakis K, Agelaki S, Kakolyris S, Souglakos J, Sarra E, Vardakis N, Hatzidaki D, Sarmonis G, Georgoulias V: Front-line treatment of advanced gastric cancer with docetaxel and granulocyte colony-stimulating factor: A phase II trial. Am J Clin Oncol 2000;23:341–344.

21 Park YH, Ryoo BY, Choi SJ, Kim HT: A phase II study of capecitabine and docetaxel combination chemotherapy in patients with advanced gastric cancer. Br J Cancer 2004;90: 1329–1333.

22 Cunningham D, Pyrhonen S, James RD, Punt CJ, Hickish TF, Heikkila R, Johannesen TB, Starkhammar H, Topham CA, Awad L, Jacques C, Herait P: Randomized trial of irinotecan plus supportive care versus supportive care alone after fluorouracil failure for patients with metastatic colorectal cancer. Lancet 1998; 352:1413–1418.

23 Chun JH, Kim HK, Lee JS, Choi JY, Lee HG, Yoon SM, Choi IJ, Ryu KW, Kim YW, Bae JM: Weekly irinotecan in patients with metastatic gastric cancer failing cisplatin-based chemotherapy. Jpn J Clin Oncol 2004;34:8–13.

24 Bugat R: Irinotecan in the treatment of gastric cancer. Ann Oncol 2003;14(suppl 2):37–40.

25 Assersohn L, Brown G, Cunningham D, Ward C, Oates J, Waters JS, Hill ME, Norman AR: Phase II study of irinotecan and 5-fluorouracil/leucovorin in patients with primary refractory or relapsed advanced oesophageal and gastric carcinoma. Ann Oncol 2004;15:64–69.

26 Kohne CH, Catane R, Klein B, Ducreux M, Thuss-Patience P, Niederle N, Gips M, Preusser P, Knuth A, Clemens M, Bugat R, Figer I, Shani A, Fages B, Di Betta D, Jacques C, Wilke HJ: Irinotecan is active in chemonaive patients with metastatic gastric cancer: A phase II multicentric trial. Br J Cancer 2003;89:997–1001.

27 Souglakos J, Syrigos K, Potamianou A, Polyzos A, Boukovinas I, Androulakis N, Kouroussis C, Vardakis N, Christophilakis C, Kotsakis A, Georgoulias V: Combination of irinotecan (CPT-11) plus oxaliplatin (L-OHP) as first-line treatment in locally advanced or metastatic gastric cancer: A multicentre phase II trial. Ann Oncol 2004;15:1204–1209.

28 Bouche O, Raoul JL, Giovanini M, Etienne PL, Bedenne L, Lledo G, Arsene D, Paitel JF, Seitz JF, Milan C: Randomized phase II trial of LV5FU2, LV5FU2-cisplatinum or LV5FU2-irinotecan in patients with metastatic gastric or cardial adenocarcinoma: Final results of study FFCF 9803. Proc Am Soc Clin Oncol 2003;22: A1033.

29 Ajani JA, Baker J, Pisters PW, Ho L, Mansfield PF, Feig BW, Charnsangavej C: CPT-11 plus cisplatin in patients with advanced, untreated gastric or gastroesophageal junction carcinoma: Results of a phase II study. Cancer 2002; 94:641–646.

30 Boku N, Ohtsu A, Shimada Y, Shirao K, Seki S, Saito H, Sakata Y, Hyodo I: Phase II study of a combination of irinotecan and cisplatin against metastatic gastric cancer. J Clin Oncol 1999;17:319–323.

31 Pozzo C, Peschel C, Gorbunova V, Valvere V, Zalusky J, Biakhov M: Irinotecan in combination with CDDP or 5-FU and folinic acid is active in patients with advanced gastric or gastro-oesophageal junction adenocarcinoma: Final results of a randomized phase II study. Proc Am Soc Clin Oncol 2001:20:A531.

32 Moehler M, Hoehler T, Siebler J, Jansen J, Wein A, Menges M, Flieger D, Geer T, Galle P, Heike M: Safety and efficacy of CPT11/FA/5-FU (ILF) versus ELF in previously untreated advanced or metastatic adenocarcinoma of stomach or gastroesophageal junction. Proc Am Soc Clin Oncol.2003;22:A258.

33 Hoehler T, Moehler M: Neue Chemotherapeutika in der Therapie des fortgeschrittenem oder metastasierten Magenkarzinoms. Onkologie 2003;26:54–59.

34 Louvet C, Andre T, Tigaud JM, Gamelin E, Douillard JY, Brunet R, Francois E, Jacob JH, Levoir D, Taamma A, Rougier P, Cvitkovic E, de Gramont A: Phase II study of oxaliplatin, fluorouracil, and folinic acid in locally advanced or metastatic gastric cancer patients. J Clin Oncol 2002;20:4543–4548.

35 Murad AM, Garcia RF, Vinholes J, et al: A phase II multicentric trial of docetaxel (Taxotere), 5-fluorouracil and epirubicin in previously untreated advanced gastric cancer: a novel and effective regimen. Proc Eur Soc Med Oncol 2002, abstr 710.

Review Article

Digestive Diseases

Dig Dis 2004;22:366–373
DOI: 10.1159/000083600

Treatment of Peritoneal Carcinomatosis in Gastric Cancers

C. Brigand[a] C. Arvieux[b, c] F.N. Gilly[b, d] O. Glehen[b, d]

[a]Service de Chirurgie Generale et Digestive, Hopital Hautepierre, Strasbourg; [b]Equipe Accueil 3738, Faculté de Médecine Lyon-Sud, Oullins; [c]Département de Chirurgie Digestive et de l'Urgence, CHU Michallon, Grenoble, et [d]Service de Chirurgie Endocrinienne et Digestive, Centre Hospitalier Lyon-Sud, Pierre-Bénite, France

Key Words

Gastric cancer · Hyperthermia · Intraperitoneal chemotherapy · Peritoneal carcinomatosis

Abstract

Peritoneal carcinomatosis may occur after curative surgery of any gastrointestinal carcinoma, but it is however the most frequent form of evolution after curative resection of gastric carcinoma and is present at the time of surgery in many cases. This locoregional extension of cancer has a poor prognosis, with a great mortality and a poor quality of life. It is sometimes considered of such a poor prognosis that patients do not go through any resection or palliative procedure. Techniques of radiotherapy, chemotherapy and intraperitoneal chemotherapy have been used with moderate clinical efficacy. Since the 1990s, intraoperative hyperthermic peritoneal chemotherapy combined with comprehensive cytoreductive surgery has been proposed to improve prognosis of patients with peritoneal carcinomatosis from gastric origin as well as carcinomatosis from colorectal origin or pseudomyxoma peritonei.

Natural History

The description of outcomes after curative resection of gastric cancer helps in understanding the mechanism of peritoneal carcinomatosis development. In 2003, Roviello et al. [1] reported a prospective multicentric study of recurrence predictive factors. After potentially curative surgery, with adequate lymphadenectomy according to the criteria described by the Japanese Research Society for Gastric Cancer [2], and without adjuvant therapy, the regular follow-up after a median period of 48 months showed a recurrence in 215 of the 441 patients (49%). Peritoneal recurrence occurred in 77 cases (36%) associated with locoregional recurrence in 16 cases. Both locoregional and peritoneal recurrence represented 80% of cases. The clinicopathological features associated with this peritoneal evolution were diffuse-mixed Lauren histological type [3], depth of invasion and particularly the serosal involvement, lymph node involvement and tumor size. Maehara et al. [4] in 1996, with a cohort of 1,117 patients, as well as Yoo et al. [5] in 2000 with a cohort of 2,328 patients, had already published the same conclusions of poor prognosis for patients with gastric cancer operated with a curative intent, when pathologic results showed poorly differentiated tissue type with serosal involvement and lymph node metastasis. A high growth pattern represented by the level of proliferating cell nuclear antigen and by younger age is also reported [4, 5].

KARGER

Fax +41 61 306 12 34
E-Mail karger@karger.ch
www.karger.com

0257–2753/04/0224–0366$21.00/0

Accessible online at:
www.karger.com/ddi

Olivier Glehen, MD, PhD
Département de Chirurgie Générale, Thoracique et Endocrinienne
Centre Hospitalier Lyon-Sud
FR–69495 Pierre-Bénite Cedex (France)
Tel. +33 478 861375, Fax +33 478 863343, E-Mail olivier.glehen@chu-lyon.fr

The role of peritoneal free cells seems to be another main prognostic factor. Bando et al. [6] examined the prognostic value of intraoperative peritoneal lavage for cytological examination in 1,297 patients with gastric cancer. A strong correlation was found between positive cytology and carcinomatosis: 50% of positive cytology in case of peritoneal carcinomatosis, versus 5% in its absence. But most interesting was the correlation between the depth of the tumor invasion and the positive cytology with 0 positive cytology for pT1 tumor, 9% for pT2 and 30% for pT3 and pT4 tumors. Cytology was also more often positive for undifferentiated carcinoma. A peritoneal positive cytology was a significant poor prognostic indicator: 77% of patients without macroscopic carcinomatosis but with positive cytology developed peritoneal recurrence (risk ratio = 31.8). Further, in 1994, Ikeguchi et al. [7] calculated the area of serosal invasion. When it was <10 cm^2, only 17% of patients had positive cytology, versus 68.5% when it was >20 cm^2.

Many mechanisms of peritoneal carcinomatosis have been proposed: not only spreading of free cancers cells due to serosal involvement of the primary tumor [8], with implantations of cells due to the presence of adherence molecules [9], but also lymphatic and venous dissemination of malignant cells. With surgery, manipulation of the tumor, transsection of the lymphatic channels and blood vessels will draw malignant cells out of their primary site, in the peritoneal cavity. Healing of all surgical wounds could include these malignant free cells and enhance their proliferation, increased by their own capabilities of multiplication [10].

Terminal evolution of patients with peritoneal carcinomatosis leads to ascites, bowel occlusion, pain, and death in all cases. The EVOCAPE 1 trial [11] showed that death occurred after diagnosis within a mean of 6.5 months and median of 3.1 months (range 0.1–48.0) in a cohort of 125 patients.

Adjuvant Chemotherapy

Drugs found to be effective for treatment against gastric cancer are 5-fluorouracil, cisplatin, epirubicin, doxorubicin, etoposide, mitomycin C, taxol, oxaliplatin or irinotecan (CPT-11), but there is no standard treatment for gastric cancer. Many studies evaluated the role of chemotherapy on survival and cure after surgery, but their results are controversial. Three meta-analyses tried to conclude thanks to a greater number of patients included in the statistical analysis. However, as described by Hu et al. [12], many of these prospective comparative studies were of low methodological quality.

The first meta-analysis reported by Hermans et al. [13] in 1993 included 2,096 patients from 11 trials published between 1980 and 1993. The odds ratio (OR) calculated by comparison of the adjuvant chemotherapy arm versus the surgery-only arm was 0.88 (95% CI 0.78–1.08). In conclusion, there was no additional survival benefit of adjuvant chemotherapy for patients treated by surgery with curative intent.

The second meta-analysis published by Hu et al. [12] in 2002 on 4,543 patients from 14 trials concluded on the survival benefit of adjuvant chemotherapy versus surgery alone, with an OR of 0.81 (95% CI 0.70–0.94), but the authors concluded that this result was not very strong because studies compiled were not of good methodological quality.

Janunger et al. [14] reported the third meta-analysis showing a similar significant survival benefit for adjuvant chemotherapy versus surgery alone (OR 0.84; 95% CI 0.74–0.96). However a second analysis in this study, which compared results obtained in Western countries to those of Asian countries, showed no benefit of chemotherapy for patients treated in Western countries (OR 0.96; 95% CI 0.83–1.12). More recent trials testing 'new drugs' like oxalipatin or irinotecan showed interesting results in phase II trials, when compared with historical studies, but median survival did not exceed 8.5–12 months [15, 16].

In conclusion, adjuvant chemotherapy does not appear to really improve survival of patients with gastric cancer.

Preoperative Chemotherapy

To improve the chance of complete surgical resection and patient survival, several trials were conducted testing preoperative chemotherapy. The theoretical base is that vascularization is impaired after surgery with multiple vascular ligations. Drugs given before surgery could then be better delivered in all sites and lead to a downstaging of the tumor which could offer more possibilities of complete resection. Moreover, destruction of free circulating cells could be more effective before surgery, because of often delayed postoperative chemotherapy due to complicated postoperative courses. This significant prognostic advantage seems to be reached with the results published by Newman et al. [17] in 2002 in a trial with only 22 patients; 19 could undergo surgery with 18 R0 resections. Understaging was effective with 16% pT3 after chemotherapy versus 85% uT3 preoperatively, and 37% stage IIIA versus 70% before treatment. The authors agreed with a probably overstaging in the initial evaluation, but downstaging was important. Only 1 postoperative death was described, and median survival was not reached at 15 months.

In 2001, Schumacher et al. [18] reported a phase II trial with 42 patients treated preoperatively by doxorubicin + cisplatin + etoposide for 3–4 cycles followed by surgery 28 days after the completion of chemotherapy. Side effects were described as 'substantial', but only 28/42 patients received the whole treatment. Thirty-one patients underwent a curative resection and 5 a palliative one. Specific severe postoperative complications occurred in 7 patients, linked to abdominal abscesses. Median survival for patients with complete resection was 28.4 months versus 7.6 for those with R1–R2 resections ($p = 0.0001$) and response to chemotherapy was a significant prognosis factor of survival ($p = 0.008$). Recurrence appeared to be more frequent in locoregional and peritoneal sites than visceral metastasis.

In the trial of Ott et al. [19], 49 patients received preoperative treatment with cisplatin, leucovorin and 5-fluorouracil (5-FU) for 2 cycles and the surgical procedure was programmed 2 weeks after. Only 38/49 patients received the scheduled treatment because of toxicity or general health status deterioration, and 32/42 patients underwent a curative resection versus 5 patients a palliative one. Median survival was 32 months (range 7.6–80) after complete resection and 7.5 (range 5.8–73) after the palliative one ($p < 0.0001$). Recurrence appeared to be more frequently local or peritoneal than hepatic. Moreover, in these trials, postoperative morbidity was not increased by neoadjuvant chemotherapy. In another publication. Marcus et al. [20] reported the same conclusions for neoadjuvant therapy with cisplatin + 5-FU, but morbidity was high after such extensive surgery: 39% with neoadjuvant chemotherapy versus 41% for surgery alone.

Nevertheless, the Dutch FAMTX trial [21] prematurely closed after inclusion of 59 patients. A high rate of adverse effects from preoperative chemotherapy with 5-FU + doxorubicin + methotrexate was observed with no advantage in survival: median survival after randomization was 18.2 months in the FAMTX group versus 30 months in the surgery-alone group. Authors concluded that chemotherapy delayed surgical resection and was a loss of chance for patients.

Although results of preoperative chemotherapy seem promising, large randomized trials are needed to prove its efficacy.

Surgery

Peritoneal seeding is one of the statuses that makes the surgeon hesitant about the usefulness of his actions for patients. However, it is not a rare situation. For 10–20% of patients preoperatively well explored with no pejorative sign, no ascites or macroscopic node, a peritoneal carcinomatosis will be discovered at the time of surgical exploration. Then, the first thought to decide the type of surgery must be to assess the goal that can be reached: Is curative surgery possible? Is palliative surgery necessary? A decision must be taken knowing that palliation should provide an acceptable quality of life and avoid potential complications like bleeding, perforation or intestinal obstruction. Moreover, adjuvant therapy could be more effective for smaller tumor nodules, and reduction of peritoneal carcinomatosis should limit ascites occurrence. All these theoretical points should influence the surgeon to do a maximal resection.

For years, many trials have shown that resection of the tumor with total or partial gastrectomies improves quality of life and survival when compared to palliative bypass. Historical studies like those published in 1988 by Hallissey et al. [22] from the Birmingham Cancer Registry or in 1989 by Haugstvedt et al. [23] with the national Norwegian Stomach Cancer Trial showed significant improvement of survival after surgical resection of tumor even in stage IV disease. However, because of poor survival results for advanced cancer, some studies tried to identify if such resections should be performed for all tumors. Isozaki et al. [24] in 1993, Maekawa et al. [25] in 1996 and Hartgrink et al. [26] in 2002, agreed that large resections were not beneficial for all patients. Analyzing the type of extension of the primary tumor, these authors separated prognosis factors like peritoneal carcinomatosis, liver metastasis, lymph nodes invasion, serosal invasion of adjacent organs or positive resection margins. They demonstrated that prognosis of patients with more than one site invaded was not improved by surgical resection. Age >70 years was another factor of poor prognosis. And Hagiwara et al. [27] emphasized that resection of peritoneal carcinomatosis was beneficial only for patients with local peritoneal extent but not with distant peritoneal involvement. More recently, under the impulsion of Japanese centers which have studied intraperitoneal hyperthermic chemotherapy for about 20 years, maximal cytoreductive surgery demonstrates its usefulness. Not only gastrectomy should be performed, but also resection of adjacent organs in T4 tumors and peritonectomies in case of peritoneal carcinomatosis [27, 28].

Usual procedures of oncologic gastrectomy should be performed: total gastrectomy, or partial distal gastrectomy with adequate margins for distal well-differentiated adenocarcinoma.

Locoregional lymphadenectomy should be achieved as recommended by the Japanese Research Society for Gastric Cancer [2] with a D2 resection. Thus, a European randomized trial from the Dutch Gastric Cancer Group trial first published by Bonenkamp et al. [29] in 1995 showed an increased morbidity and mortality with D2 lymphadenectomy compared with the D1 procedure (43 vs. 25% and 10 vs. 4%, respectively) due to the harmful consequences of pancreatectomy and splenectomy. In 2004, Hartgrink et al. [30] published the final results of this trial and demonstrated that the higher postoperative mortality withdrew the beneficent long-term results of the D2 procedure. The conclusion was that extended lymph node dissection may be of benefit if morbidity and postoperative mortality can be avoided.

Peritonectomy procedures have been well described by Sugarbaker [31], with five steps according to the extension of the peritoneal seeding. The epigastric peritonectomy removes the preperitoneal fat pad with the round and falciform ligaments of the liver. The anterolateral peritonectomy removes the greater omentum, the right paracolic gutter with the appendix and the subhepatic space, in continuity with the right subphrenic peritonectomy. The omental burse peritonectomy includes cholecystectomy and stripping of the peritoneum recovering the hepatic pedicule, the hepatoduodenal ligament and the peritoneal floor of the omental bursa. The last step is the pelvic peritonectomy associated if necessary with a rectosigmoid resection and/or a peritonectomy of the left paracolic gutter. Mesenteric peritoneum is rarely extensively removed and some acceptable small bowel resections can be performed for the localized area of tumor nodes. Other small peritoneal localizations can be destroyed by electrosurgical fulguration. These extensive peritonectomies should be realized in order to remove all macroscopic disease to increase the efficacy of intraoperative intraperitoneal chemotherapy. However, Hagiwara et al. [27] showed in 126 patients that survival was also increased after peritonectomy in cases without intraperitoneal chemotherapy, but only when the extension of the carcinomatosis did not reach the distant peritoneum.

Intraperitoneal Hyperthermic Chemotherapy

This technique was described in the 1980s, mainly in Asia by Fujimoto et al. [32] and Fujimura et al. [33]. Fujimoto's group described peritoneal chemotherapy using mitomycin C in association with a thermosensitizing drug at perfusion temperatures of about 43–44.5°C. Intraperitoneal hyperthermic chemotherapy (IPHC) combined the effects of hyperthermia with those of chemotherapeutic drugs, locally delivered for a best distribution to peritoneal tumoral cells, hardly reached by intravenous drugs.

Hyperthermia

The curative antitumoral effects of hyperthermia were established a long time ago. The cytotoxicity of hyperthermia starts at 41°C in human cells, as well described by Armour et al. [34], with exponential inactivation of tumoral cells. Mechanisms of action are multiple: impairment of DNA repair, denaturation of proteins and ionizing radiation-like effects. Thus, thermoresistance exists, dependent of genetic and of previous exposure to the same hyperthermic situations. Overcoming this phenomenon is possible, by increasing the heating temperature [35].

Thus, hyperthermia is not only used for its own anticellular properties, but also for its ability to enhance the antitumoral effects of some chemotherapeutic drugs.

Hyperthermic Chemotherapy

Many tests have been made to prove that hyperthermia does not denature chemotherapeutic drugs and to find whether drug effects should be enhanced by hyperthermia.

First we must understand that hyperthermia, in vivo, increases cell membrane permeability, alters cell metabolism and alters active drug transport and evacuation out of cells [36]. Therefore, a high cell concentration of therapeutic drugs can be locally achieved without high plasma concentration and its potential toxicity [37]. Moreover, many drugs have been shown not to be altered by hyperthermia and on the contrary to have synergy with it. One of them is mitomycin C (MMC), which is the most frequently used for IPHC. The synergistic effect between MMC and hyperthermia was demonstrated in vitro by Teicher et al. [38], where MMC was 40-fold more effective at 43°C than at 37°C. In vivo, regular dosages showed a rapid absorption by peritoneal tissues, with a low plasmatic concentration [39].

Other drugs were found to be more efficient with hyperthermia: platinum complex like cisplatin, carboplatin and more recently oxaliplatin, doxorubicin, bleomycin, gemcitabine or irinotecan [40].

Techniques

Different techniques have been described for administration of the hyperthermic drug solution immediately after the resection time of surgery. Most authors use a 'closed' sterile circuit with a closed or an open abdominal wall. In all cases, 3 or 4 drains are inserted through the abdominal wall for inflow and outflow drainage, and thermic probes are disposed to measure thermic homogeneity in the abdominal cavity. Sugarbaker et al. [10] promoted the so-called 'coliseum' technique, using a ring retractor sutured to the skin of the open abdomen, allowing a large volume of perfusion and hand manipulation of the bowel to control distribution of drugs. However, loss of temperature is very high and the health risk for the operating room staff is not negligible. Asian surgeons and the Lyon Center preferentially use a closed abdominal technique with an ingenious device for running and heating the chemotherapeutic solution. This closed technique increases abdominal pressure which might increase the penetration of drugs into tissues. Moreover, it avoids drug spillage and allows more stability in the drug's healing ability and intra-abdominal temperature. But homogeneity of distribution of the drugs is not absolutely certain [41] and a gentle massage of the abdomen throughout the procedure can be useful to improve peritoneal drug distribution [42].

Results

Cytoreductive surgery and peritonectomy procedures affect the reduction of tumor volume which has always been considered an important factor in achieving a response to chemotherapy [43, 44]. However, combining two aggressive procedures (surgery and IPCH) can lead to greater mortality and morbidity rates. Glehen et al. [45] reported a morbidity rate of 16% in patients who underwent IPCH with limited cytoreductive surgery and reported a considerably higher rate of 47% in patients who underwent IPCH combined with extensive cytoreductive surgery. The number of resections and peritonectomy procedures, the number of anastomoses, and in particular the duration of surgery contribute to a significantly higher rate of complications [46]. It would be expected that morbidity would correlate with the magnitude of surgery. Surgeons must use their judgment to achieve a balance between the postoperative risk of extensive surgery and potential benefit in survival and quality of life. The risk of postoperative complications also emphasizes the necessity for patient selection using the current strict criteria (young patients with good performance status, acceptable renal and myocardial function, no systemic chemotherapy administration 1 month prior to the procedure, no extra-abdominal metastases, no previous abdominal radiation therapy, evaluation of carcinomatosis extent by abdominal CT scan).

Glehen et al. [45] reported 1-, 2- and 5-year survival rates which were 48.1, 19.9 and 16%, respectively, in 6 patients who had a prolonged survival (2 > 3 years and 4 > 5 years). These survival results are similar to those previously reported by Yonemura et al. [47] (table 1). They updated their experience in 1996 with 83 patients who had peritonectomy in addition to IPCH with MMC, cisplatin, and etoposide. They were the only authors who reported 5-year survivors in patients with peritoneal seeding arising from gastric cancer. As Sayag-Beaujard et al. [48] reported, carcinomatosis with localized or small tumor nodules seems to be the best indications for IPCH. Their updated results showed that median survival of limited carcinomatosis was 19 months whereas it was 6.6 months for extended carcinomatosis. All 5-year survivors had a carcinomatosis with limited and small tumor nodules. Fujimoto et al. [49] also reported impressive survival in patients with limited carcinomatosis (P1: peritoneal dissemination limited to the adjacent peritoneum, and P2: several scattered metastases in the distant peritoneum). For P1 and P2 PC, the 5-year survival rates were 55 and 42%, respectively, whereas the 1-year survival rate was only 18% for P3 PC (numerous metastases to the distant peritoneum).

The most important prognostic indicator seems to be the completeness of cytoreduction. IPCH appears to be most effective when cytoreduction achieves a complete or nearly complete resection, with the intent to cure. Glehen et al. [45] reported that patients treated by complete or sub-complete surgery had a median survival of 21.3 months whereas patients treated by incomplete cytoreductive surgery had a median survival of only 6.1 months ($p < 0.0001$). The same observations have been reported by other peritoneal surface malignancy centers, for carci-

Table 1. Treatment of peritoneal carcinomatosis with cytoreductive surgery combining with IPCH

Group (first author)	Year	n	Follow-up months	Treatment	Median survival months	1-Year survival, %	5-Year survival, %	5-Year survivor
Yonemura [47]	1996	83	46	CC+IPCH (MMC, CDDP, Etop)	–	43	11	5
R0		28			13.9	61	17	3
R2		55			6.8	30	2	2
Fujimoto [49]	1997	48	–	CC+IPCH (MMC)	16.5	54	31	–
P1 PC		21				73	55	–
P2 PC		8			52.8	62	42	–
P3 PC		19			8.3	18	0	No
Hirose [50]	1999	17	14.6	CC+IPCH (MMC, CDDP, Etop)	11	44	–	–
Glehen [45]	2002	49	99	CC+IPCH (MMC)	10.3	48	16	4
Stage 1–2 PC		18			19	71	30	4
Stage 3–4 PC		31			6.6	32	0	No
CCR-0 or 1		25			21.3	75	29	4
CCR-2		24			6.1	16	0	No

CC = Cytoreductive surgery; CDDP = cisplatin; Etop = etoposide; R0 = complete cytoreduction; R2 = residual disease; P1 = PC limited to the adjacent peritoneum; P2 = several scattered metastases in the distant peritoneum; P3 = numerous metastases to the distant peritoneum. Stage 1 and 2 disease = tumor nodules <5 mm; stage 3 and 4 PC: tumor nodules >5 mm; CCR-0 or 1 = residual tumor nodules <5 mm; CCR-2 = residual tumor nodules >5 mm.

nomatosis arising from gastric cancer (5-year survival rates in patients treated by complete cytoreduction and IPCH ranging between 11 and 31% [47, 50]). Similar results for carcinomatosis arising from other origins have been reported [43, 51, 52]. An aggressive attempt at complete resection including surgical excision of all sites of macroscopic disease may add to the efficacy of IPCH. When the cytoreductive surgery does not allow a sufficient downstaging, the survival benefit of IPCH remains extremely low, and the median survival does not exceed 6–8 months [47, 49]. In the light of the risk of postoperative complications, IPCH may be not indicated in patients who are not candidates for complete or sub-complete cytoreductive surgery.

IPHC as Prophylaxis

For many Korean and Japanese authors, IPCH has been performed prophylactically or in an adjuvant setting [53–56]. They report encouraging survival results in pT3 gastric adenocarcinoma. Yonemura et al. [55] recently conducted a randomized controlled study on 139 patients with T3 or T4 gastric tumor, allocated in three groups: IPCH + surgery, intraperitoneal normothermic chemotherapy + surgery and surgery alone. After a median follow-up >5 years, the 5-year survival rate of patients treated by the combination of IPCH with surgery was significantly higher at 60% than those of the two other groups, with similar morbidity rates. But these promising results were not confirmed by all Japanese studies [56]. In Western countries, only one German study reported the use of IPCH for the prevention of carcinomatosis recurrence in advanced gastric cancer [57]. Nine patients were included in the study with a high postoperative morbidity rate (66%). Prospective randomized studies are needed in Europe to demonstrate the benefit of IPCH in earlier stages of carcinomatosis. Positive peritoneal cytology is a risk factor for the development of peritoneal carcinomatosis and may be indicative of poor prognosis. A prospective multicenter study, EVOCAPE 2, is currently being conducted in France to evaluate if patients with positive peritoneal cytology are at risk for peritoneal carcinomatosis. This study could define a group of patients at risk for carcinomatosis development for whom IPCH would be indicated.

Conclusion

While peritoneal carcinomatosis is a common evolution for gastric cancer, it has been considered for a long time without therapeutic resources. Systemic chemotherapy was a poor treatment in such situations and surgeons avoided operating because of the potential high risks involved with such interventions. However, many trials showed an interest of the primary tumor resection on quality of life and survival. For about 15 years now, experimental, then phase I and phase II studies on IPHC with MMC and cisplatin have had a tendency to provide hopeful results. On the other side, randomized trials showed an interest in prophylactic IPHC for advanced gastric cancer without carcinomatosis at the time of surgery. After adequate cytoreduction, IPHC works on both free peritoneal tumoral cells and residual microscopic disease, increasing then both local disease-free survival and general survival, with some long-term survivors. But morbidity of such an aggressive procedure is high and patient selection should be strict, not only on age, health status and medical past, but on the current disease extension, to avoid useless procedures. Moreover, we need large prospective randomized trials to conclude on efficiency of IPHC according to a standardized peritoneal staging, with standardized types of drugs and procedure.

References

1 Roviello F, Marrelli D, De Manzoni G, Morgagni P, Di Leo A, Saragoni L, De Stefano A: Prospective study of peritoneal recurrence after curative surgery for gastric cancer. Br J Surg 2003;90:1113–1119.
2 Japanese Gastric Cancer A: Japanese Classification of Gastric Carcinoma, 2nd Engl ed. Gastric Cancer 1998;1:10–24.
3 Lauren PA, Nevalainen TJ: Epidemiology of intestinal and diffuse types of gastric carcinoma. A time-trend study in Finland with comparison between studies from high- and low-risk areas. Cancer 1993;71:2926–2933.
4 Maehara Y, Emi Y, Baba H, Adachi Y, Akazawa K, Ichiyoshi Y, Sugimachi K: Recurrences and related characteristics of gastric cancer. Br J Cancer 1996;74:975–979.
5 Yoo CH, Noh SH, Shin DW, Choi SH, Min JS: Recurrence following curative resection for gastric carcinoma. Br J Surg 2000;87:236–242.
6 Bando E, Yonemura Y, Takeshita Y, Taniguchi K, Yasui T, Yoshimitsu Y, Fushida S, Fujimura T, Nishimura G, Miwa K: Intraoperative lavage for cytological examination in 1,297 patients with gastric carcinoma. Am J Surg 1999;178:256–262.
7 Ikeguchi M, Oka A, Tsujitani S, Maeta M, Kaibara N: Relationship between area of serosal invasion and intraperitoneal free cancer cells in patients with gastric cancer. Anticancer Res 1994;14:2131–2134.
8 Iitsuka Y, Kaneshima S, Tanida O, Takeuchi T, Koga S: Intraperitoneal free cancer cells and their viability in gastric cancer. Cancer 1979; 44:1476–1480.
9 Sugarbaker PH: Observations concerning cancer spread within the peritoneal cavity and concepts supporting an ordered pathophysiology. Cancer Treat Res 1996;82:79–100.
10 Sugarbaker PH, Yu W, Yonemura Y: Gastrectomy, peritonectomy, and perioperative intraperitoneal chemotherapy: The evolution of treatment strategies for advanced gastric cancer. Semin Surg Oncol 2003;21:233–248.
11 Sadeghi B, Arvieux C, Glehen O, Beaujard AC, Rivoire M, Baulieux J, Fontaumard E, Brachet A, Caillot JL, Faure JL, Porcheron J, Peix JL, Francois Y, Vignal J, Gilly FN: Peritoneal carcinomatosis from non-gynecologic malignancies: Results of the EVOCAPE 1 multicentric prospective study. Cancer 2000;88:358–363.
12 Hu JK, Chen ZX, Zhou ZG, Zhang B, Tian J, Chen JP, Wang L, Wang CH, Chen HY, Li YP: Intravenous chemotherapy for resected gastric cancer: Meta-analysis of randomized controlled trials. World J Gastroenterol 2002;8: 1023–1028.
13 Hermans J, Bonenkamp JJ, Boon MC, Bunt AM, Ohyama S, Sasako M, Van de Velde CJ: Adjuvant therapy after curative resection for gastric cancer: Meta-analysis of randomized trials. J Clin Oncol 1993;11:1441–1447.
14 Janunger KG, Hafstrom L, Glimelius B: Chemotherapy in gastric cancer: A review and updated meta-analysis. Eur J Surg 2002;168: 597–608.
15 Souglakos J, Syrigos K, Potamianou A, Polyzos A, Boukovinas I, Androulakis N, Kouroussis C, Vardakis N, Christophilakis C, Kotsakis A, Georgoulias V: Combination of irinotecan (CPT-11) plus oxaliplatin (L-OHP) as first-line treatment in locally advanced or metastatic gastric cancer: A multicentre phase II trial. Ann Oncol 2004;15:1204–1209.
16 Yoshida M, Boku N, Ohtsu A, Muto M, Nagashima F, Yoshida S: Combination chemotherapy of irinotecan plus cisplatin for advanced gastric cancer: Efficacy and feasibility in clinical practice. Gastric Cancer 2001;4: 144–149.
17 Newman E, Marcus SG, Potmesil M, Sewak S, Yee H, Sorich J, Hayek M, Muggia F, Hochster H: Neoadjuvant chemotherapy with CPT-11 and cisplatin downstages locally advanced gastric cancer. J Gastrointest Surg 2002;6:212–223.
18 Schuhmacher CP, Fink U, Becker K, Busch R, Dittler HJ, Mueller J, Siewert JR: Neoadjuvant therapy for patients with locally advanced gastric carcinoma with etoposide, doxorubicin, and cisplatinum. Closing results after 5 years of follow-up. Cancer 2001;91:918–927.
19 Ott K, Sendler A, Becker K, Dittler HJ, Helmberger H, Busch R, Kollmannsberger C, Siewert JR, Fink U: Neoadjuvant chemotherapy with cisplatin, 5-FU, and leucovorin (PLF) in locally advanced gastric cancer: A prospective phase II study. Gastric Cancer 2003;6:159–167.
20 Marcus SG, Cohen D, Lin K, Wong K, Thompson S, Rothberger A, Potmesil M, Hiotis S, Newman E: Complications of gastrectomy following CPT-11-based neoadjuvant chemotherapy for gastric cancer. J Gastrointest Surg 2003;7:1015–1023.
21 Hartgrink HH, van de Velde CJ, Putter H, Songun I, Tesselaar ME, Kranenbarg EK, de Vries JE, Wils JA, van der Bijl J, van Krieken JH: Neo-adjuvant chemotherapy for operable gastric cancer: Long-term results of the Dutch randomised FAMTX trial. Eur J Surg Oncol 2004; 30:643–649.
22 Hallissey MT, Allum WH, Roginski C, Fielding JW: Palliative surgery for gastric cancer. Cancer 1988;62:440–444.
23 Haugstvedt T, Viste A, Eide GE, Soreide O: The survival benefit of resection in patients with advanced stomach cancer: The Norwegian multicenter experience. Norwegian Stomach Cancer Trial. World J Surg 1989;13:617–622.

24 Isozaki H, Okajima K, Kawashima Y, Yamada S, Nakata E, Nishimura J, Ichinona T: Prognostic value of the number of metastatic lymph nodes in gastric cancer with radical surgery. J Surg Oncol 1993;53:247–251.
25 Maekawa S, Saku M, Maehara Y, Sadanaga N, Ikejiri K, Anai H, Kuwano H, Sugimachi K: Surgical treatment for advanced gastric cancer. Hepatogastroenterology 1996;43:178–186.
26 Hartgrink HH, Putter H, Klein Kranenbarg E, Bonenkamp JJ, van de Velde CJ: Value of palliative resection in gastric cancer. Br J Surg 2002;89:1438–1443.
27 Hagiwara A, Sawai K, Sakakura C, Shirasu M, Ohgaki M, Yamasaki J, Togawa T, Takahashi T: Complete omentectomy and extensive lymphadenectomy with gastrectomy improves the survival of gastric cancer patients with metastases in the adjacent peritoneum. Hepatogastroenterology 1998;45:1922–1929.
28 Yonemura Y, Fujimura T, Fushida S, Fujita H, Bando E, Nishimura G, Miwa K, Endou Y, Tanaka M, Sasaki T: A new surgical approach (peritonectomy) for the treatment of peritoneal dissemination. Hepatogastroenterology 1999;46:601–609.
29 Bonenkamp JJ, Songun I, Hermans J, Sasako M, Welvaart K, Plukker JT, van Elk P, Obertop H, Gouma DJ, Taat CW: Randomised comparison of morbidity after D1 and D2 dissection for gastric cancer in 996 Dutch patients. Lancet 1995;345:745–748.
30 Hartgrink HH, van de Velde CJ, Putter H, Bonenkamp JJ, Klein Kranenbarg E, Songun I, Welvaart K, van Krieken JH, Meijer S, Plukker JT, van Elk PJ, Obertop H, Gouma DJ, van Lanschot JJ, Taat CW, de Graaf PW, von Meyenfeldt MF, Tilanus H, Sasako M: Extended lymph node dissection for gastric cancer: who may benefit? Final results of the randomized Dutch Gastric Cancer Group trial. J Clin Oncol 2004;22:2069–2077.
31 Sugarbaker PH: Peritonectomy procedures. Ann Surg 1995;221:29–42.
32 Fujimoto S, Shrestha RD, Kokubun M, Ohta M, Takahashi M, Kobayashi K, Kiuchi S, Okui K, Miyoshi T, Arimizu N, et al: Intraperitoneal hyperthermic perfusion combined with surgery effective for gastric cancer patients with peritoneal seeding. Ann Surg 1988;208: 36–41.
33 Fujimura T, Yonemura Y, Fushida S, Urade M, Takegawa S, Kamata T, Sugiyama K, Hasegawa H, Katayama K, Miwa K: Continuous hyperthermic peritoneal perfusion for the treatment of peritoneal dissemination in gastric cancers and subsequent second-look operation. Cancer 1990;65:65–71.
34 Armour EP, McEachern D, Wang Z, Corry PM, Martinez A: Sensitivity of human cells to mild hyperthermia. Cancer Res 1993;53: 2740–2744.
35 Reed RA, Bedford JS: Thermal tolerance. Br J Radiol 1980;53:920–921.
36 Hahn GM: Potential for therapy of drugs and hyperthermia. Cancer Res 1979;39:2264–2268.
37 Bull JM: An update on the anticancer effects of a combination of chemotherapy and hyperthermia. Cancer Res 1984;44(suppl):4853–4856.
38 Teicher BA, Kowal CD, Kennedy KA, Sartorelli AC: Enhancement by hyperthermia of the in vitro cytotoxicity of mitomycin C toward hypoxic tumor cells. Cancer Res 1981;41: 1096–1099.
39 Jacquet P, Averbach A, Stephens AD, Stuart OA, Chang D, Sugarbaker PH: Heated intraoperative intraperitoneal mitomycin C, early postoperative intraperitoneal 5-fluorouracil: Pharmacokinetic studies. Oncology 1998;55: 130–138.
40 Ceelen WP, Hesse U, de Hemptinne B, Pattyn P: Hyperthermic intraperitoneal chemoperfusion in the treatment of locally advanced intraabdominal cancer. Br J Surg 2000;87:1006–1015.
41 Averbach AM, Sugarbaker PH: Methodologic considerations in treatment using intraperitoneal chemotherapy. Cancer Treat Res 1996;82: 289–309.
42 Hall JJ, Loggie BW, Shen P, Beamer S, Douglas Case L, McQuellon R, Geisinger KR, Levine EA: Cytoreductive surgery with intraperitoneal hyperthermic chemotherapy for advanced gastric cancer. J Gastrointest Surg 2004;8: 454–463.
43 Elias D, Blot F, El Otmany A, Antoun S, Lasser P, Boige V, Rougier P, Ducreux M: Curative treatment of peritoneal carcinomatosis arising from colorectal cancer by complete resection and intraperitoneal chemotherapy. Cancer 2001;92:71–76.
44 Barakat RR, Sabbatini P, Bhaskaran D, Revzin M, Smith A, Venkatraman E, Aghajanian C, Hensley M, Soignet S, Brown C, Soslow R, Markman M, Hoskins WJ, Spriggs D: Intraperitoneal chemotherapy for ovarian carcinoma: Results of long-term follow-up. J Clin Oncol 2002;20:694–698.
45 Glehen O, Schreiber V, Cotte E, Sayag-Beaujard AC, Osinski D, Freyer G, Francois Y, Vignal J, Gilly FN: Treatment of peritoneal carcinomatosis arising from gastric cancer by cytoreductive surgery and intraperitoneal chemohyperthermia. Arch Surg 2004;139:20–26.
46 Stephens AD, Alderman R, Chang D, Edwards GD, Esquivel J, Sebbag G, Steves MA, Sugarbaker PH: Morbidity and mortality analysis of 200 treatments with cytoreductive surgery and hyperthermic intraoperative intraperitoneal chemotherapy using the coliseum technique. Ann Surg Oncol 1999;6:790–796.
47 Yonemura Y, Fujimura T, Nishimura G, Falla R, Sawa T, Katayama K, Tsugawa K, Fushida S, Miyazaki I, Tanaka M, Endou Y, Sasaki T: Effects of intraoperative chemohyperthermia in patients with gastric cancer with peritoneal dissemination. Surgery 1996;119:437–444.
48 Sayag-Beaujard AC, Francois Y, Glehen O, Sadeghi-Looyeh B, Bienvenu J, Panteix G, Garbit F, Grandclement E, Vignal J, Gilly FN: Intraperitoneal chemohyperthermia with mitomycin C for gastric cancer patients with peritoneal carcinomatosis. Anticancer Res 1999; 19:1375–1382.
49 Fujimoto S, Takahashi M, Mutou T, Kobayashi K, Toyosawa T, Isawa E, Sumida M, Ohkubo H: Improved mortality rate of gastric carcinoma patients with peritoneal carcinomatosis treated with intraperitoneal hyperthermic chemoperfusion combined with surgery. Cancer 1997;79:884–891.
50 Hirose K, Katayama K, Iida A, Yamaguchi A, Nakagawara G, Umeda S, Kusaka Y: Efficacy of continuous hyperthermic peritoneal perfusion for the prophylaxis and treatment of peritoneal metastasis of advanced gastric cancer: Evaluation by multivariate regression analysis. Oncology 1999;57:106–114.
51 Glehen O, Mithieux F, Osinski D, Beaujard AC, Freyer G, Guerscht P, et al: Digestive surgery combined with peritonectomy procedures and intraperitoneal chemo-hyperthermia in abdominal cancers with peritoneal carcinomatosis: A phase II study. J Clin Oncol 2003;21: 789–806.
52 Shen P, Levine EA, Hall J, Case D, Russell G, Fleming R, McQuellon R, Geisinger KR, Loggie BW: Factors predicting survival after intraperitoneal hyperthermic chemotherapy with mitomycin C after cytoreductive surgery for patients with peritoneal carcinomatosis. Arch Surg 2003;138:26–33.
53 Kim JY, Bae HS: A controlled clinical study of serosa-invasive gastric carcinoma patients who underwent surgery plus intraperitoneal hyperthermo-chemo-perfusion. Gastric Cancer 2001;4:27–33.
54 Hamazoe R, Maeta M, Kaibara N: Intraperitoneal thermochemotherapy for prevention of peritoneal recurrence of gastric cancer. Final results of a randomized controlled study. Cancer 1994;73:2048–2052.
55 Yonemura Y, de Aretxabala X, Fujimura T, Fushida S, Katayama K, Bandou E, Sugiyama K, Kawamura T, Kinoshita K, Endou Y, Sasaki T: Intraoperative chemohyperthermic peritoneal perfusion as an adjuvant to gastric cancer: Final results of a randomized controlled study. Hepatogastroenterology 2001; 48:1776–1782.
56 Kunisaki C, Shimada H, Nomura M, Akiyama H, Takahashi M, Matsuda G: Lack of efficacy of prophylactic continuous hyperthermic peritoneal perfusion on subsequent peritoneal recurrence and survival in patients with advanced gastric cancer. Surgery 2002;131: 521–528.
57 Samel S, Singal A, Becker H, Post S: Problems with intraoperative hyperthermic peritoneal chemotherapy for advanced gastric cancer. Eur J Surg Oncol 2000;26:222–226.

Review Article

Digestive Diseases

Dig Dis 2004;22:374–379
DOI: 10.1159/000083601

Gene Therapy and Virotherapy of Gastric Cancer: Preclinical Results and Clinical Developments

Daniëlle A.M. Heideman

Department of Pathology, VU University Medical Center, Amsterdam, The Netherlands

Key Words
Gene transfer · Viral vector · Oncolytic virus · Gastric cancer · Stomach cancer · Gastrointestinal cancer

Abstract
Despite advances in current treatment modalities, the clinical outcome of gastric cancer remains dismal. New treatment modalities are urgently required to improve the prognosis of patients with gastric cancer. Cancer gene therapy and virotherapy comprise a potential category of new therapeutics and will be discussed in this review. To date, various gene therapy strategies have been developed, but first clinical trials reported only limited therapeutic efficacy as a result of limited gene transfer efficiency. Consequently, targeted viral vectors for enhanced delivery of transgenes to tumor cells and replicative viral systems designed to replicate selectively in malignant tissue were developed. Replication-selective oncolytic viral vectors have the advantage over non-replicative systems to cause pronounced bystander effect via self-perpetuating infection of adjacent cells after cytolysis of primary targeted cells. So far, clinical studies on virotherapy showed encouraging results; especially promising are combinations of virotherapy with current modes of treatment like chemo- and radiotherapy, or insertion of therapeutic genes in the viral genome such as combination with enzyme-prodrug therapy. Further research aiming to enhance anti-tumor efficacy and to improve selectivity of infection and replication, will eventually lead to full realization of the therapeutic potential of (replicating) viral vector systems for gastric cancer.

Introduction

Worldwide, cancer of the stomach is the second most common form of cancer with about 800,000 new cases per year and with a mortality that counts for almost 10% of all new cancer deaths [1]. Despite advances in conventional cancer treatment strategies, the prognosis of gastric cancer is poor, with reported overall 5-year survival rates rarely exceeding 20%. Thus, gastric cancer is a disease that urgently requires development of new therapeutic modalities. Gene therapy and virotherapy represent rational approaches to treat this cancer entity.

Cancer Gene Therapy

Cancer gene therapy involves the introduction of therapeutic genes into tumor cells of a cancer patient aiming to result, directly or indirectly, in eradiation of the tumor [reviewed in 2]. Originally, gene therapy was based on curing a disease by manipulating genes related to the de-

KARGER

Fax +41 61 306 12 34
E-Mail karger@karger.ch
www.karger.com

0257–2753/04/0224–0374$21.00/0

Accessible online at:
www.karger.com/ddi

Daniëlle A.M. Heideman
Department of Pathology, VU University Medical Center
PO Box 7057
NL–1007 MB Amsterdam (The Netherlands)
Tel. +31 20 444 8424, Fax +31 20 444 8168, E-Mail dam.heideman@vumc.nl

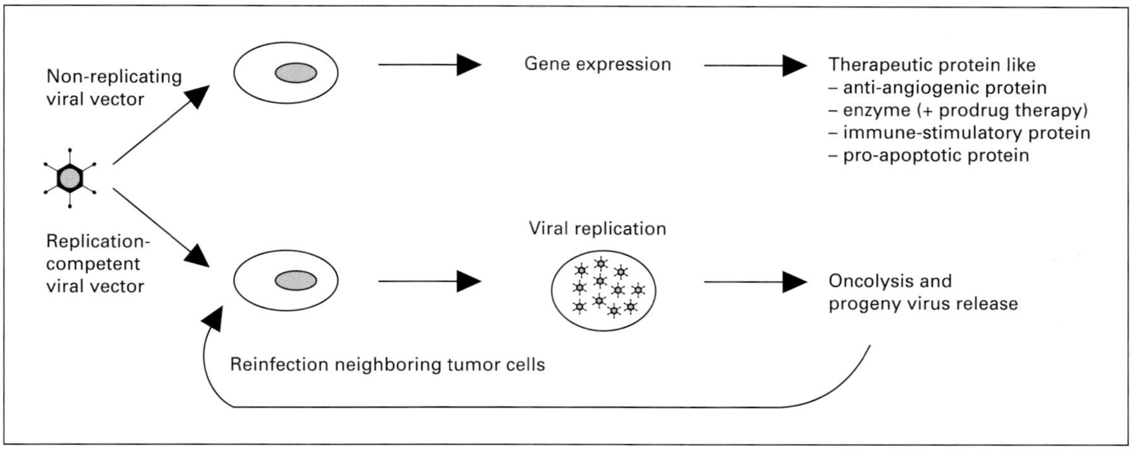

Fig. 1. Strategies for gene therapy and virotherapy. Schematic representation of different approaches available for gene therapy and virotherapy (see text for details).

velopment and maintenance of the disease [3]. Initially, this type of gene therapy was believed to easily cure most diseases, however, it finally showed a promising therapeutic outcome in only a few disease contexts [4, 5]. In case of cancer gene therapy, the concept of compensating altered genes by a normal copy in tumor cells remains challenging. The efficacy of mutation-compensation therapy is highly dependent on the efficiency of gene transfer into tumor cells. Since it is difficult to reach all tumor cells by gene transfer vectors and tumors often involve multiple genetic disorders, the gene replacement strategy is realized to be a relatively unsuitable method for cancer gene therapy.

As a result, various other gene transfer approaches have been developed, which focus on a 'bystander effect', i.e. both tumor cells containing the transgene and neighboring non-transduced tumor cells will be killed, directly or indirectly, by the therapeutic protein encoded by the transgene. These strategies include enzyme-prodrug therapy [6], genetic immunopotentiation [7] or approaches that induce death of tumor cells via inhibition of neovascularization and inactivation of signal transduction pathways involved in the malignant phenotype, e.g. NK4 gene therapy [8] (fig. 1).

Enzyme-prodrug therapy is based on the selective delivery and expression of a drug-sensitivity gene into cancer cells in order to eradicate them after drug treatment. Most widely used enzyme-prodrug systems are herpes simplex virus thymidine kinase (HSV-TK) gene together with ganciclovir, *Escherichia coli* cytosine deaminase (CD) gene together with 5-fluorocytosine (5-FC), carboxyl esterase (CE) gene together with irinotecan (CPT-11), and *E. coli* nitroreductase (NR) gene together with CB1954 [6]. To date, a phase I and pharmacokinetic study of the prodrug CB1954 has been evaluated on gastrointestinal malignancies, including gastric cancer [9]. This study demonstrated that sufficient serum and peritoneal prodrug levels needed for an enzyme-prodrug approach could be achieved after intraperitoneal administration and that the prodrug at that dose was well tolerated. A subsequent clinical trial evaluating adenovirus-mediated nitroreductase gene transfer was performed in patients with liver tumors (no patients with gastric cancer were included), indicating tolerability of the adenoviral vector and transgene expression after intratumoral injection [10]. The trial continues to evaluate the combination of prodrug and nitroreductase gene transfer as treatment for patients with non-resectable primary or secondary liver cancer (www.wiley.co.uk/genetherapy/clinical/).

Genetic immunopotentiation involves approaches that augment the immune response against tumor cells. Several genes have been investigated for their potential to induce an immune response against tumor cells, including, among others, expression of cytokines like IL-2, tumor-specific antigens like CEA, or co-stimulatory molecules like CD80 (B7-1). So far, a phase I–II study evaluating Adv-IL-2 in patients with unresectable gastric cancer has been performed [11]. Results from the clinical trial demonstrated safety of administration of adenovirus to patients.

Altogether, numerous cancer gene therapy clinical trials using enzyme-prodrug therapy or genetic immunopotentiation have been carried out to date. Many patients with gastrointestinal tract tumors were recruited in these trials; however, patients with gastric carcinoma were hardly included. These cancer gene therapy clinical trials have fallen short of expectations. Although most studies indicated safety of administration of the gene transfer vectors to patients (the adenovirus was by far the most used vector), only limited clinical responses were reported. The trials demonstrated limited tumor transduction frequencies thereby limiting therapeutic outcome [7, 12, 13]. Since also these 'bystander-effect'-inducing gene therapy approaches are dependent on the ability to deliver the therapeutic gene to target cells with a requisite level of efficiency, adequate tumor transduction is a key factor that must be addressed to realize gene therapy for cancer. Therefore, cancer gene therapy research has focused a lot on engineering vectors that more efficiently transfer the therapeutic genes into tumor cells than conventional vectors, including genetic and immunological targeting strategies, and the use of replication-competent viral systems.

Genetic, Immunological, and Transcriptional Targeting

A lot of research in the field of cancer gene therapy has focused on enhancement of gene transfer to tumor cells and selectivity of transduction. In order to make treatment effective and safe, the transgene should only be expressed in the tumor cells and not in the functionally normal epithelium of the stomach. For the use of adenovirus as gene transfer vehicle, for example, it has been shown that the natural tropism of the adenoviral vector favors the transduction of normal gastric epithelium versus gastric cancer cells [14], indicating that targeting strategies are needed to prevent unwanted gene transfer and expression in normal cells.

In recent years, a number of innovative strategies have been proposed to address the problem of 'targeting' [2]. Methods to modify the tropism of vectors are: (1) immunological targeting by using ligands for cellular receptors or antibodies against cellular antigens to redirect the vector to tumor-specific markers, in combination with the use of genetically modified vectors with ablated native tropism. Successful for gastric cancer is, for example, the use of CAR and integrin binding-ablated adenoviral vectors (also known as doubly-ablated adenoviral vectors) in combination with bispecific EpCAM-targeting conjugates [15]. (2) Genetic targeting by incorporation of new binding domains in the vector in combination with deleted native tropism, for example an integrin-binding RGD motif replacing the knob domain in the adenoviral vector [16]. (3) Transcriptionally targeting of gene expression using a cell-specific promoter, whereby the expression of the transgene will only occur in cells in which the promoter is activated. Interesting examples for gastric cancer are CEA, EpCAM, or COX-2 [17].

Virotherapy

In parallel with efforts to develop more efficient and selective gene transfer vectors, the ongoing progress in vector development and virology has led to the creation of replication-competent viral vectors. The use of replication-competent viral vector systems may overcome the limitation of replication-defective viral gene transfer systems which demonstrate only modest anti-tumor efficacy due to poor transduction efficiency and penetration capacity in solid tumor masses, even after intratumoral injection of the viral vector. Transduction of tumor cell by a replicative viral vector results in viral replication and subsequent release of viral progeny from the tumor cells which offers the potential to amplify viral vectors in situ and to achieve lateral spread to neighboring cells in a solid tumor, thus resulting in efficient tumor penetration (fig. 1). Moreover, the use of viruses that replicate through a lytic cycle allows amplification of therapeutic effect through virus-mediated oncolysis. After several rounds of viral replication and cell lysis, the tumor will ultimately be destroyed.

To date, various replicative viral vector systems based on relatively well-known viruses have been explored as novel anti-cancer agents, e.g. adenovirus [18–21], herpes simplex virus [22], influenza virus [23], Newcastle disease virus [24, 25], poliovirus [26], reovirus [27, 28], vaccinia virus [29, 30], vesicular stomatitis virus [31], and parvovirus [32–35]. Important in the design of virotherapy for cancer is the use of viruses which possess the ability to replicate specifically in tumor cells, leading to direct tumor cell lysis while leaving normal cells unaffected. Therefore, oncotropic viruses have been used or attenuated strains have been developed that possess the ability to replicate only within specific tissues; some of which will be described in detail below.

An example of an oncotropic virus is the parvovirus [32–35]. Parvoviruses, including minute virus of mice (MVM) and H-1, have been shown to preferentially replicate and exert cytopathological effect (CPE) in various oncogene-transformed cells while sparing their non-transformed counterparts in vitro and in vivo. Parvovirus exhibits oncotropism because of the strong cell-cycle and oncogene-inducible parvoviral promoter P4. MVM and H-1 viral vectors have been constructed for virotherapeutic purposes, which retain in particular the oncogene-responsive parvoviral expression cassette, including the gene coding for the multifunctional (replicative, transactivating and cytotoxic) non-structural protein 1 (NS1). Due to their oncotropism, parvoviral vectors are promising agents for virotherapy. So far, no clinical trials have been reported evaluating parvoviral vector-mediated virotherapy in patients with gastric cancer.

Conditionally replicating adenoviral vectors (CRAd) and herpes simplex viruses (HSV) also belong to the group of oncolytic viral therapeutics. However, in contrast to the replicative viral vector system described above, adenoviruses and HSV lack endogenous oncotropism. Importantly, much is known about the replication cycle of these viruses, making it feasible to exploit this knowledge for the development of replication-competent adenoviral and HSV vector systems with precise replication on the basis of cancer-specific markers. Thus, CRAds and HSV are designed to take advantage of tumor-specific changes creating preferential replication in tumor cells [36, 37]. For example, selective replication of CRAds in cancer cells is achieved through the introduction of mutations in adenoviral genes that abrogate the interaction of the encoded proteins with cellular proteins that are necessary to complete the viral life cycle in normal cells but can be selectively compensated by particular mutations existing in cancer cells (e.g. ONYX-15 [18], and AdΔ24 [20, 21]), or by placing adenoviral genes that are needed for replication under a tumor-specific promoter (e.g. α-fetoprotein promoter [38], CEA promoter [39], or cycloxygenase-2 (COX-2) promoter [40]).

So far, a clinical trial examining virotherapy based on *dl*1520, also known as ONYX-015, that as a result of *E1B-55kD* deletion cannot inactivate p53 and is able to replicate in cells with dysfunctional p53 [18], has been performed in patients with metastatic gastric carcinoma to the liver. The CRAd was delivered by intra-arterial administration and combined with chemotherapy (5-FU and leucovorin) [41]. The study demonstrated that intra-arterial administration of replicating adenoviral vectors was safe, though response to therapy was modest with no complete responses.

At the moment, replication-competent HSV expressing granulocyte-macrophage colony-stimulating factor (OncoVEX^{GM-CSF}) is under investigation in patients with gastric cancer that has spread to the skin (www.wiley.co.uk/genetherapy/clinical/). An intermediate study report described safety of administration of OncoVEX^{GM-CSF} to patients, and that signs suggestive of anti-tumor activity have been observed, including evidence of virus replication (virus in tumor swabs up to 2 weeks following virus administration), tumor necrosis, and significant inflammation consistent with the activity of GM-CSF [42].

Taken together, clinical trials performed so far evaluating oncolytic viruses show that administration of oncolytic viruses is a safe procedure without the manifestation of severe side effects; however, they also demonstrate that oncolytic virotherapy has not yet been effective in complete tumor eradication in clinical studies.

Ways to Enhance Efficacy of Virotherapy

Several problems were encountered in the above-described clinical trials that need to be addressed to guarantee oncolytic viruses as therapeutic agent in cancer treatment in future, as single agent or in combination therapy. First, like for non-replicative viral vector systems, low infectivity may be key problem hindering full realization of the therapeutic potential of oncolytic viral vector systems because infection efficiency of the progeny virus affects viral spread during each round of viral amplification. Therefore, research is ongoing to overcome low infectivity by engineering oncolytic viruses with genetic modification of their target cell-binding motif (e.g. CRAds with an integrin-binding RGD motif in the HI-loop of the fiber knob region [40]), or retargeted viruses which have incorporated an expression cassette for their targeting molecule in the genome (i.e. bispecific retargeting conjugate is produced by infected tumor cells, thereby the progeny virus subsequently produced will have retargeting ability as well [43]).

Secondly, identification of novel methods to control viral replication must continue and combination of various control mechanisms should be pursued to achieve greater safety for clinical application. So far, for example, truly selective replication of CRAds has not yet been accomplished by introduction of viral gene mutations and concerns about their selectivity restrict the use of CRAds in clinical trials. Therefore, research has focused on novel CRAds with enhanced selectivity of viral replication by introduction of multiple deletions in the adenoviral genome, e.g. combining two different E1A deletions (like in AdCB016 [44], and Ad*dl*01-07 [45]). More preclinical and clinical data are needed to test if introduction of multiple mutations in the adenoviral genome may render these vectors into truly selective CRAds that still exhibit effective oncolytic capacity.

Thirdly, viruses with greater oncolytic potency will have to be engineered to ensure therapeutic efficacy. Because the best chance of completely curing cancer patients lies with attacking tumor cells through combination of different agents with diverse mechanisms of action, investigation of incorporation of therapeutic genes into oncolytic viruses and combinations of oncolytic virotherapy with conventional therapy have to be considered to enhance anti-tumor efficacy. Since many oncolytic viruses have the cloning capacity for small transgenes, the oncolytic virus can be used as potent expression vector for anti-cancer therapeutics, e.g. drug sensitivity genes, immune response-stimulating genes, or anti-angiogenic genes. Also, the gene product can be used to enhance the inherent cancer cell killing potency of oncolytic viruses to realize full anti-tumor potential, e.g. incorporation of wt-p53 in CRAd AdΔ24 to provide functional p53 expression during adenovirus replication in cancer cells thereby accelerating cell death and progeny virus release [46–48]. Furthermore, several clinical trials on combination of oncolytic virotherapy and chemotherapy (including the study described above using combination of *dl*1520, 5-FU, and leucovorin for treatment of metastatic gastric cancer [41]) or preclinical studies combining oncolytic viruses with radiation treatment have confirmed improved anti-cancer efficacies without an increase in toxicity [49]. Since viruses kill cells by oncolytic mechanisms differing from standard anti-cancer therapies, there is a rational for synergistic interactions when used in combination with chemo-, radio-, and/or immunotherapy.

Conclusion, Discussion and Future Perspectives

Considering the poor therapeutic outcome of inoperable gastric cancer patients, continued attempts to develop successful therapeutic strategies are needed. Gene therapy and virotherapy are rational novel therapeutic modalities for gastric cancer. To date, however, there is no gene or virotherapeutic strategy that shows outstanding clinical efficacy for gastric cancer. Despite significant advances in vector development, current problems hindering clinical implementation include therapeutic potency and tumor-selectivity for safety. Therefore, to ensure the full realization of the clinical potential of gene and virotherapy in future, continuous research is needed to improve tumor-targeting strategies, to obtain truly tumor-specific control of viral replication required for clinical safety, and to enhance anti-tumor activity.

In summary, the field of gene therapy and oncolytic virotherapy has now matured beyond the first high expectancy. Valuable lessons have been learnt from first clinical trials and directed future research. Further development and evaluation of second- and third-generation agents is important to ensure full therapeutic potential. Most likely, inclusion of gene and virotherapy into multimodal cancer treatment regimens combined with surgery, chemo- and radiotherapy, will be most effective in improving the overall survival of patients with gastric cancer.

References

1 World Health Report, 1997: Conquering Suffering, Enriching Humanity. Geneva, WHO, 1997.

2 Heideman DAM, Gerritsen WR, Craanen ME: Gene therapy for gastrointestinal tract cancer: A review. Scand J Gastroenterol Suppl 2000; 232:93–100.

3 Anderson WF: Prospects for human gene therapy. Science 1984;226:401–409.

4 Losordo DW, Vale PR, Hendel RC, Milliken CE, Fortuin FD, Cummings N, Schatz RA, Asahara T, Isner JM, Kuntz RE: Phase 1/2 placebo-controlled, double-blind, dose-escalating trial of myocardial vascular endothelial growth factor 2 gene transfer by catheter delivery in patients with chronic myocardial ischemia. Circulation 2002;105:2012–2018.

5 Hacein-Bey-Abina S, Le Deist F, Carlier F, Bouneaud C, Hue C, De Villartay JP, Thrasher AJ, Wulffraat N, Sorensen R, Dupuis-Girod S, Fischer A, Davies EG, Kuis W, Leiva L, Cavazzana-Calvo M: Sustained correction of X-linked severe combined immunodeficiency by ex vivo gene therapy. N Engl J Med 2002; 346:1185–1193.

6 Springer CJ, Niculescu-Duvaz I: Prodrug-activating systems in suicide gene therapy. J Clin Investig 2000;105:1161–1167.

7 Roth JA, Cristiano RJ: Gene therapy for cancer: What have we done and where are we going? J Natl Cancer Inst 1997;89:21–39.

8 Heideman DAM, van Beusechem VW, Bloemena E, Snijders PJF, Craanen ME, Offerhaus GJA, Derksen WB, de Bruin M, Witlox MA, Molenaar B, Meijer CJLM, Gerritsen WR: Suppression of tumor growth, invasion and angiogenesis of human gastric cancer by adenovirus-mediated expression of NK4. J Gene Med 2004;6:317–327.

9 Chung-Faye C, Palmer D, Anderson D, Clark J, Downes M, Baddeley J, Hussain S, Murray PI, Searle P, Seymour L, Harris PA, Ferry D, Kerr DJ: Virus-directed, enzyme prodrug therapy with nitroimidazole reductase: A phase I and pharmacokinetic study of its prodrug, CB1954. Clin Cancer Res 2001;7:2662–2668.

10 Palmer DH, Mautner V, Mirza D, Oliff S, Gerritsen WR, van der Sijp JRM, Hubscher S, Reynolds G, Bonney S, Rajaratnam R, Hull D, Horne M, Ellis J, Mountain A, Hill S, Harris PA, Searle PF, Young LS, James ND, Kerr DJ: Virus-directed enzyme prodrug therapy: Intratumoral administration of a replication-deficient adenovirus encoding nitroreductase to patients with respectable liver cancer. J Clin Oncol 2004;22:1546–1552.

11 Gilly FN, Beaujard A, Bienvenu J, Trillet Lenoir V, Glehen O, Thouvenot D, Malcus C, Favrot M, Dumontet C, Lombard-Bohas O, Garbit F, Gueugniaud PY, Vignal J, Aymard M, Touraine Moulin F, Roos M, Pavirani A, Courtney M: Gene therapy with Adv-IL-2 in unresectable digestive cancer: Phase I–II study, intermediate report. Hepatogastroenterology 1999;46(suppl):1268–1273.

12 Herrmann F: Cancer gene therapy: Principles, problems, and perspectives. J Mol Med 1995; 73:157–163.
13 Vile RG, Russell SJ, Lemoine NR: Cancer gene therapy: Hard lessons and new courses. Gene Ther 2000;7:2–8.
14 Heideman DAM, Snijders PJF, Craanen ME, Bloemena E, Meijer CJLM, Meuwissen SGM, van Beusechem WR, Pinedo HM, Curiel DT, Haisma HJ, Gerritsen WR: Selective gene delivery towards gastric and esophageal adenocarcinoma cells via EpCAM-targeted adenoviral vectors. Cancer Gene Ther 2001;8:342–351.
15 Heideman DAM, van Beusechem VW, Offerhaus GJA, Wickham TJ, Roelvink PW, Craanen ME, Pinedo HM, Meijer CJLM, Gerritsen WR: Selective gene transfer into primary human gastric tumors using epithelial cell adhesion molecule-targeted adenoviral vectors with ablated native tropism. Hum Gene Ther 2002; 13:1677–1685.
16 Magnusson MK, See Hong S, Henning P, Boulanger P, Lindholm L: Genetic retargeting of adenovirus: Novel strategy employing 'deknobbing' of the fiber. J Virol 2001;75:7280–7289.
17 Yamamoto M, Alemany R, Adachi Y, Grizzle WE, Curiel DT: Characterization of the cyclooxygenase-2 promoter in an adenoviral vector and its application for the mitigation of toxicity in suicide gene therapy of gastrointestinal cancers. Mol Ther 2001;3:385–394.
18 Bischoff JR, Kirn DH, Williams A, Heise C, Horn S, Muna M, Ng L, Nye JA, Sampson-Johannes A, Fattaey A, McCormick F: An adenovirus mutant that replicates selectively in p53-deficient human tumor cells. Science 1996; 274:373–376.
19 Rodriguez R, Schuur ER, Lim HY, Henderson GA, Simons JW, Henderson DR: Prostate attenuated replication competent adenovirus (ARCA) CN706: A selective cytotoxic for prostate-specific antigen-positive prostate cancer cells. Cancer Res 1997;57:2559–2563.
20 Fueyo J, Gomez-Manzano C, Alemany R, Lee PS, McDonnell TJ, Mitlianga P, Shi YX, Levin VA, Yung WK, Kyritsis AP: A mutant oncolytic adenovirus targeting the Rb pathway produces anti-glioma effect in vivo. Oncogene 2000;19:2–12.
21 Heise C, Hermiston T, Johnson L, Brooks G, Sampson-Johannes A, Williams A, Hawkins L, Kirn D: An adenovirus E1A mutant that demonstrates potent and selective systemic anti-tumoral efficacy. Nat Med 2000;6:1134–1139.
22 Martuza RL: Conditionally replicating herpes vectors for cancer therapy. J Clin Invest 2000; 105:841–846.
23 Bergmann M, Romirer I, Sachet M, Fleischhacker R, Garcia-Sastre A, Palese P, Wolff K, Pehamberger H, Jakesz R, Muster T: A genetically engineered influenza A virus with ras-dependent oncolytic properties. Cancer Res 2001;61:8188–8193.
24 Phuangsab A, Lorence RM, Reichard KW, Peeples ME, Walter RJ: Newcastle disease virus therapy of human tumor xenografts: Antitumor effects of local or systemic administration. Cancer Lett 2001;172:27–36.
25 Schirrmacher V, Griesbach A, Ahlert T: Antitumor effects of Newcastle disease virus in vivo: Local versus systemic effects. Int J Oncol 2001;18:945–952.
26 Gromeier M, Lachmann S, Rosenfeld MR, Gutin PH, Wimmer E: Intergeneric poliovirus recombinants for the treatment of malignant glioma. Proc Natl Acad Sci USA 2000;97: 6803–6808.
27 Strong JE, Coffey MC, Tang D, Sabinin P, Lee PW: The molecular basis of viral oncolysis: Usurpation of the Ras signaling pathway by reovirus. EMBO J 1998;17:3351–3362.
28 Wilcox ME, Yang W, Senger D, Rewcastle NB, Morris DG, Brasher PM, Shi ZQ, Johnston RN, Nishikawa S, Lee PW, Forsyth PA: Reovirus as an oncolytic agent against experimental human malignant gliomas. J Natl Cancer Inst 2001;93:903–912.
29 Timiryasova TM, Li J, Chen B, Chong D, Langridge WH, Gridley DS, Fodor I: Antitumor effect of vaccinia virus in glioma model. Oncol Res 1999;11:133–144.
30 McCart JA, Ward JM, Lee J, Hu Y, Alexander HR, Libutti SK, Moss B, Bartlett DL: Systemic cancer therapy with a tumor-selective vaccinia virus mutant lacking thymidine kinase and vaccinia growth factor genes. Cancer Res 2001;61:8751–8757.
31 Stojdl DF, Lichty B, Knowles S, Marius R, Atkins H, Sonenberg N, Bell JC: Exploiting tumor-specific defects in the interferon pathway with a previously unknown oncolytic virus. Nat Med 2000;6:821–825.
32 Telerman A, Tuynder M, Dupressoir T, Robaye B, Sigaux F, Shaulian E, Oren M, Rommelaere J, Amson R: A model for tumor suppression using H-1 parvovirus. Proc Natl Acad Sci USA 1993;90:8702–8706.
33 Ponnazhagan S: Parvovirus vectors for cancer gene therapy. Expert Opin Biol Ther 2004;4: 53–64.
34 Dupont F: Risk assessment of the use of autonomous parvovirus-based vectors. Curr Gene Ther 2003;3:567–582.
35 Cornelis JJ, Lang SI, Stroh-Dege AY, Balboni G, Dinsart C, Rommelaere J: Cancer gene therapy through autonomous parvovirus-mediated gene transfer. Curr Gene Ther 2004;4:249–261.
36 Oosterhoff D, van Beusechem VW: Conditionally replicating adenoviruses as anticancer agents and ways to improve their efficacy. J Exp Ther Oncol 2004;4:37–57.
37 Varghese S, Rabkin SD: Oncolytic herpes simplex virus vectors for cancer virotherapy. Cancer Gene Ther 2002;9:967–978.
38 Takahashi M, Sato T, Sagawa T, Lu Y, Sato Y, Iyama S, Yamada Y, Fukaura J, Takahashi S, Miyanishi K, Yamashita T, Sasaki K, Kogawa K, Hamada H, Kato J, Niitsu Y: E1B-55K-deleted adenovirus expressing E1A-13S by AFP-enhancer/promoter is capable of highly specific replication in AFP-producing hepatocellular carcinoma and eradication of established tumor. Mol Ther 2002;5:627–634.
39 Li Y, Chen Y, Dilley J, Arroyo T, Ko D, Working P, Yu DC: Carcinoembryonic antigen-producing cell-specific oncolytic adenovirus, OV798, for colorectal cancer therapy. Mol Cancer Ther 2003;2:1003–1009.
40 Yamamoto M, Davydova J, Wang M, Siegal GP, Krasnykh V, Vickers SM, Curiel DT: Infectivity enhanced, cyclooxygenase-2 promoter-based conditionally replicative adenovirus for pancreatic cancer. Gastroenterology 2003; 125:1203–1218.
41 Reid T, Galanis E, Abbruzzese J, Sze D, Wein LM, Andrews J, Randlev B, Heise C, Uprichard M, Hatfield M, Rome L, Rubin J, Kirn D: Hepatic arterial infusion of a replication-selective oncolytic adenovirus (dl1520): Phase II viral, immunological and clinical endpoints. Cancer Res 2002;62:6070–6079.
42 Hu JC, McNeish I, Shorrock C, Steiner J, Love C, Coffin R, Coombes C: A phase I clinical trial with OncoVEX$^{GM\text{-}CSF}$. Proc Am Soc Clin Oncol 2003;22:185(abstr 742).
43 Van Beusechem VW, Mastenbroek DC, van den Doel PB, Lamfers ML, Grill J, Wurdinger T, Haisma HJ, Pinedo HM, Gerritsen WR: Conditionally replicative adenovirus expressing a targeting adapter molecule exhibits enhanced oncolytic potency on CAR-deficient tumors. Gene Ther 2003;10:1982–1991.
44 Balague C, Noya F, Alemany R, Chow LT, Curiel DT: Human papillomavirus E6E7-mediated adenovirus cell killing: Selectivity of mutant adenovirus replication in organotypic cultures of human keratinocytes. J Virol 2001; 75:7602–7611.
45 Howe JA, Demers GW, Johnson DE, Neugebauer SE, Perry ST, Vaillancourt MT, Faha B: Evaluation of E1-mutant adenoviruses as conditionally replicating agents for cancer therapy. Mol Ther 2000;2:485–495.
46 Van Beusechem VW, van den Doel PB, Grill J, Pinedo HM, Gerritsen WR: Conditionally replicative adenovirus expressing p53 exhibits enhanced oncolytic potency. Cancer Res 2002; 62:6165–6171.
47 Geoerger B, Vassal G, Opolon P, Dirven CM, Morizet J, Laudani L, Grill J, Giaccone G, Vandertop WP, Gerritsen WR, van Beusechem VW: Oncolytic activity of p53-expressing conditionally replicative adenovirus AdΔ24-p53 against human malignant glioma. Cancer Res 2004;64:5753–5759.
48 Geoerger B, Van Beusechem VW, Opolon P, Morizet J, Laudani L, Lecluse Y, Barrois M, Idema S, Grill J, Gerritsen WR, Vassal G: Expression of p53, or targeting towards EGFR, enhances the oncolytic potency of conditionally replicative adenovirus against neuroblastoma. J Gene Med 2005, in press.
49 Chu RL, Post DE, Khuri FR, Van Meir EG: Use of replicating oncolytic adenoviruses in combination therapy for cancer. Clin Cancer Res 2004;10:5299–5312.

Review Article

Digestive Diseases

Dig Dis 2004;22:380–385
DOI: 10.1159/000083602

Recent Advances in Molecular Diagnosis and Therapy of Gastric Cancer

Jie Chen[a] Christoph Röcken[b] Peter Malfertheiner[a] Matthias P.A. Ebert[a]

Departments of [a]Gastroenterology, Hepatology and Infectious Diseases, and [b]Pathology, Otto von Guericke University, Magdeburg, Germany

Key Words
Gastric cancer, molecular basis · Gastric cancer, molecular diagnosis · Gastric cancer, molecular therapy

Abstract
Gastric cancer is the fourth most common malignancy and the second most frequent cause of cancer-related death in the world. It is often diagnosed in advanced stages when treatment options are limited, leading to a poor prognosis. During the past 15 years, much has been learnt about the molecular mechanisms of gastric carcinogenesis and the development of metastases. This coincided with the development of new techniques for functional genomics, including both transcriptomics and proteomics, which significantly improve the ability to explore new molecular alterations involved in carcinogenesis and tumor progression. An improved understanding of the molecular pathology and pathogenesis of gastric cancer may lead to a more rapid development of molecular diagnostic and patient tailored therapeutic targets.

Introduction

Gastric cancer is one of the most common cancers worldwide, accounting for over 870,000 new cases and over 650,000 deaths annually [1]. Mortality from gastric cancer is second only to lung cancer. A history of infection and chronic inflammation is strongly associated with the risk of gastric cancer and its precursor lesions [2]. In Western countries, two-thirds of the gastric cancer patients are diagnosed in advanced stages, when surgery can only be palliative; meanwhile, gastric cancers are largely resistant to chemotherapy and radiotherapy [3]. Due to late diagnosis and limited treatment options, gastric cancer has a poor prognosis. Despite a decreasing incidence the overall prevalence of gastric cancer is increasing and it will remain a major clinical problem in the future.

Over 90% of gastric cancers are adenocarcinomas [4, 5]. The recent WHO classification of tumors of the digestive system divides four common histological patterns of gastric adenocarcinomas, i.e. the papillary, tubular, mucinous and signet ring cell pattern [2]. The older Laurén classification separates intestinal and diffuse type of gastric adenocarcinoma [6], and has validated its usefulness multiple times, both in terms of patient management, and in understanding the pathogenesis of gastric cancer: these two subtypes differ in their epidemiology and etiology, molecular biology, as well as clinical outcome. During the

KARGER
Fax +41 61 306 12 34
E-Mail karger@karger.ch
www.karger.com

0257–2753/04/0224–0380$21.00/0

Accessible online at:
www.karger.com/ddi

Matthias Ebert, MD
Department of Gastroenterology, Hepatology and Infectious Diseases
Otto von Guericke University, Leipziger Strasse 44
DE–39120 Magdeburg (Germany), Tel. +49 391 6721520
Fax +49 391 67190054, E-Mail Matthias.Ebert@medizin.uni-magdeburg.de

past 15 years, much has been learnt about the molecular basis of the development and progression of gastric cancer [7, 8], which enables us to find new molecular biomarkers particularly for the detection of gastric cancer in its early stages, and helps us to develop new molecular therapies for gastric cancer.

Molecular Basis of Gastric Cancer

Carcinogenesis of gastric cancer is a complex multistep process, including numerous genetic and epigenetic alterations. Environmental risk factors interplay with the host genetic profile and both influence gastric carcinogenesis. *Helicobacter pylori* is the most important environmental risk factor for the development of gastric cancer. More than 70% of cases with gastric cancer are attributable to *H. pylori*-associated chronic gastritis. However, the individual host response to infection, influenced by, e.g., the genetic polymorphisms of pro-inflammatory cytokines also contributes to the risk of gastric cancer [3, 8]. The interleukin-1 *(IL-1)* gene cluster polymorphisms were found to be associated with an increased risk of gastric cancer in *H. pylori*-infected patients [9]. Genomic instability is also a fundamental event in gastric carcinogenesis. Two molecular phenotypes with distinct pathways of genomic instability have been uncovered in gastric cancer: the phenotype with a high-level microsatellite instability caused by inactivation of DNA repair genes, and the phenotype with chromosomal or intrachromosomal instability caused by mutations in genes controlling the segregation of genetic material during mitosis. The latter is characterized by chromosomal rearrangement and loss or gain of chromosomes, which in turn can induce the activation of oncogenes (i.e. *c-met*, *c-erbB-2*, *K-sam*), or inactivation of tumor-suppressor genes (i.e. *p53, p16, APC*), abnormal alterations of genes implicated in cell proliferation and apoptosis (i.e. *cyclin D1, bcl-2, E2F -1, SC-1*), as well as telomerase activation of genes involved [8]. With regard to gastric cancer invasion and metastasis, molecular alterations in cell-cell or cell-matrix interactions (i.e. E-cadherin, β-catenin, ICAM-1, VCAM-1, MMPs) and neo-angiogenesis (i.e. VEGF, HIF-1α, ECM1) are considered to play important roles [10–13]. Apart from genetic alterations, epigenetic alterations have recently drawn increasing attention in gastric carcinogenesis and metastasis. Cancer-related epigenetic alterations include a global genomic hypomethylation and a dense hypermethylation of the CpG islands in gene regulatory regions by DNA methyltransferases (DNMTs), as well as formation of transcriptionally repressive chromatin states by histone deacetylase (HDAC) activity [14–16]. Global genomic hypomethylation may lead to chromosomal instability, activation of endogenous parasitic DNA sequences (i.e. *L1* and *Alu* repeats) and loss of imprinting (i.e. 11p15) [16–19]. Hypermethylation of the CpG islands in gene regulatory regions and formation of transcriptionally repressive chromatin states can result in gene transcriptional silencing [15, 16, 20]. A significant proportion of tumor-related genes, including well-characterized tumor suppressor genes ($p16^{INK4a}$, $p15^{INK4b}$, $p14^{ARF}$, *p73*, *APC*, and *BRCA1)*, DNA repair genes *(hMLH1)*, and genes related to metastasis and invasion *(CDH1*, *TIMP3*, and *DAPK)* have been demonstrated to be silenced by aberrant promotor hypermethylation in different cancers including gastric cancer [16, 20].

Molecular Diagnosis

To date, most of the classic cancer-associated molecular alterations have also been found in gastric cancer. Some of these changes occur commonly in all various types of malignant tumors and some differ depending on the histological type. For instance, loss of functional *p53* and telomerase activation, are common to all tumor subtypes [8]. Down-regulation of cell adhesion molecules, such as cadherins, however, is associated mainly with cancers showing a diffuse, non-cohesive growth pattern; germline mutations of E-cadherin *(CDH1)* gene have been detected in 50–70% of diffuse-type gastric cancers and are responsible for a small subset of familial gastric cancer [21, 22]. Conversely, mutation or loss of heterozygosity (LOH) of the adenomatous polyposis coli *(APC)* gene occurs mainly in intestinal-type gastric cancers [8]. Despite the large body of data, none of the molecular errors identified thus far in gastric cancer are totally specific or unique for gastric cancer, in a more general sense, and for specific histological subtypes of gastric cancer in particular. It is very likely that a combination of different molecular markers is necessary to effectively predict individual gastric cancer risk, and to detect gastric cancer in its early stages. In 1993, Yasui et al. [23, 24] established a genetic diagnosis system for gastrointestinal pathology specimens and performed this as a routine service in an analysis of more than 10,000 cases, using so-called classical molecular and genetic markers, including *p53, APC, p27, EGFR*, microsatellite assay and others. Recent findings of the spectrum of epigenetic alterations for a relatively small subset of genes involved in important cellular pathways in tumorigenesis indicate that this is specially present in certain tumors of the gastrointestinal tract. For example, gastrointestinal tumors (colon and gastric) share a set of genes silenced by hypermethylation such as *p16INK4a*, *p14ARF*, *MGMT*, *APC*, and *hMLH1*. Therefore, a molecular marker system for cancer based on aberrant methylation is proposed for the early detection of the major forms of human cancers including gastric cancer [16, 20].

In recent years, with the progress of the Human Genome Project (HGP), molecular diagnosis of gastric cancer enters into the post-genomic era. New techniques of functional genomics include methods of gene expression profiling at the transcriptional level (transcriptomics, i.e. cDNA microarray, serial analysis of gene expression (SAGE), differential display, subtractive hybridization) and protein level (proteomics). These techniques have been used in conjunction with laser capture microdissection (LCD) to study the pathology and pathogenesis of gastric cancer [25–34]. These novel and powerful techniques permit the analysis of thousands of genes and their products simultaneously in a quick and high-throughput way and hold great promise in the molecular diagnosis of gastric cancer. New strategies from basic cancer research to clinical molecular diagnosis of gastric cancer can be proposed by combining these new functional genomic techniques with classical clinic detection techniques. Firstly (basic research stage), by using SAGE, differential display, or subtractive hybridization together with LCD to analyze normal gastric tissue, gastric cancer tissue and metastatical tissue, comparative gene expression profiles can be obtained from gastric cancer, cancer metastases, and matching non-neoplastic mucosa or precursor lesions. Subsequent proteome analyses provide the corresponding protein expression profiles. Finally, comparing the gene expression profiles with the protein expression profiles, helps to identify putative differentially expressed genes, gene products and regulatory pathways involved in the development of gastric cancer and metastases. Secondly (pre-clinical study stage), the expression of specifically up or down-regulated genes/proteins is confirmed by real-time RT-PCR, immunohistochemistry or enzyme-linked immunosorbent assays in a larger number of gastric cancer patients leading to the selection of biomarkers for clinical application. Thirdly (clinical diagnostic stage), the confirmed gastric cancer-specific biomarkers can be used to prepare custom-made cDNA microarrays or protein chips, and establish clinical detection systems for blood or tissue specimens.

Molecular Therapy

Based on the understanding of the molecular mechanisms underlying gastric carcinogenesis and metastasis, new molecular therapies directed at tumor-specific molecular defects in gastric cancer have been investigated in recent years. These molecular strategies include direct induction of tumor cell death, reversal of tumorigenesis by correcting genetic abnormalities, enhancing tumor response to conventional chemo- and radiotherapy, modulation of the host immune response against tumors, and protection of normal tissue from toxic effects of antitumor treatment by means of drug or gene therapy. Although most of these molecular strategies for gastric cancer treatment are currently only performed on cell lines or animal models, promising results from these studies indicate their future clinical application. New strategies for molecular therapy of gastric cancer are summarized in figure 1.

Molecular therapy targeting oncogene transcripts and products include antisense oligonucleotides or specific hammerhead ribozymes, as well as monoclonal antibodies or drugs antagonizing protein function. Oncogene (i.e. *c-myc*, *K-ras*, *c-erbB-2*, *EGFR*) inhibition has been widely studied in gastric cancer cell lines and animal models. Promising results in growth inhibition and apoptosis induction of gastric cancer have been reported [35–38]. Reactivation of tumor suppressor genes presents an alternative approach that includes the direct transfer of wild-type tumor suppressor genes (i.e. *p53*, $p16^{INK4A}$, *FHIT*) into gastric cancer cells [39–41] or more recently the so-called 'transcriptional therapy' using DNA demethylating drugs (i.e. 5′-azadeoxycytidine, procainamide) and/or histone hyperacetylating drugs (i.e. 4-phenylbutyrate, trichostatin A). These therapies aim to reactivate silenced tumor suppressor genes by reversing methylation of CpG islands in gene promotor regions and/or histone deacetylase activity [42, 43]. Inhibition of extracellular proteolytic systems (i.e. MMPs) or blockage of factors involved in neo-angiogenesis (i.e. VEGF, HIF-1α) have also been reported to inhibit the formation of gastric cancer metastases [44–47]. Recently, several groups reported the induction of cell cycle arrest and the inhibition of cell growth in gastric cancer cells by treatment with antisense telomerase RNA (anti-hTR). Anti-hTR targets rather specifically and selectively cancer tissue, making it highly attractive for the treatment of gastric cancer [48, 49].

Gastric cancer is largely resistant to chemotherapy, however, based on the knowledge of the molecular mechanisms underlying gastric carcinogenesis and anticancer

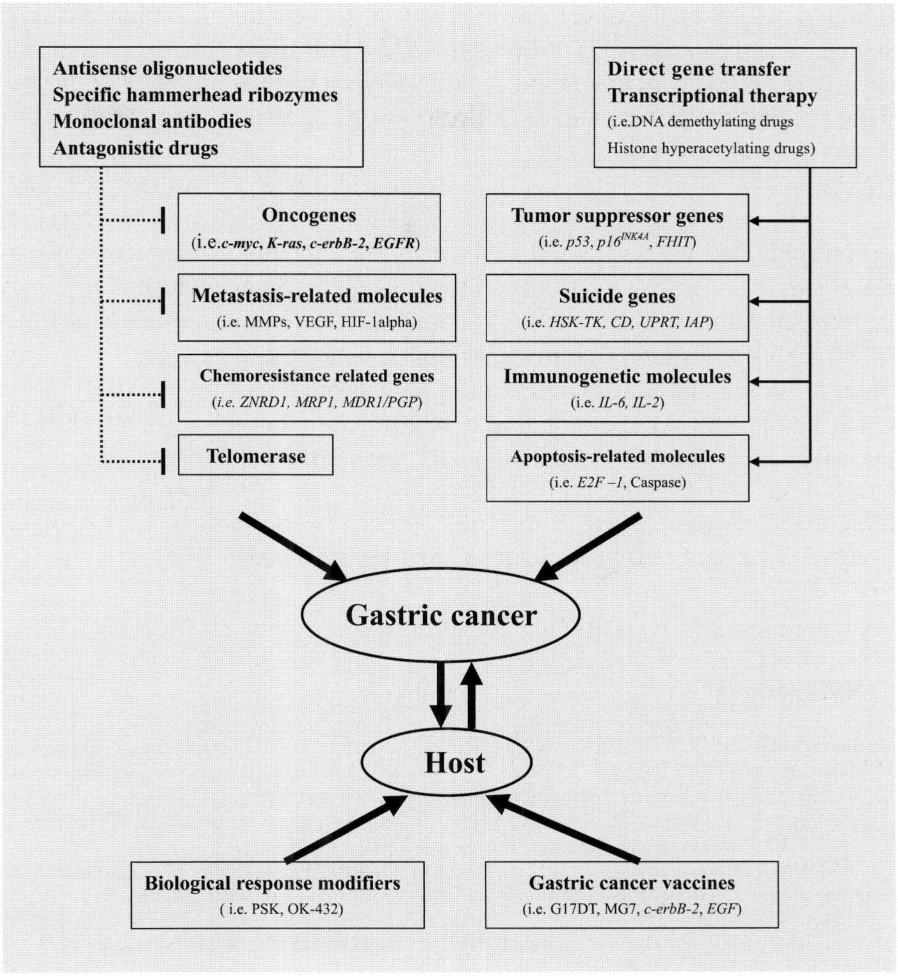

Fig. 1. Summary of strategies and molecular targets in treatment of gastric cancer. Adapted from the review by Chen et al. [63]. ···· = Inhibition; → = activation.

drug metabolism, a new strategy termed 'gene-chemotherapy' has been introduced more recently. One type of gene-chemotherapy is aimed at the reversal of the chemoresistance of gastric cancer cells in chemotherapy. Chemoresistance of cancer cells is due to abnormal alterations of oncogenes (i.e. *c-erbB-2*), tumor suppressor genes (i.e. *ERCC1*), apoptosis-related genes (i.e. *Bcl-2*) and specific or multidrug resistance (MDR) genes (i.e. *ZNRD1, MRP1, MDR1/PGP*) [50–52]. Gene therapy targeted at these chemoresistance-related genes can reverse tumors with drug-resistance phenotype to drug-sensitive and thereby enhance the effect of chemotherapy. A further approach of gene-chemotherapy is the 'cytotoxic gene therapy' or 'suicide gene therapy'. The strategy of cytotoxic gene therapy or suicide gene therapy involves the transduction of tumor cells with a foreign enzyme, following administration of a prodrug. The transduced enzyme catalyses the formation of toxic molecules, that induce tumor cell death. By using tissue-specific promoters, the enzyme transduction can be targeted at special tumor sites. The most frequently investigated enzyme/prodrug systems in cytotoxic gene therapy of gastric cancer are the HSK-TK/GCV (herpes simplex virus thymidine kinase/ganciclovir) system, the CD/5-FC (cytosine deaminase/5-fluorocytosine) system, the UPRT/5-FU (uracil phosphoribosyltransferase/5-fluorouracil) system and very recently the IAP/EP (intestinal alkaline phosphatase/etoposide phosphate) system [53–56].

Although gastric cancer cells, in general, have a low sensitivity to chemotherapy and low immunogenicity related to the stimulation of immune competent cells, new methods including biochemical modulation and non-specific immunopotentiation with biological response modifiers (BRMs) (i.e. PSK, OK-432) have permitted us to augment the clinical efficacy of immunochemotherapy in gastric cancer [57]. Apart from the non-specific immunotherapy, several novel cancer vaccines have also been designed recently (i.e. G17DT, MG7, *c-erbB-2*, *EGF*); pilot clinical trials indicate that these cancer vaccines can induce specific antibodies and T-cell responses in gastric cancer patients [58–62].

Conclusion

In conclusion, during the past 15 years, much has been learnt about molecular alterations in gastric cancer, and many of these molecular changes can be used as biomarkers in gastric cancer diagnosis. Based on the understanding of the molecular mechanisms underlying gastric carcinogenesis and metastasis, new therapeutic strategies, targeting molecular defects in gastric cancer, have been designed and many new promising principles have been developed in recent years. There is, however, still a gap between identification of molecular defects and the successful application of a specific therapy in clinical practice. The use of new techniques of functional genomics, including the combined approach of transcriptomics and proteomics, may allow the final molecular characterization of gastric cancers in the individual patient and may form the basis for new therapeutic strategies specific for the molecular changes present in a single subject with gastric cancer in the future.

Acknowledgements

M. Ebert is supported by a grant from the Deutsche Forschungsgemeinschaft (Eb 187/4-1) and a Heisenberg-Stipend (Eb 187/5-1). Additional support is granted from the Land Sachsen-Anhalt.

References

1 Stewart BW, Kleihues P (eds): World Cancer Report. Lyon, IARC Press, 2003.
2 Hamilton SR, Aaltonen LA (eds): Pathology and Genetics. Tumours of the Digestive System. WHO Classification of Tumours. Lyon, IARC Press, 2000, vol 2.
3 Hohenberger P, Gretschel S: Gastric cancer. Lancet 2003;362:305–315.
4 Fuchs CS, Mayer RJ: Gastric carcinoma. N Engl J Med 1995;333:32–41.
5 Blok P, Craanen ME, Offerhaus GJ, et al: Gastric carcinoma: Clinical, pathogenic, and molecular aspects. QJM 1997;90:735–749.
6 Lauren P: The two histological main types of gastric carcinoma: Diffuse and so-called intestinal-type carcinoma. Acta Path Microbiol Scand 1965;64:31–49.
7 Hanahan D, Weinberg RA: The hallmarks of cancer. Cell 2000;100:57–70.
8 Nardone G: Review article: Molecular basis of gastric carcinogenesis. Aliment Pharmacol Ther 2003;17(suppl 2):75–81.
9 El-Omar EM, Carrington M, Chow WH, et al: Interleukin-1 polymorphisms associated with increased risk of gastric cancer. Nature 2000; 404:398–402.
10 Murray GI, Duncan ME, Arbuckle E, et al: Matrix metalloproteinases and their inhibitors in gastric cancer. Gut 1998;43:791–797.
11 Sunami T, Yashiro M, Chung KH: ICAM-1 (intercellular adhesion molecule-1) gene transfection inhibits lymph node metastasis by human gastric cancer cells. Jpn J Cancer Res 2000;91:925–933.
12 Kakeji Y, Maehara Y, Sumiyoshi Y, et al: Angiogenesis as a target for gastric cancer. Surgery 2002;131(suppl):48–54.
13 Gulubova MV: Expression of cell adhesion molecules, their ligands and tumour necrosis factor-α in the liver of patients with metastatic gastrointestinal carcinomas. Histochem J 2002;34:67–77.
14 Cameron EE, Bachman KE, Myohanen S, et al: Synergy of demethylation and histone deacetylase inhibition in the re-expression of genes silenced in cancer. Nat Genet 1999;21: 103–107.
15 Baylin SB, Esteller M, Rountree MR, et al: Aberrant patterns of DNA methylation, chromatin formation and gene expression in cancer. Hum Mol Genet 2001;10:687–692.
16 Esteller M, Herman JG: Cancer as an epigenetic disease: DNA methylation and chromatin alterations in human tumours. J Pathol 2002; 196:1–7.
17 Gaudet F, Hodgson JG, Eden A, et al: Induction of tumors in mice by genomic hypomethylation. Science 2003;300:489–492.
18 Eden A, Gaudet F, Waghmare A, et al: Chromosomal instability and tumors promoted by DNA hypomethylation. Science 2003;300: 455.
19 Feinberg AP: Imprinting of a genomic domain of 11p15 and loss of imprinting in cancer: An introduction. Cancer Res 1999;59(suppl): 1743–1746.
20 Esteller M, Corn PG, Baylin SB, et al: A gene hypermethylation profile of human cancer. Cancer Res 2001;61:3225–3229.
21 Caldas C, Carneiro F, Lynch HT, et al: Familial gastric cancer: Overview and guidelines for management. J Med Genet 1999;36:873–880.
22 Ebert MP, Malfertheiner P: Review article: Pathogenesis of sporadic and familial gastric cancer – Implications for clinical management and cancer prevention. Aliment Pharmacol Ther 2002;16:1059–1066.
23 Yasui W, Yokozaki H, Shimamoto F, et al: Molecular-pathological diagnosis of gastrointestinal tissues and its contribution to cancer histopathology. Pathol Int 1999;49:763–774.
24 Yasui W, Oue N, Kuniyasu H, et al: Molecular diagnosis of gastric cancer: Present and future. Gastric Cancer 2001;4:113–121.
25 Ebert MP, Gunther T, Hoffmann J, et al: Expression of metallothionein II in intestinal metaplasia, dysplasia, and gastric cancer. Cancer Res 2000;60:1995–2001.
26 Kim B, Bang S, Lee S, et al: Expression profiling and subtype-specific expression of stomach cancer. Cancer Res 2003;63:8248–8255.
27 Tay ST, Leong SH, Yu K, et al: A combined comparative genomic hybridization and expression microarray analysis of gastric cancer reveals novel molecular subtypes. Cancer Res 2003;63:3309–3316.
28 Aoyagi K, Tatsuta T, Nishigaki M, et al: A faithful method for PCR-mediated global mRNA amplification and its integration into microarray analysis on laser-captured cells. Biochem Biophys Res Commun 2003;300: 915–920.
29 Takenawa H, Kurosaki M, Enomoto N, et al: Differential gene-expression profiles associated with gastric adenoma. Br J Cancer 2004;90: 216–223.

30 Oue N, Hamai Y, Mitani Y, et al: Gene expression profile of gastric carcinoma: Identification of genes and tags potentially involved in invasion, metastasis, and carcinogenesis by serial analysis of gene expression. Cancer Res 2004; 64:2397–2405.
31 Yasui W, Oue N, Ito R, et al: Search for new biomarkers of gastric cancer through serial analysis of gene expression and its clinical implications. Cancer Sci 2004;95:385–392.
32 Sinha P, Poland J, Schnolzer M, et al: Characterization of the differential protein expression associated with thermoresistance in human gastric carcinoma cell lines. Electrophoresis 2001;22:2990–3000.
33 Tomlinson AJ, Hincapie M, Morris GE, et al: Global proteome analysis of a human gastric carcinoma. Electrophoresis 2002;23:3233–3240.
34 Ryu JW, Kim HJ, Lee YS, et al: The proteomics approach to find biomarkers in gastric cancer. J Korean Med Sci 2003;18:505–509.
35 Chen JP, Lin C, Xu CP, et al: Molecular therapy with recombinant antisense c-myc adenovirus for human gastric carcinoma cells in vitro and in vivo. J Gastroenterol Hepatol 2001;16: 22–28.
36 Song JJ, Lee H, Kim E, et al: Transduction effect of antisense K-ras on malignant phenotypes in gastric cancer cells. Cancer Lett 2000; 157:1–7.
37 Bi F, Fan D, Hui H, et al: Reversion of the malignant phenotype of gastric cancer cell SGC7901 by c-erbB-2-specific hammerhead ribozyme. Cancer Gene Ther 2001;8:835–842.
38 Hirao T, Sawada H, Koyama F, et al: Antisense epidermal growth factor receptor delivered by adenoviral vector blocks tumor growth in human gastric cancer. Cancer Gene Ther 1999;6: 423–427.
39 Ohashi M, Kanai F, Ueno H, et al: Adenovirus mediated p53 tumour suppressor gene therapy for human gastric cancer cells in vitro and in vivo. Gut 1999;44:366–371.
40 Jeong YW, Kim KS, Oh JY, et al: Exogenous wild-type p16INK4A gene induces delayed cell proliferation and promotes chemosensitivity through decreased pRB and increased E2F-1 expressions. Int J Mol Med 2003;12:61–65.
41 Ishii H, Zanesi N, Vecchione A, et al: Regression of upper gastric cancer in mice by FHIT gene delivery. FASEB J 2003;17:1768–1770.
42 Jung M: Inhibitors of histone deacetylase as new anticancer agents. Curr Med Chem 2001; 8:1505–1511.
43 Chiurazzi P, Neri G: Reactivation of silenced genes and transcriptional therapy. Cytogenet Genome Res 2003;100:56–64.
44 Matsuoka T, Yashiro M, Sawada T, et al: Inhibition of invasion and lymph node metastasis of gastrointestinal cancer cells by R-94138, a matrix metalloproteinase inhibitor. Anticancer Res 2000;20:4331–4338.
45 Matsuoka T, Yashiro M, Sawada T, et al: Effect of a matrix metalloproteinase inhibitor on a lymph node metastatic model of gastric cancer cells passaged by orthotopic implantation. J Exp Clin Cancer Res 2001;20:213–218.
46 Mori A, Arii S, Furutani M, et al: Soluble Flt-1 gene therapy for peritoneal metastases using HVJ-cationic liposomes. Gene Ther 2000;7: 1027–1033.
47 Yeo EJ, Chun YS, Cho YS, et al: YC-1: a potential anticancer drug targeting hypoxia-inducible factor 1. Natl Cancer Inst 2003;95: 516–525.
48 Yang SM, Fang DC, Yang JL, et al: Effect of antisense human telomerase RNA on malignant phenotypes of gastric carcinoma. J Gastroenterol Hepatol 2002;17:1144–1152.
49 Wong SC, Yu H, Moochhala SM, et al: Antisense telomerase induced cell growth inhibition, cell cycle arrest and telomerase activity down-regulation in gastric and colon cancer cells. Anticancer Res 2003;23:465–469.
50 Funato T, Kozawa K, Fujimaki S, et al: Increased sensitivity to cisplatin in gastric cancer by antisense inhibition of the her-2/neu (c-erbB-2) gene. Chemotherapy 2001;47:297–303.
51 Kim R, Minami K, Nishimoto N, et al: Enhancement of antitumor effect by intratumoral administration of bax gene in combination with anticancer drugs in gastric cancer. Int J Oncol 2001;18:363–367.
52 Stein U, Lage H, Jordan A, et al: Impact of BCRP/MXR, MRP1 and MDR1/P-Glycoprotein on thermoresistant variants of atypical and classical multidrug resistant cancer cells. Int J Cancer 2002;97:751–760.
53 Terazaki Y, Yano S, Yuge K, et al: An optimal therapeutic expression level is crucial for suicide gene therapy for hepatic metastatic cancer in mice. Hepatology 2003;37:155–163.
54 Ueda K, Iwahashi M, Nakamori M, et al: Carcinoembryonic antigen-specific suicide gene therapy of cytosine deaminase/5-fluorocytosine enhanced by the cre/loxP system in the orthotopic gastric carcinoma model. Cancer Res 2001;61:6158–6162.
55 Inaba M, Sawada H, Sadata A, et al: Circumvention of 5-fluorouracil resistance in human stomach cancer cells by uracil phosphoribosyltransferase gene transduction. Jpn J Cancer Res 1999;90:349–354.
56 Kim KY, Cho YJ, Jeon GA, et al: Membrane-bound alkaline phosphatase gene induces antitumor effect by G2/M arrest in etoposide phosphate-treated cancer cells. Mol Cell Biochem 2003;252:213–221.
57 Toge T: Effectiveness of immunochemotherapy for gastric cancer: A review of the current status. Semin Surg Oncol 1999;17:139–143.
58 Watson SA, Gilliam AD: G17DT – A new weapon in the therapeutic armoury for gastrointestinal malignancy. Expert Opin Biol Ther 2001;1:309–317.
59 Kerr C: Promising results in stomach cancer trial. Lancet Oncol 2002;3:523.
60 Guo CC, Ding J, Pan BR, et al: Development of an oral DNA vaccine against MG7-Ag of gastric cancer using attenuated *Salmonella typhimurium* as carrier. World J Gastroenterol 2003;9:1191–1195.
61 Kono K, Takahashi A, Sugai H, et al: Dendritic cells pulsed with HER-2/neu-derived peptides can induce specific T-cell responses in patients with gastric cancer. Clin Cancer Res 2002;8:3394–3400.
62 Gonzalez G, Crombet T, Catala M, et al: A novel cancer vaccine composed of human-recombinant epidermal growth factor linked to a carrier protein: Report of a pilot clinical trial. Ann Oncol 1998;9:431–435.
63 Chen J, Chen MH, Röcken C, et al: Molecular therapy of gastric cancer. Cancer Therapy 2003;1:323–333.

Original Paper

Digestive Diseases

Dig Dis 2004;22:386–389
DOI: 10.1159/000083603

Helicobacter pylori Seropositivity and Atherosclerosis Risk Factors

Aydın Köksal[a] Yakup Ekmekçi[b] Yasemin Karadeniz[c] Seyfettin Köklü[a] Teoman Apan[d] Murat Yılmaz[b] Mesut Sezikli[b] Birsen Ünal[c] Tolga Demirel[b] Akın Yıldız[b]

[a]Department of Gastroenterology, Yüksek İhtisas Hospital, Ankara and Departments of [b]Internal Medicine, [c]Radiology, and [d]Microbiology, Kırıkkale University Medical School, Kırıkkale, Turkey

Key Words

Atherosclerosis · *Helicobacter pylori* · Infections · Carotid artery · Intima-media thickness

Abstract

Certain viral and bacterial infections may contribute to the initiation and progression of atherosclerosis. The aim of this study is to determine whether *Helicobacter pylori* (HP) seropositivity contributes to conventional atherosclerosis risk factors in the development of an early sign of atherosclerosis: intima-media thickness (IMT) of the carotid artery. Eighty-four patients who had at least two conventional atherosclerosis risk factors and a control group of 50 patients having no risk factors for atherosclerosis were enrolled in the study. None of the patients had ever received HP eradication treatment. HP IgG antibodies were determined by enzyme-linked immunosorbent assay. Carotid artery IMT was measured 1 cm before the carotid bifurcation. Seventy-five percent of the study group was HP seropositive. HP seropositive (n = 64) and seronegative (n = 21) groups were identical in terms of sex distribution, smoking pattern, mean age, hemoglobin, leukocyte, platelet, C-reactive protein, erythrocyte sedimentation rate, glucose, cholesterol, triglyceride, low-density lipoprotein, high-density lipoprotein, systolic blood pressure and diastolic blood pressure levels. There was no significant difference between the mean carotid IMT of HP seropositive (0.8 ± 0.3 mm) and negative (0.8 ± 0.3 mm) patients in the study group. Similar to the study group, there was no statistically significant difference between mean carotid IMT of HP seropositive (0.56 ± 0.19 mm) and negative patients (0.67 ± 0.13 mm) in the control group (p = 0.2). Future studies concerning virulent strains are needed to determine the probable role of HP in atherosclerosis.

Introduction

Helicobacter pylori (HP) is a Gram-negative microaerophilic bacterium which colonizes the gastric mucosa of approximately 50% of all adults. It is a major cause of chronic gastritis and peptic ulcer disease [1].

In recent studies, atherosclerosis is appreciated as an inflammatory disease and there is growing belief that certain viral and bacterial infections such as cytomegalovirus, herpes simplex virus, *Chlamydia pneumoniae* and HP may contribute to the initiation and progression of atherosclerosis [2–4]. Modifications in the serum lipid profile, increased serum levels of cytokines and acute-phase reactants, alterations in fibrinolysis and coagulation pathway, increased endothelial inflammatory activity, direct infection of arterial wall with macrophages and increased serum antibodies to mycobacterial heat-shock protein are the potential mechanisms that are suggested to contribute to the pathogenesis of atherosclerosis [5–12].

KARGER

Fax +41 61 306 12 34
E-Mail karger@karger.ch
www.karger.com

0257–2753/04/0224–0386$21.00/0

Accessible online at:
www.karger.com/ddi

Dr. Aydın Köksal
Feneryolu sok. 5/21 Etlik
TR–06010 Ankara (Turkey)
Tel. +90 312 3212904, Fax +90 312 312 41 20
E-Mail dckoksal@hotmail.com

Among the infections, the causal link to atherosclerosis is strongest for *C. pneumoniae* [13, 14]. The reports concerning the causal relation between HP and atherosclerosis are conflicting and are potentially biased by factors such as socioeconomic status and genetic characteristics of the patients [15].

Intima media of arterial wall thickens during the development of atherosclerosis. There is accumulating evidence that intima-media thickness (IMT) is an early sign of atherosclerosis and can be used as an indicator of atherosclerosis in clinical studies [16]. High-resolution B-mode ultrasonography can be used to visualize the IMT of carotid arteries for this purpose.

The aim of this study is to determine whether HP seropositivity contributes to conventional risk factors in the development of atherosclerosis.

Methods

Patients

The study group consisted of 100 patients. They were randomly chosen among patients attending to our clinic who had at least two of the conventional risk factors for atherosclerosis including hypertension, hyperlipidemia, obesity, diabetes, smoking, female gender, personal history of atherosclerosis and family history of premature atherosclerosis. All of the patients underwent a physical examination. Smoking behavior and family history of atherosclerosis were recorded. Blood pressure was measured twice after 5 min of rest in the sitting position. Hypertension was defined on the basis of the fifth report Joint National Committee on Detection, Evaluation and Treatment of High Blood Pressure, or as current use of antihypertensive drugs. Hyperlipidemia was defined as a serum cholesterol level of ≥ 200 mg/dl, or current use of a hypolipidemic drug. Height and weight of each patient was measured and body mass index (BMI) was calculated (kg/m^2). Obesity was defined as a BMI of ≥ 30 kg/m^2. Diabetes was defined on the basis of American Diabetes Association criteria, or as current use of oral hypoglycemic agents or insulin. Smoking history was obtained as pack/year. With respect to smoking behavior, patients were grouped as smokers and non-smokers. Patients who quitted smoking <10 years ago were classified as smokers. Patients with clinical signs or symptoms of infectious diseases and those taking any medication known to interfere with acute phase reactants were excluded from the study. Patients who received HP eradication treatment during their lifetime were also excluded. Eighty-four patients (24 male, 60 female) fulfilled the criteria and were enrolled in the study.

Taking the variety of risk factors and the limited number of patients in the study group into consideration, a control group (50 patients) having no risk factors for atherosclerosis were incorporated into the study. All of the patients gave informed consent to participate in the study.

Biochemical Measurements

Blood samples were drawn from each patient after an overnight fasting. Lipid analysis including total cholesterol, lipoprotein analysis (low-density lipoprotein, high-density lipoprotein), triglycerides and acute phase reactants such as erythrocyte sedimentation rate (ESR) and C-reactive protein (CRP) were measured immediately using a Boehringer Mannheim Hitachi 717 automatic analyzer. Complete blood count was measured by using a Beckman P Coulter MaxM blood count analyzer.

Serology

Serum was centrifuged at 4,000 *g* for 10 min and frozen at –20°C until analysis. HP-specific serum IgG antibodies were measured by a commercial enzyme-linked immunosorbent assay test kit (EUROIMMUN, Lübeck, Germany). Calibration was performed in relative units per milliliter (RU/ml). According to the manufacturer's instructions titers, >20 RU/ml were considered to be seropositive.

Ultrasound Methods

A linear-array real-time ultrasound equipment with a 7.5-MHz transducer (GE LOGIQ MD 400, Milwaukee, Wisc., USA) was used by two radiologists. Common carotid artery IMT was measured 1 cm before the carotid bifurcation at the far wall of the carotid artery. The distance between the echoes arising from the intima-media interface and media-adventitia interface was taken as the measure of IMT. At least 6 longitudinal and cross-sectional measurements of both common carotid arteries were summarized and a mean carotid IMT was calculated for each patient.

Statistical Analysis

SPSS for Windows 6.0 statistical software was used for the statistics. Results were expressed as mean ± SD. Groups were compared with Mann-Whitney U test and χ^2 test. Correlations between variables were examined by using the Pearson's and Spearman's test. Any p value <0.05 was considered to be significant.

Results

The study group consisted of 84 patients (24 male, 60 female) with a mean age of 48 ± 13 years. Seventy-five percent of the study group (17 male, 46 female) was HP seropositive. Hypertension was present in 60 patients (45 HP seropositive, 15 HP seronegative; p = 0.7); hypercholesterolemia, in 16 (11 HP seropositive, 5 HP seronegative; p = 0.3); obesity, in 52 (40 HP seropositive, 12 HP seronegative; p = 0.8); diabetes, in 4 (3 HP seropositive, 1 HP seronegative, p = 0.6); smoking, in 25 (19 HP seropositive, 6 HP seronegative; p = 0.7); personal history of atherosclerosis, in 12 (9 HP seropositive, 3 HP seronegative; p = 0.8) and family history of premature atherosclerosis, in 18 (13 HP seropositive, 5 HP seronegative; p = 0.5). The results of blood biochemistry, atherosclerosis risk factors and IMT of the carotid artery classified according to HP seropositivity is presented in table 1. There was no significant difference between the sex distribution, smoking pattern, mean age, hemoglobin, leukocyte, platelet, CRP, ESR, glucose, cholesterol, triglyceride, low-density lipoprotein,

Table 1. Blood biochemistry, atherosclerosis risk factors and IMT of the carotid artery of the HP seropositive and negative groups

	HP(+) (n = 63)	HP(–) (n = 21)	p	Total (n = 84)
Age, years	46.7 ± 14.7	45.1 ± 7.1	0.2	46.3 ± 13.1
Sex, M/F	17/46	7/14	0.5	24/60
BMI, kg/m^2	32.8 ± 6.5	31.9 ± 3.2	0.5	32.8 ± 5.9
Smokers, packs/year	5.6 ± 10.2	12.7 ± 22.2	0.4	6.8 ± 13.5
Hemoglobin, g/dl	14.1 ± 1.4	13.8 ± 1.9	0.6	13.9 ± 1.4
Leukocytes, 10^9/l	6.1 ± 1.1	6.2 ± 1.9	0.6	6.2 ± 1.7
Platelets, 10^9/l	225.0 ± 66.2	216.3 ± 73.1	0.6	222.4 ± 66.5
CRP, mg/dl	0.3 ± 0.3	0.5 ± 0.8	0.6	0.3 ± 0.5
ESR, mm/h	25.0 ± 17.4	17.7 ± 12.1	0.1	23.6 ± 16.6
Glucose, mg/dl	100.8 ± 17.4	101.1 ± 11.2	0.3	100.5 ± 16
Cholesterol, mg/dl	231.0 ± 38.4	213.8 ± 43.1	0.1	227.3 ± 39.3
Triglyceride, mg/dl	150.8 ± 70.5	167.6 ± 127.3	0.4	158.5 ± 87.7
HDL, mg/dl,	57.2 ± 11.9	54.4 ± 14.0	0.4	56.4 ± 12.2
LDL, mg/dl	142.2 ± 35.1	124.2 ± 36.8	0.06	137.8 ± 35.5
SBP, mm Hg	155.0 ± 21.0	160.8 ± 27.0	0.3	151.3 ± 26.6
DBP, mm Hg	93.8 ± 11.0	94.4 ± 17.8	0.9	91.9 ± 13.6
IMT, mm	0.8 ± 0.3	0.8 ± 0.3	0.3	0.8 ± 0.3

high-density lipoprotein, systolic blood pressure (SBP) and diastolic blood pressure (DBP) of HP seropositive and negative groups. There was no significant difference between the mean carotid IMT of HP seropositive (0.85 ± 0.38 mm) and negative groups (0.88 ± 0.3 mm), which were statistically indifferent in response to conventional atherosclerosis risk factors. In a univariate and multivariate analysis, none of the risk factors were found to correlate with the mean carotid IMT of the patients.

The control group consisted of 30 HP seropositive (10 male, 20 female, mean age 45 ± 11 years) and 20 HP seronegative (6 male, 14 female, mean age 45 ± 10 years) patients. None of the patients in the control group had any of the risk factors for atherosclerosis. Similar to the study group, there was no statistically significant difference between mean carotid IMT of HP seropositive (0.56 ± 0.19 mm) and negative groups (0.67 ± 0.13 mm) (p = 0.2). The mean carotid intima media of the patients in the study group were significantly thicker than the control group both in the HP seropositive (0.85 ± 0.38 vs. 0.56 ± 0.19 mm; p = 0.02) and HP seronegative patients (0.88 ± 0.3 vs. 0.67 ± 0.13 mm; p = 0.04).

Discussion

Although it is still not widely accepted, infectious diseases appear to be implicated in the occurrence of atherosclerotic disease. Among the microorganisms the causal link between atherosclerosis and infections is strongest for *C. pneumoniae*. Reports concerning the causal relation between HP and atherosclerosis are conflicting. In the USA, peak in the incidence of coronary heart disease from the 1940s through the 1970s coincides with the peak in duodenal ulcer, suggesting a causal association between HP and coronary heart disease [17]. The association between coronary heart disease and HP was first reported by Mendall et al. [18] in 1994. The authors reported an increased prevalence of HP seropositivity in patients with coronary heart disease and concluded that childhood HP infection may be an important risk factor for the development of adult coronary heart disease. Since the first report by Mendall et al., the studies published in the following years have conflicting results. In a meta-analysis of 18 studies, Danesh and Peto [15] found no significant correlation between HP seropositivity and coronary heart disease risk factors. In that meta-analysis, only increased BMI and increased HDL cholesterol had a significant correlation with HP seropositivity but they were not accepted to present a causal relation. Atherosclerosis Risk in Communities Study Investigators observed a significant relation between HP seropositivity and low homocysteine concentrations and high fibrinogen levels. Also they found a significant correlation between HP seropositivity and increased BMI. Despite these associations they concluded that neither conventional risk factors nor mean carotid IMT is associated with HP seropositivity [19]. Blasi et al. [20] reported high seroprevalence of HP in patients with atherosclerosis, but found no evidence for the presence of HP in atherosclerotic plaques of abdominal aortic aneurysm specimens. In 1999, Danesh et al. [21] were the first to demonstrate the presence of HP genome in buffy coat samples and diseased arterial segments in living subjects. Farsak et al. [22] found HP DNA in a considerable number of atherosclerotic plaques by polymerase chain reaction and concluded that HP may have a role in the development of atherosclerosis, especially in countries where infection is prevalent. Ameriso et al. [23] isolated HP from atherosclerotic lesions by a highly sensitive polymerase chain reaction method and concluded that it is especially associated with those with inflammatory features. In a prospective analysis, Mayr et al. [24] reported that HP seropositivity correlated significantly with carotid atherosclerosis when the statistical analysis was restricted to low social status.

In Turkey the seroprevalence of HP is high and around 70–80% [25, 26]. It is thought to increase in lower socioeconomic classes, who have low folate and high homocysteine levels. We conducted our study in a less developed region of our country and our patients were in low socioeconomic class. However, we did not find any significant difference between the conventional atherosclerosis risk factors and carotid IMT of HP seropositive and negative groups. Therefore we suggest that seropositivity does not necessarily indicate persistent exposure of the vascular system to infection. We think that CagA-positive HP strains may be more strongly associated with coronary heart disease than CagA-negative strains and the virulence of the microorganism may determine the insult.

In summary, we did not find any causal relation between HP seropositivity and atherosclerosis risk factors, including carotid IMT in our study population with low socioeconomic class. However, important limitations of our study were the small number of patients and the lack of information about the virulence of the microorganisms. We believe that future studies concerning virulent HP strains in a large group of patients are needed to determine the probable role of HP in atherosclerosis.

References

1 Megraud F: Epidemiology of *Helicobacter pylori* infection. Gastroenterol Clin North Am 1993;22:73–88.
2 Danesh J, Collins R, Peto R: Chronic infections and coronary heart disease: Is there a link? Lancet 1997;350:430–436.
3 Saikku P, Leinonen M, Mattila K, et al: Serological evidence of an association of a novel *Chlamydia*, TWAR, with chronic coronary heart disease and acute myocardial infarction. Lancet 1988;ii:983–986.
4 Patel P, Mendall MA, Carrington D, et al: Association of *Helicobacter pylori* and *Chlamydia pneumoniae* infections with coronary heart disease and cardiovascular risk factors. BMJ 1995;311:711–714.
5 Laurila A, Bloigu A, Näyhä S, et al: Chronic *Chlamydia pneumoniae* infection is associated with a serum lipid profile known to be a risk factor for atherosclerosis. Arterioscler Thromb Vasc Biol 1997;17:2910–2913.
6 Laurila A, Bloigu A, Näyhä S, et al: Association of *Helicobacter pylori* infection with elevated serum lipids. Atherosclerosis 1999;142:207–210.
7 Mendall MA, Patel P, Asante M, et al: Relation of serum cytokine concentrations to cardiovascular risk factors and coronary heart disease. Heart 1997;78:273–277.
8 Miragliotta G, Del Prete R, Mosca A: *Helicobacter pylori* infection and coronary heart disease. Lancet 1994;344:751.
9 Kaukoranta-Tolvanen SSE, Ronni T, Leinonen M, et al: Expression of adhesion molecules on endothelial cells stimulated by *Chlamydia pneumoniae*. Microb Pathog 1996;21:407–411.
10 Molestina RE, Miller RD, Ramirez JA, et al: Infection of human endothelial cells with *Chlamydia pneumoniae* stimulates transendothelial migration of neutrophils and monocytes. Infect Immun 1999;67:1323–1330.
11 Xu Q, Willeit J, Marosi M, et al: Association of serum antibodies to heat-shock protein 65 with carotid atherosclerosis. Lancet 1993;341:255–259.
12 Kol A, Bourcier T, Litchman AH, et al: Chlamydial and human heat-shock protein 60s activate human vascular endothelium, smooth muscle cells and macrophages. J Clin Invest 1999;103:571–577.
13 Cook PJ, Honeybourne D, Lip GY, et al: *Chlamydia pneumoniae* antibody titers are significantly associated with acute stroke and transient cerebral ischemia: The West Birmingham Stroke Project. Stroke 1998;29:404–410.
14 Grayston JT, Kuo CC, Coulson AS, et al: *Chlamydia pneumoniae* (TWAR) in atherosclerosis of carotid artery. Circulation 1995;92:3397–3400.
15 Danesh J, Peto R: Risk factors for coronary heart disease and infection with *Helicobacter pylori*: Meta-analysis of 18 studies. BMJ 1998;316:1130–1132.
16 Heiss G, Sharett AR, Barnes R, et al: Carotid atherosclerosis measured by B-mode ultrasound in populations: Associations with cardiovascular risk factors in the ARIC study. Am J Epidemiol 1991;134:250–256.
17 Stehbens WE: The hypothetical epidemic of coronary heart disease and atherosclerosis. Med Hypotheses 1995;45:449–454.
18 Mendall MA, Goggin PM, Molineaux N, et al: Relation of *Helicobacter pylori* infection and coronary heart disease. Br Heart J 1994;71:437–439.
19 Folsom AR, Nieto FJ, Sorlie P, et al: *Helicobacter pylori* seropositivity and coronary heart disease incidence: Atherosclerosis Risk in Communities (ARIC) Study Investigators. Circulation 1998;98:845–850.
20 Blasi F, Ranzi ML, Erba M, et al: No evidence for the presence of *Helicobacter pylori* in atherosclerotic plaques in abdominal aortic aneurysm specimens. Atherosclerosis 1996;126:339–340.
21 Danesh J, Koreth J, Youngman L, et al: Is *Helicobacter pylori* a factor in coronary atherosclerosis? J Clin Microbiol 1999;37:1651.
22 Farsak B, Yıldırır A, Akyön Y, et al: Detection of *Chlamydia pneumoniae* and *Helicobacter pylori* DNA in human atherosclerotic plaques by PCR. J Clin Microbiol 2000;38:4408–4411.
23 Ameriso SF, Fridman EA, Leiguarda RC, et al: Detection of *Helicobacter pylori* in human carotid atherosclerotic plaques. Stroke 2001;32:385–391.
24 Mayr M, Kiechl S, Willeit J, et al: Associations of antibodies to *Chlamydia pneumoniae*, *Helicobacter pylori* and cytomegalovirus with immune reactions to heat-shock protein 60 and carotid or femoral atherosclerosis. Circulation 2000;102:833–839.
25 Özden A, Dumlu Ş, Dönderici Ö: *Helicobacter pylori* infeksiyonunun ülkemizde seroepidemiyolojisi. Gastroenteroloji 1992;3:664–668.
26 Us D, Hasçelik H: Seroprevalence of *Helicobacter pylori* infection in an asymptomatic Turkish population. Turk J Pediatr 1996;38:329–334.

Original Paper

Digestive Diseases

Dig Dis 2004;22:390–395
DOI: 10.1159/000083604

Down-Regulation of Secretory Leukocyte Protease Inhibitor Expression in Gastric Mucosa Is a General Phenomenon in *Helicobacter pylori*-Related Gastroduodenal Diseases

Thomas Wex[a] Aleksandra Sokic-Milutinovic[a, b] Vera Todorovic[c]
Milos Bjelovic[d] Tomica Milosavljevic[b] Predrag Pesko[d] Peter Malfertheiner[a]

[a]Clinic for Gastroenterology, Hepatology and Infectious Diseases, Otto von Guericke University, Magdeburg, Germany; [b]Clinic for Gastroenterology and Hepatology, Institute for Digestive Diseases, Clinical Center of Serbia; [c]Department of Immunohistochemistry and Electron Microscopy, Institute for Medical Research, and [d]Department of Esophageal and Gastric Surgery, The First University Surgical Hospital, Institute for Digestive Diseases, Clinical Center of Serbia, Belgrade, Serbia and Montenegro

Key Words
Secretory leukocyte protease inhibitor · Gastritis · Gastroduodenal disease · Gastric cancer · Duodenal ulcer

Abstract
Background: Secretory leukocyte protease inhibitor (SLPI) represents a multifunctional protein of the gastric mucosa exerting anti-microbial and anti-inflammatory effects. Recently, a local down-regulation of antral SLPI expression in *Helicobacter pylori* (*Hp*)-infected healthy volunteers was demonstrated. ***Aim:*** To analyze mucosal SLPI expression in patients with various gastroduodenal disorders. ***Methods:*** The prospective study included 90 patients with following gastroduodenal disorders diagnosed: gastric cancer (GC, n = 22), duodenal ulcer (DU, n = 17), *Hp*-positive dyspeptic patients (NUD, n = 31) and *Hp*-negative NUD (n = 20). During esophagogastroduodenoscopy, biopsies were taken each from antrum, corpus and tumor. SLPI expression was analyzed by quantitative RT-PCR and ELISA. ***Results:*** Antral SLPI levels were reduced in all *Hp*-infected patients (NUD, DU, GC) by about 75% (1,494–1,826 pg/50 μg protein) compared to *Hp*-negative NUD (6,563 pg/50 μg protein, $p < 0.001$, ANOVA). Tumor tissue had twofold higher SLPI levels than surrounding tumor-free gastric mucosa (3,900 vs. 1,826 pg/50 μg protein, $p = 0.013$), but revealed reduced SLPI levels compared to *Hp*-negative NUD patients ($p = 0.067$). No differences were found between SLPI expression of intestinal and diffuse GC. SLPI transcript levels were unchanged throughout all groups and locations implying that transcriptional regulation of SLPI is not involved. ***Conclusion:*** Local down-regulation of SLPI in antral mucosa is a general phenomenon of *Hp*-related diseases.

Introduction

Helicobacter pylori (Hp) infection has been linked to the development of variety of gastroduodenal diseases, including gastric and duodenal ulcers, gastric adenocarcinoma and mucosa-associated lymphatic tissue lymphoma [1–3]. The initial interaction between the bacterium

KARGER
Fax +41 61 306 12 34
E-Mail karger@karger.ch
www.karger.com

© 2004 S. Karger AG, Basel
0257–2753/04/0224–0390$21.00/0

Accessible online at:
www.karger.com/ddi

Thomas Wex, PhD
Department of Gastroenterology, Hepatology and Infectious Diseases
Otto von Guericke University, Magdeburg, Leipziger Strasse 44
DE–39120 Magdeburg (Germany), Tel. +49 391 6713106
Fax +49 391 6713105, E-Mail thomas.wex@medizin.uni-magdeburg.de

and gastric epithelial surface leads to various molecular changes in epithelial cells including cytoskeletal rearrangement, intracellular phosphorylation and the induction of pro-inflammatory cytokines, such as IL-8, IL-1β and TNF-α [4–7]. In context with chronic-active gastritis, caused by *Hp*, an activation of pro-inflammatory pathways occurs that lead subsequently to the induction of cytokines, chemokines, reactive oxygen species and proteases contributing to cellular damage seen in gastroduodenal diseases [4, 8–11]. Recently, we identified the secretory leukocyte protease inhibitor (SLPI) as a potential target gene in the course of *Hp* infection [12]. Healthy volunteers, who were *Hp*-infected, revealed a dramatic reduction of mucosal SLPI levels in their antrum (–67%) compared to *Hp*-negative subjects. The fact that after eradication therapy, the initial reduced SLPI levels reversed to normal ranges implied a pathophysiological role of *Hp* for the down-regulation of antral SLPI levels [12].

SLPI represents a serine-protease inhibitor that possesses inhibitory activity toward several serine proteases [13] and has bactericidal and anti-fungal activities [14]. Using the SLPI knock-out model, it was shown that SLPI promotes wound healing by regulating the equilibrium between proepithelin and epithelin, an epithelial growth factor [15, 16]. Furthermore, SLPI is considered as anti-inflammatory molecule that acts as negative regulator on the NF-κB signal pathway [17–19]. There are several studies showing an up-regulation of SLPI during inflammation in lung, intestinal and systemic diseases [20–23]. In contrast, *Hp* infection and associated gastritis resulted in a local loss of SLPI in the antrum that was inversely associated with activity and chronicity of inflammation [12].

In order to study whether this SLPI down-regulation represents a general phenomenon in *Hp*-associated diseases, we investigated mucosal SLPI levels in the gastric mucosa of patients suffering from duodenal ulcer, non-ulcer dyspepsia and gastric cancer (GC).

Methods

Study Population

The outpatient-based prospective study was conducted at the Clinic for Gastroenterology and Hepatology (Clinical Center of Serbia, University of Belgrade). All patients gave informed consent for participation in this study and the study protocol was approved by the local Ethics Committee.

Ninety patients with either dyspeptic symptoms (*Hp*-positive: n = 48 and *Hp*-negative: n = 20) or GC (n = 22) were included into the study. All patients with GC were *Hp*-positive. Demographic factors including age, sex and smoking are presented in table 1.

Table 1. Demographic factors of the study group

	Hp^- NUD (n = 20)	Hp^+ NUD (n = 31)	Hp^+ DU (n = 17)	GC[1] (n = 22)
Age, years	45 ± 16	53 ± 12	45 ± 14	64 ± 11
Sex, males	8	13	8	14
Smokers	9	11	10	5

[1] The GC group consisted of patients with both intestinal (n = 11) and diffuse type (n = 11) gastric adenocarcinoma.

Dyspepsia was defined in accordance to the Rome II classification of functional dyspepsia. According to this definition, dyspepsia refers to pain or discomfort centered in the upper abdomen, while pain in the right or left hypochondrium is not considered to be representative of dyspepsia [24]. Duration of symptoms was not specified by Rome II criteria, but it was advised that in research studies investigators might specify the duration of symptoms in order to improve the homogeneity of the patients studied. Therefore, we modified the definition as proposed by Knill-Jones [25] stating that symptoms should persist for at least 4 weeks. Exclusion criteria were in concordance with the recommendations from European Helicobacter Study Group [26]. In brief, age (<20 and >80 years), pregnancy, gastric outlet obstruction, administration of antibiotics, H_2 antagonists, omeprazole- and/or bismuth-containing preparations within 30 days prior to endoscopy; the use of non-steroid anti-inflammatory drugs and the presence of associated diseases (hepatic, renal, cardiac, respiratory, suspected or confirmed malignant disease) eliminated patients from the study.

Hp infection was diagnosed if simultaneous positivity existed for two of the three following tests: rapid urease test, histology and serology. Patients were divided into 4 groups according to the endoscopic findings. In duodenal ulcer (DU) group endoscopy revealed presence of active ulcer without any sign of cancer, and all patients were *Hp*-positive. Non-ulcer dyspepsia group (NUD) consisted of patients in which endoscopy did not show any signs of ulcer or cancer, and the upper gastrointestinal symptoms had persisted for at least a month. The NUD group was further divided into *Hp*-negative and *Hp*-positive subgroup. The GC group consisted of *Hp*-positive patients with tumor localized in the distal parts of the stomach and histology revealed gastric adenocarcinoma.

Esophagogastroduodenoscopy and Hp *Status*

Each patient underwent esophagogastroduodenoscopy and testing for the presence of *Hp* by rapid urease test and histology. Biopsies from antral and corpus mucosa were stained using hematoxylin-eosin and modified Giemsa staining procedures. Biopsy specimens were assessed separately according to the Sydney System [27] by an experienced pathologist who was blinded to the clinical data. Inflammation, activity of gastritis, presence of atrophy and intestinal metaplasia as well as the number of bacteria were assessed on a four-grade scale as described previously [27]. In addition to routine biopsies, two additional biopsies were taken each from antrum, corpus and gastric carcinoma if suspected.

Blood samples were taken from the patients after endoscopic examination and sera were separated by centrifugation and stored at –20°C until analyzed. The concentration of anti-*Hp* IgG antibodies was analyzed using the Pyloriset EIA-G III™ (Orion Diagnostica, Finland) according to the manufacturer's instructions and as described [28].

Extraction of Total Protein from Gastric Biopsies and ELISA

Gastric biopsies were snap-frozen in liquid nitrogen, and homogenized in 1 ml ice-cold lysis buffer containing 0.5% SDS, 0.5% Triton X-100, 0.5% Tween 20, 10% (v/w) glycerol, 62.5 m*M* Tris (pH 6.8). The lysate was centrifuged in a microcentrifuge (10,000 *g*, 4°C) for 15 min. The supernatant was transferred to a new tube and total protein content was analyzed using the Advanced™ protein assay (Tebu, Offenbach, Germany). Finally, samples were stored at –80°C in aliquots until usage. The SLPI concentration was investigated using the SLPI kit (R&D Systems, Minneapolis, Minn., USA).

RNA Extraction and Quantitative RT-PCR

Gastric biopsies were snap-frozen in liquid nitrogen and subsequently stored in 0.5 ml TRIzol Reagent™ (Life Technologies, USA) at –80°C until usage. Total RNA was extracted using a two-step protocol as described previously [29]. Briefly, after homogenization, the total RNA fraction was isolated using the TRIzol protocol according to the manufacturer's instructions. The RNA pellet was resolved in 100 µl RNase-free water and subsequently purified using the RNeasy kit™ (Qiagen, Hilden, Germany) following the protocol described by the manufacturer. RNA concentration was quantified by UV spectroscopy and its integrity was verified by gel electrophoresis. The cDNA synthesis and quantitative RT-PCR were performed as described previously [12, 29].

Statistical Analysis

All data were entered into a database and analyzed using the Microcal Origin™ 5.0 program package (Northhampton, Mass., USA). p values of <0.05 were regarded as significant. Differences between groups were analyzed by one-way analysis of variance (ANOVA).

Results

As shown recently in healthy volunteers, significantly reduced antral SLPI levels were detected in *Hp*-infected patients by ELISA. Overall, the antral SLPI levels were reduced between 40 and 78% (fig. 1A). Patients with NUD, DU and GC had significantly lower antral SLPI levels (1,494–1,826 pg/50 µg protein) than *Hp*-negative dyspeptic patients (6,563 pg/50 µg protein, $p < 0.001$). Interestingly, the SLPI expression of endoscopically normal tumor-free antral mucosa, obtained from tumor patients, showed a significant higher SLPI expression than the tumor itself (3,900 vs. 1,826 pg/50 µg protein, $p = 0.013$). Compared to *Hp*-negative dyspeptic patients, the SLPI level of the tumor-free antral mucosa was in tendency lower without reaching the significance level (fig. 1A). The down-regulation of SLPI was locally confined to the antrum regardless of the associated disease (fig. 1A, 2A).

The analysis of the antral SLPI transcript levels did not reveal significant differences among all groups (fig. 1B). The apparent slight increase of SLPI transcript levels in the tumor tissue is presumably caused by two facts. First, due to limited material, only 13 out of 22 tumor samples could be analyzed by quantitative RT-PCR. Second, 3 out of 13 samples revealed extremely high SLPI transcript levels exceeding other samples by a factor of >100.

The comparison of SLPI level with respect to location confirmed the previous finding that mucosal SLPI levels of *Hp*-negative persons are higher in antrum than corpus (fig. 1A, 2A). In contrast to antral mucosa, corresponding biopsies from corpus mucosa revealed similar SLPI levels among all patient groups. Moreover, the SLPI expression of the tumor was not different from that of the adjacent tumor-free corpus mucosa (fig. 2A). All together, no difference of SLPI expression in corpus was found with respect to the presence of *Hp* infection or GC.

The analysis of patients with GC concerning the tumor type did not reveal differences between gastric carcinoma of the intestinal or diffuse type. Both groups exhibited the same pattern of SLPI expression, the adjacent antral mucosa had in tendency higher SLPI levels than the tumor itself (fig. 2B). However, due to the limited number of patients, both observations were not significant (fig. 2B).

Discussion

Recently, we showed that in contrast to other inflammatory processes located in other types of tissues [20, 21], the inflammation of gastric mucosa was accompanied by a significant decrease of mucosal SLPI levels. It is notable that the initial study was performed in young and healthy volunteers who had *Hp* infection without any complications or associated diseases [12]. The aim of this study was to investigate this phenomenon in a routine clinical setting and to verify the general importance of this finding with respect to *Hp*-associated diseases.

Overall, the study could confirm the previous finding obtained from healthy volunteers. The *Hp* infection was found to be associated with a significant reduction of mucosal SLPI in the antrum, whereas SLPI expression of corpus mucosa was not affected. The reduction rate of SLPI was about 70–78% and very similar among all dis-

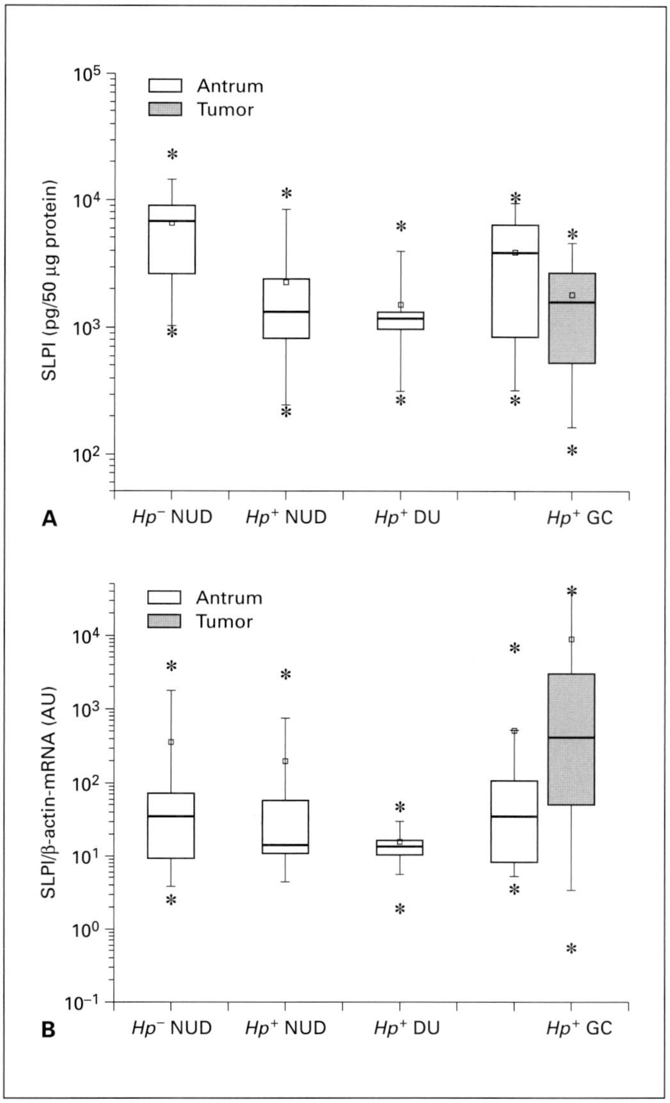

Fig. 1. Comparison of SLPI gene expression in antral mucosa of patients with different gastroduodenal diseases. **A**, **B** Data from ELISA and quantitative RT-PCR, respectively. Data are shown as box plot for each group. Boxes represent the 25th, 50th and 75th percentile values (horizontal lines of the box) and means (squares). The Y-axes illustrate the SLPI content in pg/50 µg protein (**A**) and the ratio of SLPI/β-actin mRNA expressed as arbitrary units (AU) (**B**). The X-axes show the different groups of patients as indicated. The open boxes identify antrum samples, whereas gray boxes represent samples from gastric tumors. The asterisks represent the 1 and 99% percentiles of data sets.

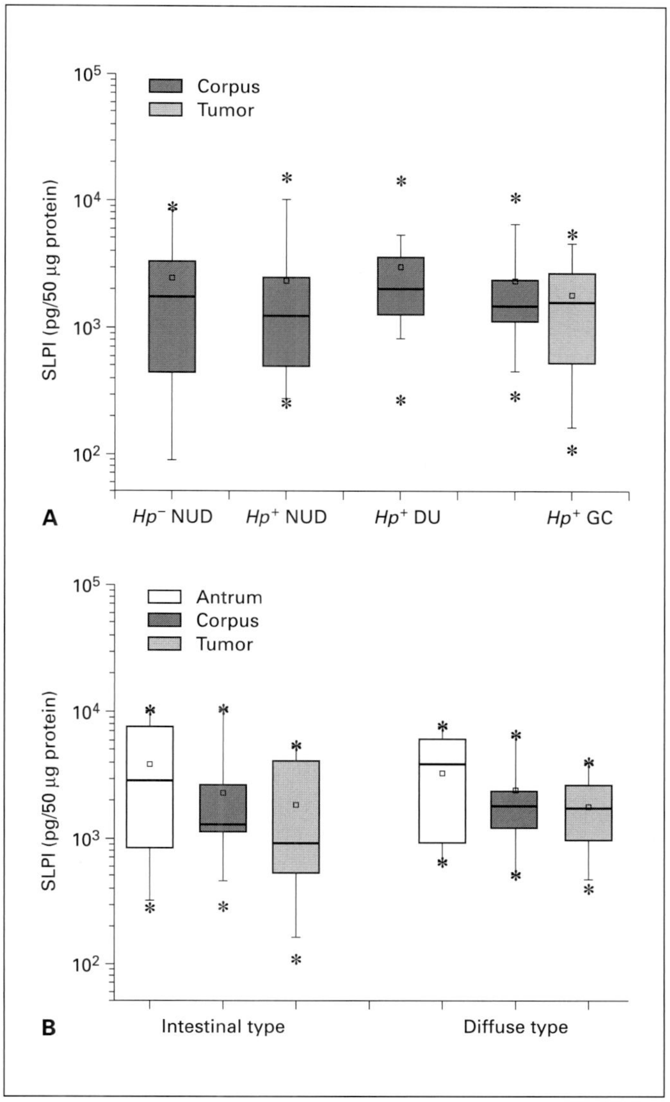

Fig. 2. Comparison of SLPI protein levels in corpus mucosa of patients with different gastroduodenal diseases and GC. Data are shown as box plot as described in figure 1. The Y-axes illustrate the SLPI content in pg/50 µg protein. The X-axes identify the different groups of patients as indicated. **A** Data for corpus mucosa. The dark gray boxes represent corpus mucosa, the light gray box represents GC and is identical to figure 1. **B** Comparison of mucosal SLPI levels between the two types of GC. The locations investigated are identified in the legend within the graph.

eases analyzed. The analysis of SLPI expression in GC revealed two findings. First, GC tissue has lower SLPI expression than the normal surrounding tissue. This is in contrast to other tumors that were shown to overexpress SLPI [30–32]. Furthermore, it was shown in a mouse model that SLPI can also promote tumorigenic and metastatic potency of tumor cells [33].

Second, the down-regulation of SLPI was restricted to the antrum only, and endoscopically normal tumor-free gastric mucosa adjacent to the tumor had higher SLPI levels than the tumor itself. The fact that the corpus mucosa, which in most cases undergoes atrophic changes during gastric carcinogenesis, had no changes in SLPI expression supports the hypothesis that there is a direct link between antral SLPI expression and the presence of *Hp*. The observation that in GC patients the antral SLPI levels were slightly higher compared to the levels found in the tumor tissue of the same patient is another hint for this hypothesis. It is well known that during the progression towards gastric neoplasia, the density of the bacterium is changing. In most patients, the colonization of *Hp* in the antrum reaches a peak in the chronic gastritis. During atrophic changes, the milieu of the stomach is changing towards higher pH, which subsequently might enable other bacteria to colonize in the stomach and to suppress the growth of *Hp*. Based on our hypothesis, the disappearance of *Hp* could lead to a recovery of mucosal SLPI expression as demonstrated by *Hp* eradication therapy in healthy volunteers [12]. The analysis of the GC patients strongly supports this model. Most of our cancer patients exhibited signs of atrophy in their endoscopically normal tumor-free antral mucosa, which in tendency had higher SLPI levels than the tumor itself. Since atrophic areas have less inflammation than normal epithelium, the partially normalized SLPI levels in the tumor-free antrum of these patients might be attributed to the reduced number of *Hp*. The fact that the tumor had similar low levels of SLPI as chronically inflamed gastric mucosa (*Hp*-positive NUD or DU patients) is a novel finding and implies that the tumor might originate from epithelial cells directly involved in the interaction with *Hp*. Since *Hp* has been recognized to be an important co-factor in the etiology of non-cardia GC of both the diffuse and intestinal type [34, 35], our findings concerning the similar SLPI expression between both groups are in line with the current concept of the role of *Hp* in gastric carcinogenesis.

The functional consequences of the decreased SLPI expression on gastric mucosa on the molecular level are not well understood. Taking the pleiotropic effects of this protein into consideration, SLPI might be involved in different processes. On the one hand, the decreased antral SLPI levels might affect the proteolytic capacity of serine proteases like cathepsin G or elastase in the mucosal microenvironment. For instance, Zhu et al. [16] reported that in the absence of SLPI, proepithelin (PEPI), an epithelial growth factor, is increasingly converted to epithelin (EPI). PEPI and EPI exert opposing activities. EPI inhibits the growth of epithelial cells but induce them to secrete the neutrophil attractant IL-8, while PEPI blocks neutrophil activation by tumor necrosis factor, preventing release of oxidants and proteases. The authors concluded that the equilibrium between SLPI and elastase determines the ratio of PEPI and EPI, which affects repair processes of gastric mucosa and represents a link between innate immunity and wound healing. On the other hand, SLPI seems to be involved in the regulation of the NF-κB-signaling pathway in lung tissue [17, 18] that could represent a further link between SLPI expression and the inflammation of the gastric mucosa as seen in gastritis. Last but not least, SLPI might also exert an anti-microbial effect against *Hp* since the molecule was shown to inhibit the growth of Gram-positive and -negative bacteria at micromolar concentrations [36, 37].

Taken together, this study provides evidence that the significant decrease of SLPI in antral mucosa of *Hp*-infected patients is a general phenomenon in *Hp*-mediated diseases. The functional role of SLPI, in particular for the antrum, and its potential involvement in gastric tumorigenesis need further investigations.

Acknowledgements

We thank Ljiljana Popovic, Milanka Perak and Branka Jovic for their assistance in endoscopy unit as well as Ursula Stolz and Simone Philipsen (Otto von Guericke University) for their experimental work. This study was supported by Serbian Ministry for Science, Technology and Development (Project No. 1752), an EAGE grant to A. Sokic-Milutinovic and by a grant of the European Helicobacter Study Group to P. Malfertheiner.

References

1 Blaser MJ: *Helicobacter pylori* and the pathogenesis of gastroduodenal inflammation J Infect Dis 1990;161:626–633.
2 Sepulveda AR, Coelho LG: *Helicobacter pylori* and gastric malignancies. Helicobacter 2002; 7(suppl 1):37–42.
3 Ebert MP, Yu J, Sung JJ, Malfertheiner P: Molecular alterations in gastric cancer –The role of *Helicobacter pylori*. Eur J Gastroenterol Hepatol 2000;12:795–798.
4 Naumann M, Crabtree JE: *Helicobacter pylori*-induced epithelial cell signaling in gastric carcinogenesis. Trends Microbiol 2004;12:29–36.
5 Segal ED, Falkow S, Tompkins LS: *Helicobacter pylori* attachment to gastric cells induces cytoskeletal rearrangements and tyrosine phosphorylation of host cell proteins. Proc Natl Acad Sci USA 1996;93:1259–1264.
6 Maeda S, Yoshida H, Ogura K, Mitsuno Y, Hirata Y, Yamaji Y, Akanuma M, Shiratori Y, Omata M: *H. pylori* activates NF-κB through a signaling pathway involving IκB kinases, NF-κB-inducing kinase, TRAF2, and TRAF6 in gastric cancer cells. Gastroenterology 2000; 119:97–108.
7 Higashi H, Tsutsumi R, Muto S, Sugiyama T, Azuma T, Asaka M, Hatakeyama M: SHP-2 tyrosine phosphatase as an intracellular target of *Helicobacter pylori* CagA protein. Science 2002;295:683–686.
8 Lindholm C, Quiding-Jarbrink M, Lonroth H, Svennerholm AM: Induction of chemokine and cytokine responses by *Helicobacter pylori* in human stomach explants. Scand J Gastroenterol 2001;36:1022–1029.
9 Smoot DT, Elliott TB, Verspaget HW, Jones D, Allen CR, Vernon KG, Bremner T, Kidd LC, Kim KS, Groupman JD, Ashktorab H: Influence of *Helicobacter pylori* on reactive oxygen-induced gastric epithelial cell injury. Carcinogenesis 2000;21:2091–2095.
10 Matsuo T, Ikura Y, Ohsawa M, Ogami M, Kayo S, Yoshimi N, Hai E, Naruko T, Ohishi M, Higuchi K, Arakawa T, Ueda M: Mast cell chymase expression in *Helicobacter pylori*-associated gastritis. Histopathology 2003;43: 538–549.
11 Danese S, Papa A, Gasbarrini A, Ricci R, Maggiano N: *Helicobacter pylori* eradication downregulates matrix metalloproteinase-9 expression in chronic gastritis and gastric ulcer. Gastroenterology 2004;126:369–371.
12 Wex T, Treiber G, Nilius M, Vieth M, Roessner A, Malfertheiner P: *Helicobacter pylori*-mediated gastritis induces local downregulation of secretory leukocyte protease inhibitor in the antrum. Infect Immun 2004;72:2383–2385.
13 Potempa J, Korzus E, Travis J: The serpin superfamily of proteinase inhibitors: Structure, function and regulation. J Biol Chem 1994; 269:15957–15960.
14 Hiemstra PS, Maassen RJ, Stolk J, Heinzel-Wieland R, Steffens GJ, Dijkman JH: Antibacterial activity of antileukoprotease. Infect Immun 1996;64:4520–4524.
15 Ashcroft GS, Lei K, Jin W, Longenecker G, Kulkarni AB, Greenwell-Wild T, Hale-Donze H, McGrady G, Song XY, Wahl SM: Secretory leukocyte protease inhibitor mediates non-redundant functions necessary for normal wound healing. Nat Med 2000;6:1147–1153.
16 Zhu J, Nathan C, Jin W, Sim D, Ashcroft GS, Wahl SM, Lacomis L, Erdjument-Bromage H, Tempst P, Wright CD, Ding A: Conversion of proepithelin to epithelins: Roles of SLPI and elastase in host defense and wound repair. Cell 2002;111:867–878.
17 Taggart CC, Greene CM, McElvaney NG, O'Neill S: Secretory leucoprotease inhibitor prevents LPS-induced IκBα degradation without affecting phosphorylation or ubiquitination. J Biol Chem 2002;277:33648–33653.
18 Lentsch AB, Jordan JA, Czermak BJ, Diehl KM, Younkin EM, Sarma V, Ward PA: Inhibition of NF-κB activation and augmentation of IκBβ by secretory leukocyte protease inhibitor during lung inflammation. Am J Pathol 1999; 154:239–247.
19 Henriksen PA, Hitt M, Xing Z, Wang J, Haslett C, Riemersma RA, Webb DJ, Kotelevtsev YV, Sallenave JM: Adenoviral gene delivery of elafin and secretory leukocyte protease inhibitor attenuates NF-κB-dependent inflammatory responses of human endothelial cells and macrophages to atherogenic stimuli. J Immunol 2004;172:4535–4544.
20 Song X, Zeng L, Jin W, Thompson J, Mizel DE, Lei K, Billinghurst RC, Poole AR, Wahl SM: Secretory leukocyte protease inhibitor suppresses the inflammation and joint damage of bacterial cell wall-induced arthritis. J Exp Med 1999;190:535–542.
21 Sallenave JM: The role of secretory leukocyte proteinase inhibitor and elafin (elastase-specific inhibitor/skin-derived antileukoprotease) as alarm antiproteinases in inflammatory lung disease. Respir Res 2000;1:87–92.
22 Duits LA, Tjabringa GS, Aarts NJ, van't Wout JW, Hiemstra PS, Nibbering PH, van Dissel JT: Plasma secretory leukocyte protease inhibitor in febrile patients. Clin Microbiol Infect 2003;9:605–613.
23 Grobmyer SR, Barie PS, Nathan CF, Fuortes M, Lin E, Lowry SF, Wright CD, Weyant MJ, Hydo L, Reeves F, Shiloh MU, Ding A: Secretory leukocyte protease inhibitor, an inhibitor of neutrophil activation, is elevated in serum in human sepsis and experimental endotoxemia. Crit Care Med 2000;28:1276–1282.
24 Talley NJ, Stanghellini V, Heading RC, Koch KL, Malagelada JR, Tytgat GNJ: Functional gastroduodenal disorders. Gut 1999;45:37–42.
25 Knill-Jones RP: A formal approach to symptoms in dyspepsia. Clin Gastroenterol 1985; 14:517–529.
26 Malfertheiner P, Megraud F, O'Morain CO, Bell D, Blanchi Porro G, Deltenre M, et al: Current European concepts in the management of *Helicobacter pylori* infection – The Maastricht consensus report. Eur J Gastroenterol Hepatol 1999;9:91–92.
27 Dixon MF, Genta RM, Yardley JH, Correa P: Classification and grading of gastritis. The updated Sydney System. International Workshop on the Histopathology of Gastritis, Houston 1994. Am J Surg Pathol 1996;20:1161–1181.
28 Sokic-Milutinovic A, Wex T, Todorovic V, Milosavljevic T, Malfertheiner P: Anti-CagA and anti-VacA antibodies in *Helicobacter pylori*-infected patients with and without peptic ulcer disease in Serbia and Montenegro. Scand J Gastroenterol 2004;39:222–226.
29 Wex T, Treiber G, Lendeckel U, Malfertheiner P: A two-step method for the extraction of high-quality RNA from endoscopic biopsies. Clin Chem Lab Med 2003;41:1033–1037.
30 Yoshida N, Egami H, Yamashita J, Takai E, Tamori Y, Fujino N, Kitaoka M, Schalkwijk J, Ogawa M: Immunohistochemical expression of SKALP/elafin in squamous cell carcinoma of human lung. Oncol Rep 2002;9:495–501.
31 Shigemasa K, Tanimoto H, Underwood LJ, Parmley TH, Arihiro K, Ohama K, O'Brien TJ: Expression of the protease inhibitor antileukoprotease and the serine protease stratum corneum chymotryptic enzyme is coordinated in ovarian tumors. Int J Gynecol Cancer 2001; 11:454–461.
32 Morita M, Arakawa H, Nishimura S: Identification and cloning of a novel isoform of mouse secretory leukocyte protease inhibitor, mSLPI-β, overexpressed in murine leukemias and a highly liver metastatic tumor, IMC-HA1 cells. Adv Enzyme Regul 1999;39:341–355.
33 Devoogdt N, Hassanzadeh Ghassabeh G, Zhang J, Brys L, De Baetselier P, Revets H: Secretory leukocyte protease inhibitor promotes the tumorigenic and metastatic potential of cancer cells. Proc Natl Acad Sci USA 2003;100:5778–5782.
34 Nardone G: Review article: Molecular basis of gastric carcinogenesis. Aliment Pharmacol Ther 2003;17(suppl 2):75–81.
35 Correa P, Piazuelo MB, Camargo MC: The future of gastric cancer prevention. Gastric Cancer 2004;7:9–16.
36 Hiemstra PS, Fernie-King BA, McMichael J, Lachmann PJ, Sallenave JM: Antimicrobial peptides: Mediators of innate immunity as templates for the development of novel anti-infective and immune therapeutics. Curr Pharm Des 2004;10:2891–2905.
37 Hiemstra PS, Maassen RJ, Stolk J, Heinzel-Wieland R, Steffens GJ, Dijkman JH: Antibacterial activity of antileukoprotease. Infect Immun 1996;64:4520–4524.

Original Paper

Digestive Diseases

Dig Dis 2004;22:396–401
DOI: 10.1159/000083605

Subtotal Esophageal Resection in Motility Disorders of the Esophagus

Ines Gockel[a] Werner Kneist[a] Volker F. Eckardt[c] Katja Oberholzer[b]
Theodor Junginger[a]

Departments of [a]General and Abdominal Surgery, and [b]Radiology, Johannes Gutenberg University, Mainz, and [c]Department of Gastroenterology, German Diagnostic Clinic, Wiesbaden, Germany

Key Words

Motility disorders of the esophagus · Advanced and decompensated stage · Subtotal esophageal resection · Perioperative course · Long-term results

Abstract

Background: Esophagectomy for motility disorders is performed infrequently. It is indicated after failed medical therapy, pneumatic dilation, non-resecting surgical and redo procedures. Patient selection in this group is challenging and the operative risk has to be weighted carefully against the poor quality of life with persistent or recurrent dysphagia. ***Patients and Methods:*** Between September 1985 and April 2004, subtotal esophageal resections for advanced esophageal motility disorders of the esophagus not responding to previous therapy were carried out in 8 patients (6 females, 2 males). The median age of these patients was 59.5 (43–78) years. Six patients had a megaesophagus secondary to achalasia; 1 patient had a non-specific esophageal motility disorder with a stenosis of the distal esophagus, and a further patient displayed a recurrent huge epiphrenic diverticulum, which occurred in the context of a collagen disease. A transhiatal esophageal resection was performed in 6, a transthoracic procedure in 2 patients. ***Results:*** Outcome assessment was done after a follow-up of 43.5 (3–92) months in median. The resection and reconstruction of the esophagus in advanced and decompensated esophageal motility disorders led to a marked functional improvement with disappearance of dysphagia. Despite previous therapeutic failures, alimentation could be restored in all patients. ***Conclusion:*** Favourable long-term results with significant improvement of symptoms can be achieved by esophageal resection even if endoscopic therapy or non-resecting surgical measures are unsuccessful. Transhiatal esophagectomy with gastric pull-up should be the preferred procedure and can be performed with low morbidity.

Introduction

Motility disorders rarely necessitate the removal of the esophagus since medical therapy, pneumatic dilation and/or non-resecting surgical procedures sufficiently palliate the patients' symptoms. Only if all of the latter treatment modalities fail is esophageal resection advisable.

The aim of any treatment is to abolish dysphagia without exposing the patient to gastroesophageal reflux or to an extreme operative risk. While the available literature suggests favorable long-term results after esophagectomy for the end stage of achalasia (AC) [1–8], little information exists with regard to its use in non-specific motility disorders of the esophagus. Over a period of 18 years, we encountered 8 patients with esophageal motility disorders in whom esophageal resection was the only remaining therapeutic option, 2 of these patients had motor disorders other than AC. The following report describes the patients' long-term clinical course.

KARGER

Fax +41 61 306 12 34
E-Mail karger@karger.ch
www.karger.com

0257–2753/04/0224–0396$21.00/0

Accessible online at:
www.karger.com/ddi

Ines Gockel, MD
Department of General and Abdominal Surgery, Johannes Gutenberg University
Langenbeckstrasse 1
DE–55101 Mainz (Germany)
Tel. +49 6131 177291, Fax +49 6131 176630, E-Mail gockel@ach.klinik.uni-mainz.de

Table 1. Demographic data and preceding therapy

Diagnosis	Sex	Age years	Duration of symptoms years	Treatment modalities prior to esophageal resection
AC	f	45	28	4 × PD
AC	f	77	42	15 × PD, Myo + SF
AC	m	64	27	3 × PD, Myo
AC	f	43	25	4 × PD, Myo + SF
AC	f	78	63	2 × PD
AC	f	63	53	1 × PD, fundic and distal esophageal resection (2 ×)
NEMD	m	47	10	Myo, 360°-FP → 180°-SF, 1 × PD
CD	f	56	8	Transthoracic resection of an epiphrenic diverticulum

AC = Achalasia, NEMD = non-specific esophageal motility disorder, CD = collagen disease, PD = pneumatic dilation, Myo = myotomy, SF = semifundoplication, FP = fundoplication.

Patients

Between September 1985 and April 2004, 424 esophageal resections were performed for carcinoma of the esophagus at the Department of General and Abdominal Surgery at the University of Mainz. During the same period, subtotal esophageal resections for advanced esophageal motility disorders of the esophagus not responding to medical therapy were carried out in 8 patients (6 females, 2 males). The median age of these patients was 59.5 (43–78) years. Two patients were classified as ASA II, and 6 as ASA III. In 6 cases, radiographic and manometric studies showed megaesophagus secondary to AC; 1 patient had a non-specific esophageal motility disorder with a stenosis of the distal esophagus after failure of multiple therapeutic options, and a further female patient displayed a recurrent huge epiphrenic diverticulum, which occurred in the context of a collagen disease (lupus erythematodes disseminatus). The demographic data of these 8 patients are presented in table 1. The median postoperative follow-up was 43.5 (3–92) months. Due to the heterogeneity of the described motility disorders, we intend to focus on patients with AC.

Clinical Course prior to Esophageal Resection

Previous Surgery

Six patients had undergone a total of nine surgical procedures at a median of 12.5 (0.75–27) years prior to esophageal resection. In 3 patients with AC, a Heller-myotomy with an anterior semifundoplication had been previously performed but was later followed by megaesophagus and a peptic stricture. Another female patient had undergone first a fundic and later a partial distal esophageal resection with esophagogastrostomy at another institution, now presenting with Barrett's esophagus and severe dysphagia refractory to conservative management.

The patient with non-specific motility disorder had been treated by thoracoscopic myotomy 2 years earlier at another institution under the presumptive diagnosis of a diffuse esophageal spasm. Two months later, a 360° Nissen fundoplication was added for newly occurring gastroesophageal reflux. This was followed by balloon dilatation, and 1 year later by laparoscopic conversion of the 360° wrap into a 180° semifundoplication as treatment of recurrent vomiting and weight loss.

In the female patient with collagen disease, an epiphrenic diverticulum measuring 15 × 13 × 12 cm in size had been removed transthoracically. Seven years later, she presented with a recurrent epiphrenic diverticulum sized 12 cm in diameter accompanied by severe dysphagia (table 1). The indications for esophageal resection are shown in table 2.

Preoperative Clinical Symptoms

Patients with AC presented with long-standing dysphagia (median: 35 (25–63) years) for solid and liquid food. All patients reported regurgitation of undigested food as well as retrosternal pain. Two patients described significant weight loss, and another 2 had pulmonal symptoms with recurrent aspiration, whereas 3 patients suffered from frequent heartburn. Bolus obstruction occurred in 3 patients and necessitated endoscopic extraction of food particles.

Radiological Findings

The median diameter of the esophageal body in patients with AC was 7.25 (6–15) cm. The criterion of a dolichomegaesophagus (DME) (>7 cm in diameter) was therefore met by 5 of 6 patients. The median maximum width of the gastric cardia amounted to 5 (3–15) mm. None of the patients showed any radiologic evidence of peristalsis.

Manometric Findings

Perfusion manometry was performed in all patients with AC: In 4 cases with a tortuous and dilated esophagus, the probe could not be passed through the lower esophageal sphincter. In the remaining 2 patients, the resting lower esophageal sphincter pressure was 5 and 12 mm Hg (respectively after preceding pneumatic dilation).

All patients exhibited aperistalsis of the esophageal body with low contraction amplitudes and partly repetitive contractions.

Table 2. Surgical therapy and follow-up

Patient	Indication for surgery	Surgical procedure	Duration of surgery min	Follow-up months
1	AC, DME	TH colon interposition	245	51
2	AC, DME peptic stenosis	TH gastric pull-up	315	72
3	AC, DME peptic stenosis	TH gastric pull-up	275	60
4	AC, DME	TH gastric pull-up	255	36
5	AC, DME	TH gastric pull-up	175	8
6	AC, Barrett's-esophagus	1. colon interposition 2. TT esophageal resection	245	3
7	NEMD, stenosis	TH gastric pull-up	205	5
8	collagenosis, recurrent epiphrenic diverticulum	TT gastric pull-up	305	92

AC = Achalasia, DME = dolichomegaesophagus, NEMD = non-specific esophageal motility disorder, TH = transhiatal, TT = transthoracic.

Surgical Procedures and Follow-Up

The median length of operation (n = 8) was 250 (175–315) min. In 6 patients, the operative procedure consisted of a transhiatal subtotal resection of the esophagus. In these cases, the esophagus was replaced by the pulled-up stomach with cervical esophagogastrostomy, while in 2 patients a colon interposition was performed. A dual operation was carried out in the female patient who had had two partial distal resections at another clinic. First, a retrosternal colon interposition with cervical esophagocolostomy and proximal closure of the remnant esophagus, which was left in situ to limit the risk of the operation was done (fig. 1). Secondary, the rest of the esophagus was removed 5 months later by means of a rethoracotomy. Surgical therapy and follow-up is shown in table 2.

During the early postoperative course, 1 female patient developed a fistula of the cervical esophagogastrostomy, which spontaneously closed during conservative therapy. The patient with a non-specific motility disorder of the esophagus developed a chylothorax and a transthoracic revision with ligation of the lymphatic vessels had to be performed. In 3 patients, repeated bouginage of the cervical esophagogastrostomy became necessary. 4½ years after surgery, 1 patient with a colon interposition developed a bleeding ulcer in the area of the distal interposition and underwent a revised cologastrostomy at an outside institution. This patient died for unknown reasons on the 7th postoperative day. The remaining patients had an uneventful postoperative course.

Patients were followed and examined in the outpatient clinic of the gastroenterologist (V.F.E.). Interviews were performed with the assessment of dysphagia, regurgitation, retrosternal pain, weight and reflux. Six patients remained free of symptoms during their long-term clinical course (median observation time: 43.5 (3–92) months). One patient complained about occasional retrosternal pain. She was found to have reflux esophagitis immediately proximal to the cervical esophagogastrostomy. Alimentation could be restored in all patients.

Histopathological Findings

All patients with a dilated esophagus in the context of AC showed a marked rarefaction of the intramural ganglion cells. In addition, they exhibited a distinct fibrosis of the smooth muscular layer and myopathic changes of the smooth muscle cells. An epithelial hyperplasia with macroscopically clearly visible polypoid changes of the complete esophageal mucosa (fig. 2a) as well as microcalcifications of the esophageal wall, probably due to stasis

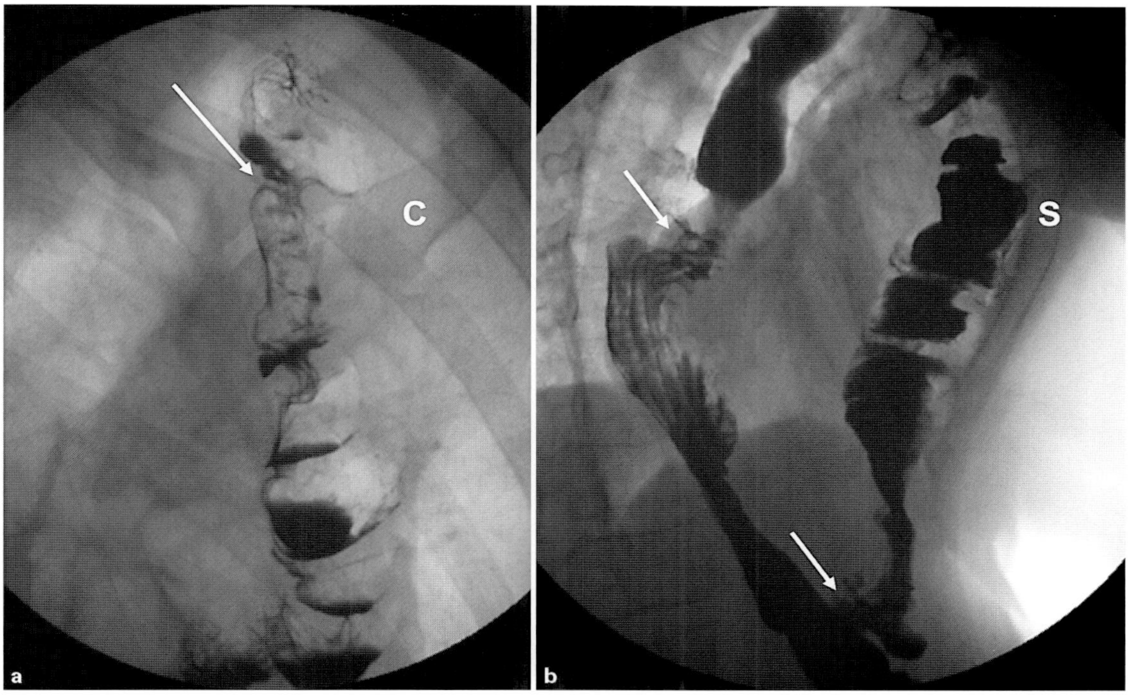

Fig. 1. A dual operation was performed in a patient with two previous partial distal (fundic and esophageal) resections: first, a retrosternal colon interposition with a cervical esophagocolostomy, a coloantral anastomosis and proximal closure of the remnant esophagus, which was left in situ to limit the risk of the operation. In a second step, the rest of the esophagus was removed by a rethoracotomy 5 months later (barium swallow shown after the first operation). **a** Arrow = cervical esophagocolostomy; c = clavicle. **b** Upper arrow = esophagofundostomy; lower arrow = coloantral anastomosis; s = sternum.

and retention esophagitis, were found in a patient who had the disease for 63 years (fig. 2b).

Discussion

The etiology of esophageal motility disorders is largely unknown. Correspondingly, any therapy remains palliative and is directed at the removal of symptoms, such as dysphagia, regurgitation and retrosternal pain. For the treatment of AC, pneumatic dilation and open or laparoscopic extramucosal myotomy are most frequently used and often alleviate symptoms. Only in cases of recurrent symptoms, if a scarring of the esophagogastric junction as a consequence of long-lasting reflux occurs, or if the esophagus has become massively dilated, may more aggressive therapy become indicated. The extensive dilation of the esophagus leads to a retention esophagitis with regurgitation and the danger of aspirations, and in rare cases it can be the cause of malign degeneration [9–11].

Such end stages of AC are fairly infrequent. Among a total group of 132 patients, which had been treated surgically at our institution during 18 years, a decompensated form of AC was found in 6 patients. In all of them, dysphagia leading to malnutrition was the prominent symptom. The median length of symptoms was 35 years, and all patients had previously undergone multiple dilation therapies or surgical procedures.

Resections of the esophagus as a result of a DME are described in the literature with a frequency of 8–9% in relation to the total number of treated AC patients [8, 12], whereas this frequency in patients with Chagas disease is markedly higher (14%) [13].

Different types of resection have been proposed. The limited distal esophageal resection with interposition of a short colon segment was shown by Hsu et al. [14] to lead to good functional results. This procedure, however, does not prevent the rare complication of esophageal carcinoma. Therefore, Orringer advocated a subtotal resection of the esophagus, which was developed further by DeMeester as a vagal-sparing procedure [15–17].

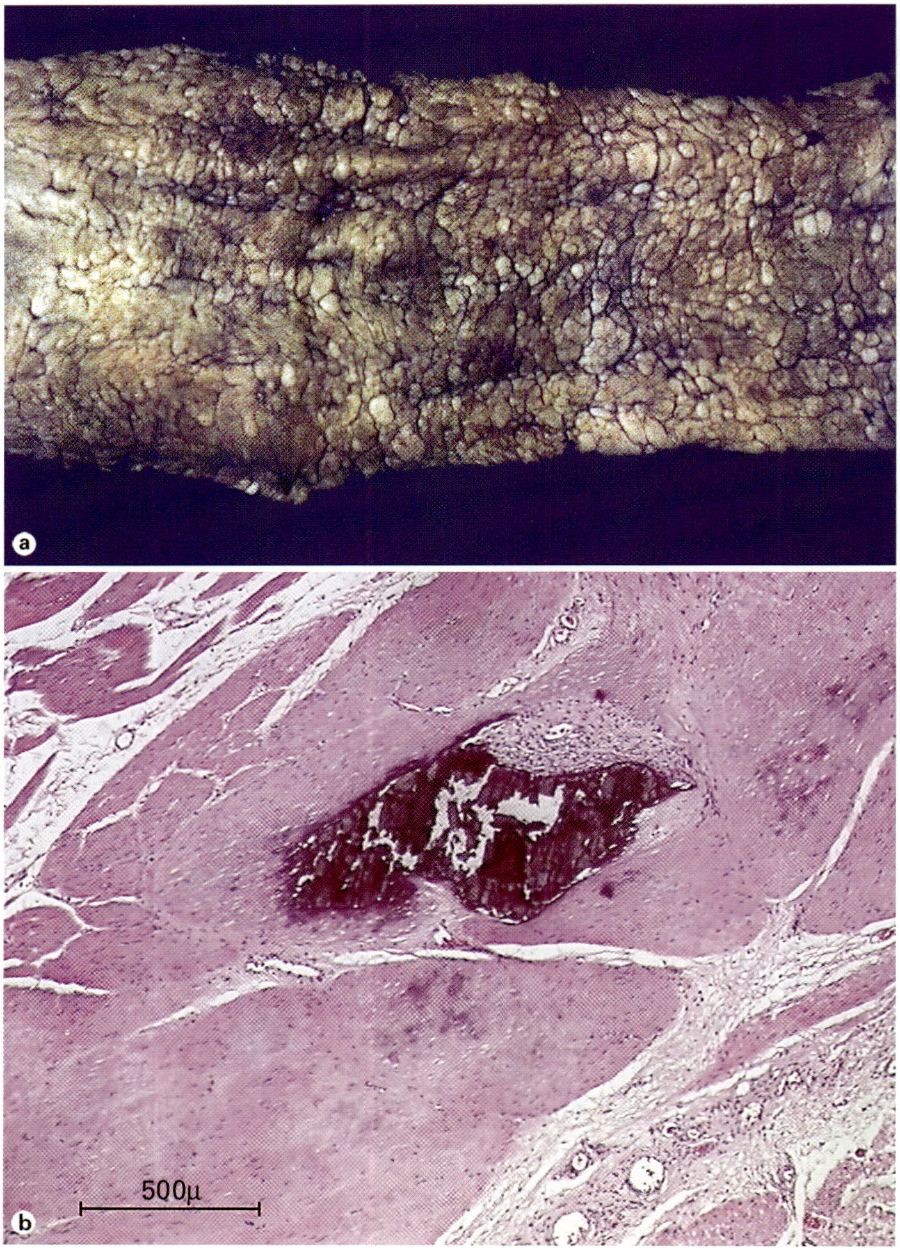

Fig. 2. a Epithelial hyperplasia with macroscopically clearly visible polypoid changes of the complete esophageal mucosa was obvious in a patient with AC and DME. **b** Microcalcifications of the esophageal wall, probably due to stasis and retention esophagitis, were found in a patient who had a history of AC for 63 years.

While most larger series used the stomach as an esophageal substitute, as described by Orringer and Devaney, a colon interposition was preferred by others [5, 6, 15, 16, 18, 19]. In a series of 255 patients with benign esophageal diseases, mostly esophageal motility disorders, Young et al. [2] performed a gastric pull-up in 65.9%, a colon interposition in 27.5%, and a small intestine interposition in 6.6% of all cases. Thus, in patients undergoing esophageal resection for benign diseases, the most frequently performed procedure is the transhiatal esophagectomy with gastric pull-up and cervical esophagogastrostomy, which may be prohibitive if scarring of the gastric cardia is encountered as a consequence of previous surgery. A colon interposition is burdened by a higher rate of long-term complications, and is therefore less suitable as an esophageal replacement in benign disease [19, 20–22].

In the long-term course, 1 female patient with a colon interposition suffered from a bleeding ulcer in the area of the distal interposition with an ensuing new formation of the cologastrostomy outside. The patient died 4½ years later of the consequences of the operation. All other patients were largely free of major complications.

Devaney et al. [6] described the anastomotic insufficiency in 10% of all cases, a lesion of the recurrent laryngeal nerve in 5%, a mediastinal bleeding with thoracotomy in 2%, and a chylothorax in 2%, with a mortality rate of 2% on account of respiratory insufficiency and sepsis as major complications.

Resection of the esophagus led in all of our patients to the disappearance of dysphagia. Such positive functional long-term result with an improvement of the quality of life has been described by other authors: Peters et al. [3] reported a satisfactory postoperative outcome with an improvement of dysphagia in 80%. Although similar data was described by others, their results have to be viewed with caution because of the use of different grading systems for functional results and the heterogeneity of the underlying syndromes [5, 7, 13, 18, 23, 24].

Motility disorders other than AC are rarely an indication for a subtotal esophageal resection. Literature on a larger series of cases does not exist. Our decision to operate was based on the failure of multiple previous therapies. The postoperative course of these patients suggests that favorable long-term results with significant improvement of dysphagia can be achieved by esophageal resection even if endoscopic therapy or non-resecting surgical measures are unsuccessful.

Conclusion

In summary, the resection and reconstruction of the esophagus in advanced esophageal motility disorders led to a marked functional improvement with disappearance of dysphagia. As these decompensated stages are irreversible and not influenced by conservative and/or non-resecting surgical procedures, symptomatic relief can be achieved by esophagectomy which is the only available treatment in order to restore alimentation and quality of life.

The choice of the operative approach and the type of interposition may be determined by the presence or absence of scarring due to previous surgery. If the latter is absent, we believe that transhiatal esophagectomy with gastric pull-up and cervical esophagogastrostomy should be the preferred procedure and can be performed with low morbidity.

References

1 Buntain WL, Payne WS, Lynn HB: Esophageal reconstruction for benign disease: A long-term appraisal. Am Surg 1980;46:67–79.
2 Young MM, Deschamps C, Trastek VF, Allen MS, Miller DL, Schleck CD, Pairolero PC: Esophageal reconstruction for benign disease: Early morbidity, mortality, and functional results. Ann Thorac Surg 2000;70:1651–1655.
3 Peters JH, Kauer WKH, Crookes PF, Ireland AP, Bremner CG, DeMeester TR: Esophageal resection with colon interposition for end-stage achalasia. Arch Surg 1995;130:632–637.
4 Kneist W, Sultanov F, Eckardt VF, Junginger T: Ösophagusresektion zur Behandlung der Achalasie. Vier Fallberichte und Übersicht über die Literatur. Chirurg 2002;73:223–229.
5 Orringer MB, Stirling MC: Esophageal resection for achalasia: Indications and results. Ann Thorac Surg 1989;47:340–345.
6 Devaney EJ, Lannettoni MD, Orringer MB, Marshall B: Esophagectomy for achalasia: Patient selection and clinical experience. Ann Thorac Surg 2001;72:854–858.
7 Malthaner RA, Todd RT, Miller L, Pearson FG: Long-term results in surgically managed esophageal achalasia. Ann Thorac Surg 1994;58:1343–1347.
8 Miller DL, Allen MS, Trastek VF, Deschamps C, Pairolero PC: Esophageal resection for recurrent achalasia. Ann Thorac Surg 1995;60:922–925.
9 Streitz JM Jr, Ellis FH Jr, Gibb SP, Heatley GM: Achalasia and squamous cell carcinoma of the esophagus: Analysis of 241 patients. Ann Thorac Surg 1995;59:1604–1609.
10 Peracchia A, Segalin A, Bardini R, Ruol A, Bonavina L, Baessato M: Esophageal carcinoma and achalasia: Prevalence, incidence and results of treatment. Hepatogastroenterology 1991;38:514–516.
11 Hankins JR, McLaughlin JS: The association of carcinoma of the esophagus with achalasia. J Thorac Cardiovasc Surg 1975;69:355–360.
12 Ellis FH, Crozier RE, Gibb SP: Reoperative achalasia surgery. J Thorac Cardiovasc Surg 1986;92:859–865.
13 Pinotti HW, Cecconello I, da Rocha JM, Zilberstein B: Resection for achalasia of the esophagus. Hepatogastroenterology 1991;38:470–473.
14 Hsu HS, Wang CY, Hsieh CC, Huang MH: Short-segment colon interposition for end-stage achalasia. Ann Thorac Surg 2003;76:1706–1710.
15 Orringer MB: Transhiatal esophagectomy for benign disease. J Thorac Cardiovasc Surg 1985;90:649–655.
16 Orringer MB, Stirling MC: Transhiatal esophagectomy for benign and malignant disease. J Thorac Cardiovasc Surg 1993;105:265–277.
17 Banki F, Mason RJ, DeMeester SR, Hagen JA, Balaji NS, Crookes PF, Bremner CG, Peters JH, DeMeester TR: Vagal-sparing esophagectomy: A more physiologic alternative. Ann Surg 2002;236:324–336.
18 Orringer MB, Orringer JS: Esophagectomy: Definite treatment for esophageal neuromotor dysfunction. Ann Thorac Surg 1982;34:237–248.
19 Watson TJ, DeMeester TR, Kauer WHK, Peters JH, Hagen JA: Esophageal replacement for end-stage benign esophageal disease. J Thorac Cardiovasc Surg 1998;115:1241–1249.
20 Tsutsui S, Moriguchi S, Morita M, Kuwano H, Matsuda H, Mori M, Matsuura H, Sugimachi K: Multivariate analysis of postoperative complications after esophageal resection. Ann Thorac Surg 1992;53:1052–1056.
21 Isolauri J, Markkula H, Autio V: Colon interposition in the treatment of carcinoma of the esophagus and gastric cardia. Ann Thorac Surg 1987;43:420–424.
22 Orringer MB, Marshall B, Stirling MC: Transhiatal esophagectomy for benign and malignant disease. J Thorac Cardiovasc Surg 1993;105:265–277.
23 Waters PF, Pearson FG, Todd TR, Patterson GA, Goldberg M, Ginsberg RJ, Cooper JD, Ramirez J, Miller L: Esophagectomy for complex benign esophageal disease. J Thorac Cardiovasc Surg 1988;95:378–381.
24 Banbury MK, Rice TW, Goldblum JR, Clark SB, Baker ME, Richter JE, Rybicki LA, Blackstone EH: Esophgectomy with gastric reconstruction for achalasia. J Thorac Cardiovasc Surg 1999;117:1077–1084.

Author Index Vol. 22, 2004

Digestive Diseases

KARGER

Fax +41 61 306 12 34
E-Mail karger@karger.ch
www.karger.com

Accessible online at:
www.karger.com/ddi

Subject Index Vol. 22, 2004

KARGER

Fax + 41 61 306 12 34
E-Mail karger@karger.ch
www.karger.com

Accessible online at:
www.karger.com/ddi

Vol. 22, 2004

Digestive Diseases

Clinical Reviews

Formerly 'Survey of Digestive Diseases'
Founded in 1983 by T.S.N. Chen and R.K. Zetterman
Former Editor: S.R. Achem (1993–2000)

KARGER

Basel · Freiburg · Paris · London · New York · Bangalore · Bangkok · Singapore · Tokyo · Sydney

S. Karger
Medical and Scientific Publishers
Basel • Freiburg • Paris • London
New York • Bangalore • Bangkok
Singapore • Tokyo • Sydney

Drug Dosage
The authors and the publisher have exerted every effort to ensure that drug selection and dosage set forth in this text are in accord with current recommendations and practice at the time of publication. However, in view of ongoing research, changes in government regulations, and the constant flow of information relating to drug therapy and drug reactions, the reader is urged to check the package insert for each drug for any change in indications and dosage and for added warnings and precautions. This is particularly important when the recommended agent is a new and/or infrequently employed drug.

P.O. Box, CH–4009 Basel (Switzerland)
Printed in Switzerland on acid-free paper by
Reinhardt Druck, Basel

KARGER

Fax +41 61 306 12 34
E-Mail karger@karger.ch
www.karger.com

Digestive Diseases

Contents Vol. 22, 2004

No. 1

No. 2

KARGER

Fax +41 61 306 12 34
E-Mail karger@karger.ch
www.karger.com

Access to full text and tables of contents, including tentative ones for forthcoming issues:
www.karger.com/ddi_issues

No. 3

No. 4